TREE CLIMBERS' GUIDE

TREE CLIMBERS' GUIDE

4TH EDITION

SHARON J. LILLY

ALEX K. JULIUS

ILLUSTRATIONS BY BRYAN KOTWICA

This book is an educational tool for introductory arboriculture. It may be used as part of, but not as a replacement for, a comprehensive training program. While some equipment and techniques are explained and illustrated, actual use requires knowledge of and experience with the equipment and techniques prior to use in an actual work environment. Equipment and techniques represented are approved at the time of publication and could change. The techniques depicted or described in this book must be analyzed, and at times modified, to meet the specific needs of the individual situation.

Workers should be familiar with local, state, provincial, national, and federal government standards and regulations applicable to the job assignment and requirements. The many training tools available through the International Society of Arboriculture are excellent resources to aid in continuing education and training. The practices and recommendations contained in this book should be used in practice only by those properly trained, educated, and experienced in the field of arboriculture. ISA is responsible only for the educational program contained in this book and not for the use or misuse of these ideas in specific field situations or by inexperienced or improperly trained individuals.

International Society of Arboriculture
270 Peachtree St. NW, Suite 1900
Atlanta, GA 30303
United States
+1 (678) 367-0981
www.isa-arbor.com

Cover Design: Shawna Armstrong
Page Design and Composition: Bookbright Media
Printed in the United States of America by Premier Print Group, Champaign, IL

ISBN: 978-1-943378-09-8

10 9 8 7 6 5 4 3 2

0322-CA-1200

CONTENTS

ACKNOWLEDGMENTS

The International Society of Arboriculture and the authors of this guide extend special thanks to Will Koomjian and John Wayne Farber for their many hours reviewing text and illustrations for this edition, and to the illustrator, Bryan Kotwica, whose talent is a gift to our profession.

The authors would also like to thank their partners at home for their patience during this process, and for reading multiple drafts.

The authors would like to thank and acknowledge the following professionals for taking time to review parts or all of this guide, and for sharing their insights and expertise:

Dr. John Ball
Tim Bushnell
Mark Chisholm
John 'Didj' Coles
Jason Diehl
Melissa Duffy
Drew Dunavant
Kevin Eckert
Rose Epperson
John Wayne Farber
Rich Herfurth
Dr. Brian Kane
Phillip Kelley
Will Koomjian
Kevin Myers
Dwayne Neustaeter
Scott Prophett
Lindsey Purcell
Don Roppolo
Rip Tompkins
Travis Vickerson
Tim Walsh

CHAPTER

1

TREE HEALTH AND SCIENCES

LEARNING OBJECTIVES

The tree worker will be able to:

- Explain how trees grow, manufacture their own food, and conduct water and minerals.
- Discuss the relationship between soil and healthy root growth and function.
- Describe how trees respond to stress and defend against decay.
- Recognize the major defects and conditions that can increase the likelihood of a tree failure.
- Explain the characteristics and terminology used to identify trees.

IMPORTANT TERMS

abiotic
absorbing roots
alternate leaf arrangement
anatomy
arborist
axillary bud
barrier zone
biotic
branch bark ridge
branch collar
buttress roots
cambium
cavity
Compartmentalization of Decay in Trees (CODIT)
compound leaf
conifer
conk
crown
deciduous
drip line
evergreen
fascicle sheath
frond
fruiting body
girdling root
growth rings
heartwood
included bark
internode
lateral bud
leaf scar
leaflet
lenticel
lobe
mineral
mycorrhizae
node
opposite leaf arrangement
phloem
photosynthesis
physiology
pore space
radius
ray
reaction zone
root crown
root mat
sapwood
serration
simple leaf
starch
stomates
stress
structural root zone (SRZ)
terminal bud
transpiration
trunk flare
vascular bundle
vascular system
vascular wilt
watersprout
whorled
woundwood
xylem

INTRODUCTION

Trees have basic needs, including sunlight, air, water, essential minerals, and adequate growing space above and below ground. When all of these fundamental needs are fulfilled, a tree can survive, grow, and thrive. If any of these is lacking, the tree will suffer and perhaps die. Safe climbing requires an **arborist** to understand the fundamental principles of tree biology and how stress factors affect tree health and stability.

Additionally, a basic knowledge of tree anatomy and physiology is the foundation for informed tree care. Trees respond to stress from wounds and poor environmental conditions, and it is important to understand and interpret the response to apply the best care practices. Poor understanding of tree processes can result in poor decisions, poor technique, and the wrong treatment, which can be damaging to trees.

It is also important for a tree climber to be able to identify trees and their distinguishing characteristics. A tree climber who cannot correctly identify tree species risks accidentally working on the wrong trees. Knowing the growth habits of a particular species can help an arborist prune trees to achieve a more natural form. Additionally, knowing the strength of trees' wood and branch attachment may save a life.

Climbing or working on a high-risk tree can pose a threat not only to the climber but also to other people and property in the area. Tree climbers must inspect the tree and identify potential hazards prior to climbing and initiating any work. Knowing how to identify signs of potential hazards is a critical component of the inspection process.

This chapter introduces the major parts of a tree and their basic functions, as well as the fundamental terminology for discussing them. It serves as an early primer for tree biology, tree identification, and recognition of potential defects and hazards. The content is presented at an introductory level without going into significant detail. As a tree worker progresses in experience and education, they are encouraged to continue learning and consider moving on to the *Arborists' Certification Study Guide,* also published by the International Society of Arboriculture.

FIGURE 1.1 Sugar is produced in the leaves in a reaction called photosynthesis. Sunlight provides the energy, water and carbon dioxide are the inputs, and sugar and oxygen are the outputs.

TREE STRUCTURE AND FUNCTION

Tree **anatomy** is the study of the structure of trees and their parts. Tree **physiology** is the study of how tree parts function and all work together.

Leaves

Leaves may be thought of as the "food factories" of the tree. Unlike humans and other animals, plants actually manufacture their own food. The process is called **photosynthesis**, which means "made with light."

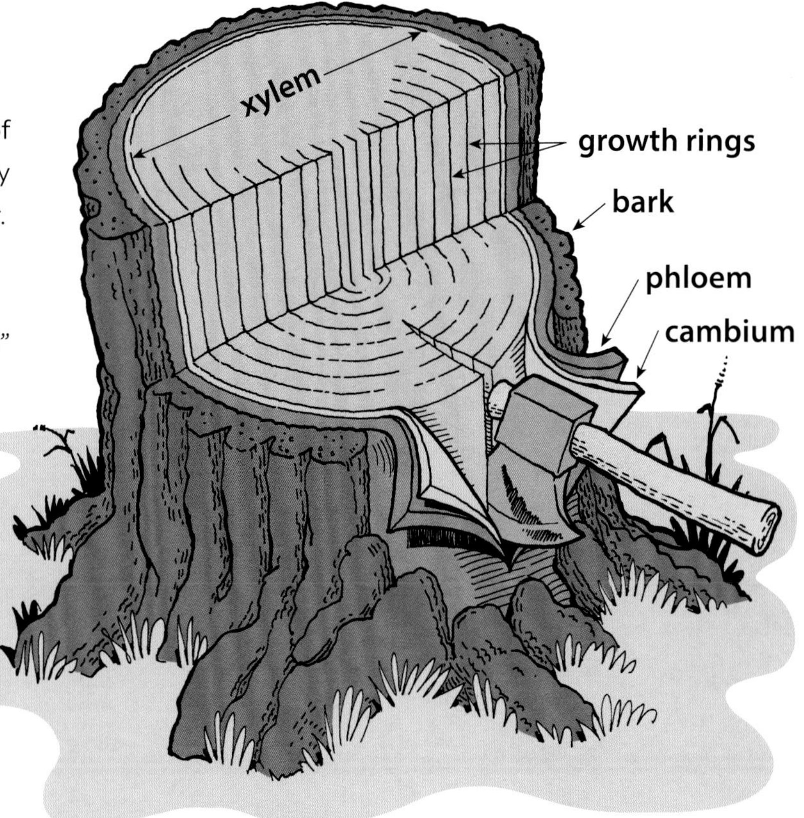

FIGURE 1.2 Not far beneath the bark of the tree is a continuous layer of dividing cells known as the cambium. Phloem is produced toward the outside of the tree. The xylem is formed toward the inside of the tree. A cut (cross) section of a branch, trunk, or root will reveal the growth rings. Usually, each ring represents one year's growth of xylem. The ring just inside the cambium is the most recent year's growth.

Sunlight powers the reaction that combines water and carbon dioxide to form sugar. Oxygen is given off into the atmosphere as a byproduct. Sugar is used to provide energy for growth and development; some of the sugar is transported through the phloem and stored as starch in certain cells in the wood or roots.

A second function of the leaves is **transpiration**. Transpiration is the loss of water, in the form of water vapor, from tiny pores in the leaf surface called **stomates**. This evaporation cools the leaves. It also creates the "transpirational pull" that helps move water up from the roots through the xylem to other parts of the tree.

Leaves are found in a variety of shapes, colors, and sizes. Some leaves are uniquely adapted for extreme environments to help with heat or drought, or even to discourage pests. Needles, found on pines, spruces, and firs, are also a form of leaves. Most **conifers**, or cone-bearing trees, are **evergreens**, meaning they keep their leaves for more than one year. Trees that lose their leaves in the fall are called **deciduous**.

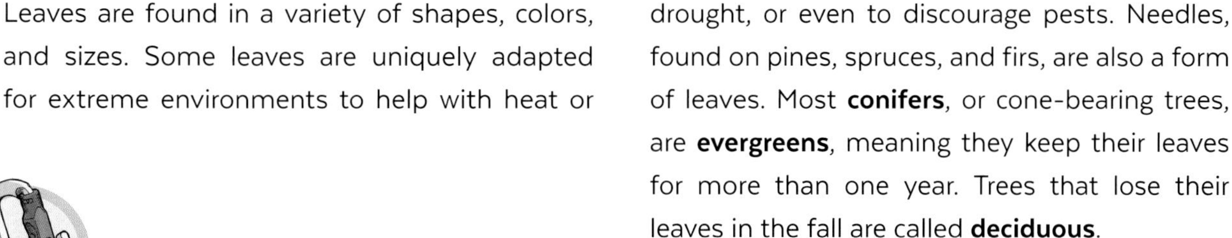

FUNCTIONS OF THE LEAVES

Photosynthesis—the production of sugar (food)

Transpiration—a cooling process that helps pull water up through the tree

Trunk and Branches

The trunk and branches of a tree provide the tree's structural framework. The branches form a scaffold system, or branching structure, which supports the tree and presents the leaves to the sun. The trunk and branches perform several important functions: they conduct water and **minerals** from the roots to the aboveground portions of the tree, they provide structural support for the tree's crown, and they store energy in the form of sugars or starches.

Just beneath the protective layer of bark on a tree is a continuous layer of dividing cells known as the **cambium**. Division of cambium cells results in growth in diameter of the trunk and branches. The cambium is also important in the closure of wounds because the cambium produces the new cells that form the **woundwood**.

Cells produced in the cambium layer toward the outside of the tree become part of the **phloem**. The phloem carries the sugars that are produced in the leaves to other parts of the tree, for use or to be stored as starch.

The **xylem** is formed in the cambium layer toward the inside of the tree. The xylem consists of wood fibers and the **vascular system** that conducts water and minerals up from the roots. It is a complex tissue composed of both living and dead cells that function not only for water conduction, but also in storage of starch, defense against decay, and structural support of the tree.

When we look at a cut (cross) section of a branch, trunk, or root, the **growth rings** (growth increments) are visible. Usually, for temperate (nontropical) trees, each ring represents one year's growth of xylem. The ring just inside the cambium layer is the most recent year's growth. The thickness of the growth rings is often an indication of growing conditions in previous years. For example, several years of drought can cause thin growth rings, representing reduced growth of the tree. It is also true that counting the growth rings can often reveal the age of many trees. This does not apply to tropical trees, however, which may have several growth periods during a year.

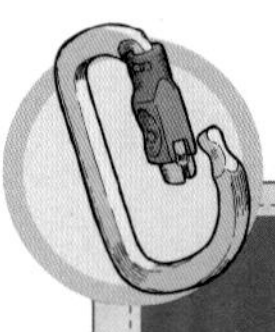

FUNCTIONS OF THE TRUNK AND BRANCHES

- Provide structural support
- Grow to present the leaves to the sun to harvest sunlight energy
- Conduct water and nutrients throughout the tree
- Store starch energy reserves
- Defend against decay

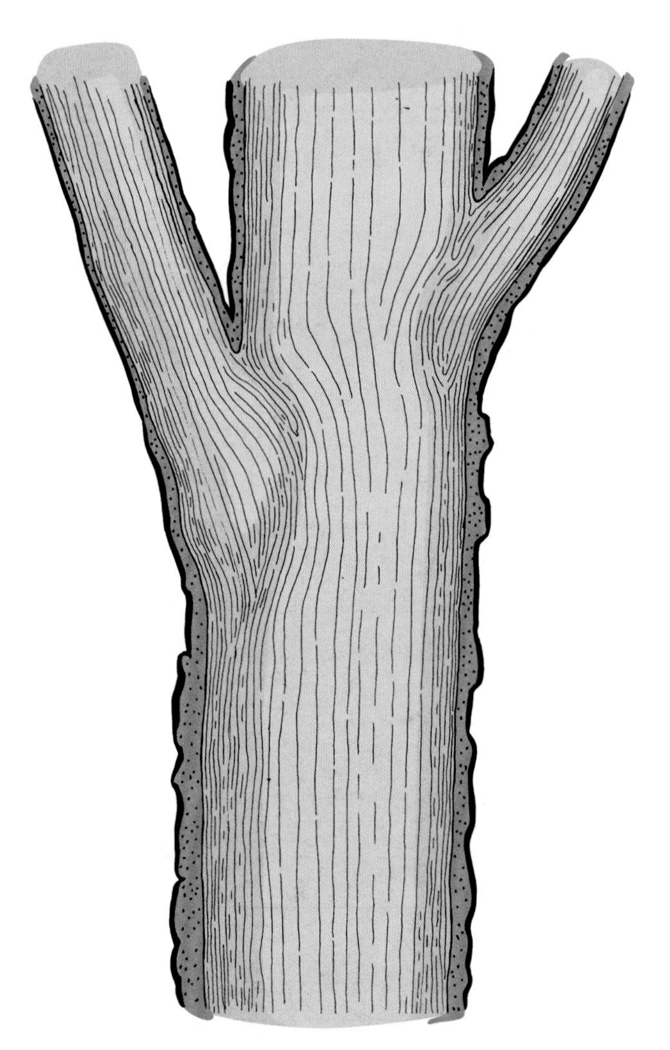

FIGURE 1.3 With the bark removed, the pattern of normal branch attachment is visible. There is no direct vascular connection between a branch and portions of the tree above that branch.

The outermost rings of the xylem, known as the **sapwood**, conduct water and minerals from the roots to the leaves. In most trees, the inner growth rings, called the **heartwood**, are dead xylem. These rings no longer carry water and minerals up through the tree, but may still serve as a storage area.

The cambium, phloem, and xylem form a continuous system running from the small roots, up through the trunk and branches, and into the tiny twigs and leaves. As cambium cells divide, an additional layer of conducting cells forms, increasing the diameter of the branch or root. Growth in branch length occurs through elongation from the ends of the twigs at the terminal buds. Branches stay in the same position on the trunk as the tree grows; they do not get higher each year.

In addition to the phloem and xylem, the trunk and branches of a tree also contain **rays**. The rays are radial sheets of living cells that cross both the phloem and xylem. When viewed in a cross section of a tree, they look like spokes of a wheel. The rays transport sugars and other materials across the stem tissues. They are also food-storage sites within the tree. Most of the stored energy that is used by the tree for growth, flowering, and fruiting comes from storage sites close to where it is utilized.

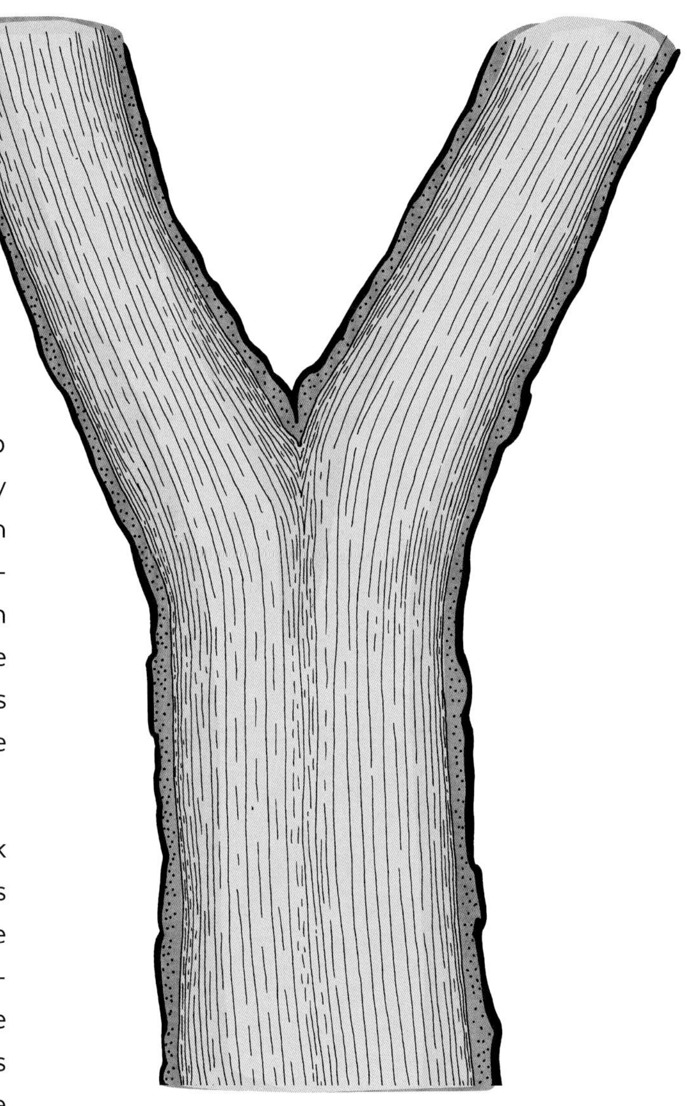

FIGURE 1.4 Codominant stems do not have a branch collar and can sometimes be weaker, especially if included bark is present.

Each branch of the tree is similar in structure and function to the entire tree crown. Yet branches are not simply outgrowths of the trunk. Instead, branches and trunks have a unique attachment form. Annual growth of trunk xylem surrounds each branch, helping to strengthen the attachment. Branches are strongly attached to the trunk beneath the branch, but more weakly attached to the trunk above the branch. There is no direct connection of vascular tissue between a branch and other branches that originate above it.

The annual production of layers formed by xylem at the connection point of the trunk and branches forms a bulge at the base of the branch called the **branch collar**. In the branch union, the branch and trunk expand against each other. As a result, bark is pushed up, forming the **branch bark ridge**. If the bark in the branch union becomes pinched between the branch and trunk, it is called **included bark**. Included bark weakens the branch connection.

Roots

The roots of trees serve four primary functions: anchorage, storage, absorption, and conduction. Larger roots are woody and similar internally to the trunk and branches. They serve to hold the tree in place, store **starches**, and carry water and minerals to the tree top. Larger roots branch many times, forming smaller networks of roots. The small, fibrous **absorbing roots** take up water and minerals. These slender roots can branch out to form fanlike mats just under the soil surface. Most tree roots coexist in a beneficial relationship with certain fungi, which help in the absorption of water and minerals. These root-fungus relationships are called **mycorrhizae**.

FIGURE 1.5 Root tip anatomy.

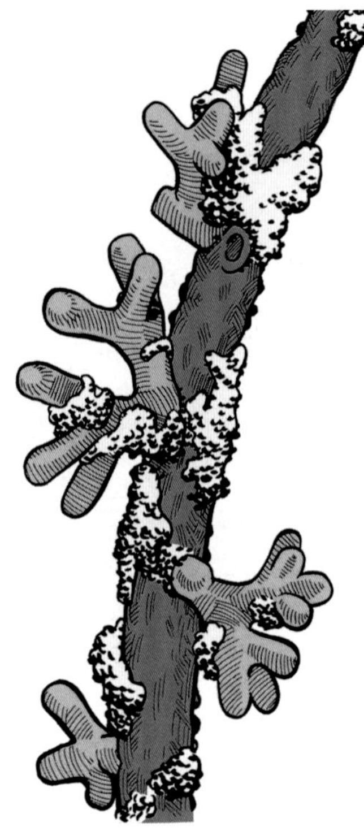

FIGURE 1.6 Most tree roots coexist in a beneficial relationship with fungi. This relationship, called mycorrhizae, helps in the absorption of water and minerals.

Roots grow where moisture and oxygen are available. Although tree roots can grow very deep in certain sites, most absorbing roots are found in the upper 8 in (20 cm) of soil. Even the largest roots are found predominantly in the upper 3 ft (1 m) of soil. The **structural root zone (SRZ)**, which includes the portion of the root zone most critical for a tree's structural support, is usually within a **radius** of at least three times the diameter of the trunk. The idea that the root system is a mirror image of the tree's **crown** is absolutely false.

FIGURE 1.7 Most absorbing roots grow very near the surface, where moisture and oxygen are available. There is generally little root growth under buildings or paved surfaces.

Roots grow outward from the tips; this growth occurs the most where growing conditions are most

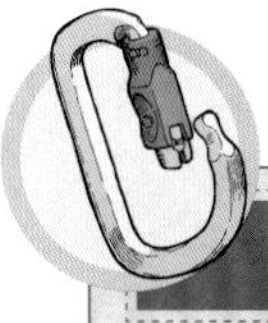

FUNCTIONS OF THE ROOTS

- Absorption of water and minerals
- Conduction of water and minerals
- Anchorage to hold the tree upright
- Storage of nutrients
- Defense against decay

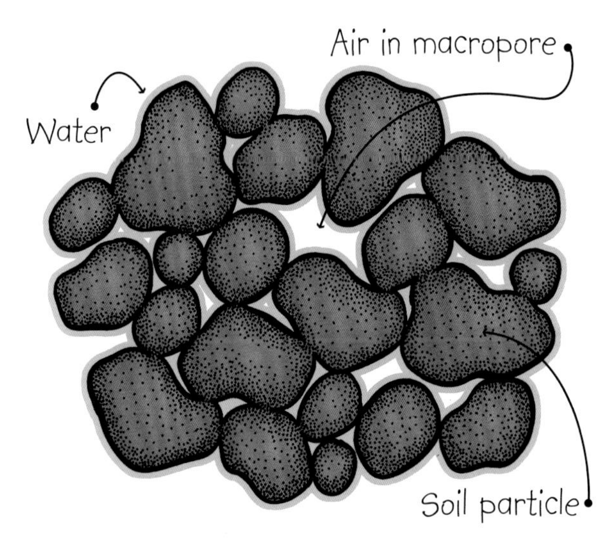

FIGURE 1.8 An ideal soil is about 50 percent pore space. The spaces between the soil particles may be filled with air or water.

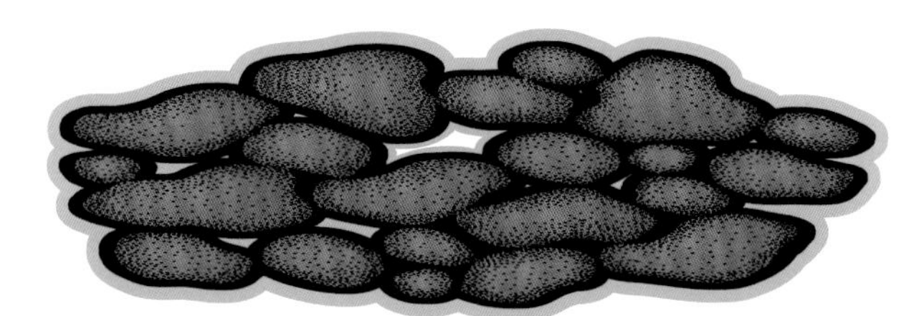

FIGURE 1.9 When a soil is compacted, the pore space is reduced. Oxygen and available water levels decrease, and root growth is inhibited.

favorable. **Pore spaces** between the soil particles contain the necessary oxygen and water for root growth. If pore space is inadequate or if there is not enough oxygen, roots cannot function. Thus, roots are less likely to be found in compacted soils that lack adequate pore space. Where soils

FIGURE 1.10 Roots grow where growing conditions are most favorable. They normally extend much farther from the tree than the drip line.

are severely compacted from vehicles or pedestrians, tree growth and health usually suffer.

The direction of root growth and its distance from the trunk depends largely on the surrounding soil conditions and availability of space. Roots of trees grown in open areas often extend two to three times the radius of the tree's crown. However, if structures or pavements limit growth, the roots of a tree may grow only a short distance in one direction and a great distance in the other. Roots normally grow much farther from the tree than the **drip line**.

DEFENSE AGAINST DECAY

A developmental process unique to woody plants is the ability to compartmentalize decay. Compartmentalization is a process by which trees limit the spread of decay. After a tree has been wounded, reactions are triggered that cause the tree to form protective boundaries around the wounded area.

Alex Shigo, a prominent tree researcher, proposed a model of this compartmentalization process called **CODIT**, **C**ompartmentalization **O**f **D**ecay **I**n **T**rees. In Dr. Shigo's model, the tree forms four "walls." Wall 1 resists vertical spread by plugging xylem cells. Wall 2 resists inward spread across the annual rings. Wall 3 inhibits lateral spread by activating ray cells to resist decay. Together, these three walls are known as the **reaction zone**. Wall 4 is formed with the next layer of wood to form after the injury. It protects against the outward spread of decay. The fourth wall is the **barrier zone**. Wall 1 is the weakest and Wall 4 is the strongest, chemically.

At times, the tree cannot resist the spread of aggressive decay-causing pathogens. It is common for Walls 1, 2, and 3 to fail, allowing decay to spread inside the tree. Decay can ultimately result in the formation of a **cavity**. Wall 4 usually does not fail unless the cambium is killed or injured, so the decay can often be confined to tissues that were present at the time of injury.

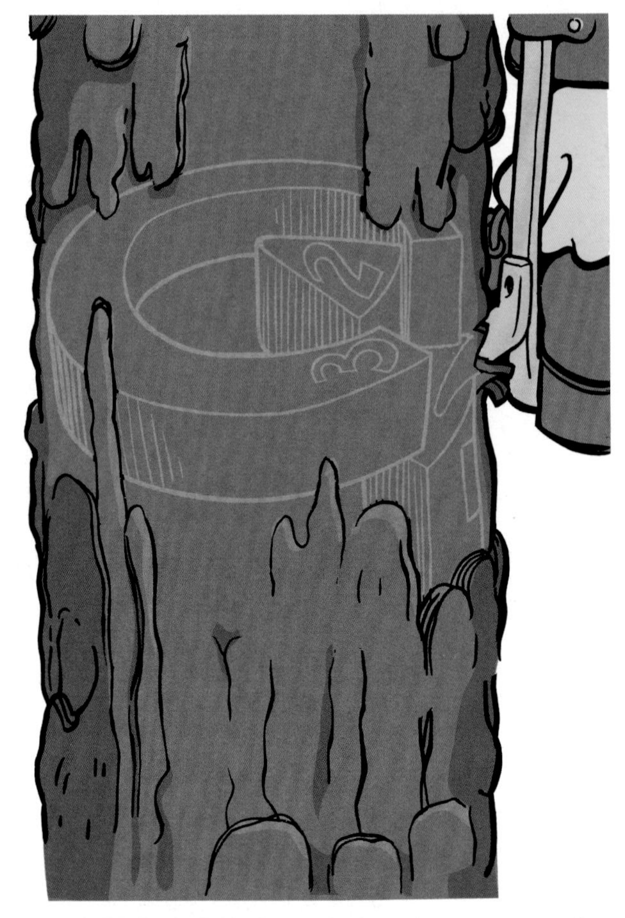

FIGURE 1.11 Wall 1 is formed when the tree responds to wounding by "plugging" the upper and lower vascular elements to limit vertical spread of decay. Wall 2 is formed by the last cells of the growth ring limiting inward spread. Wall 3 has the ray cells compartmentalize decay by limiting lateral spread. Wall 4 (shown in Figure 1.12), the strongest wall, is the new growth ring that forms after the injury. Wall 4 prevents decay from entering new wood.

FIGURE 1.12 Wall 4 is formed with the next layer of wood to form after the injury. Wall 4 usually does not fail unless the cambium is killed or injured, so the decay can often be confined to tissues that were present at the time of injury.

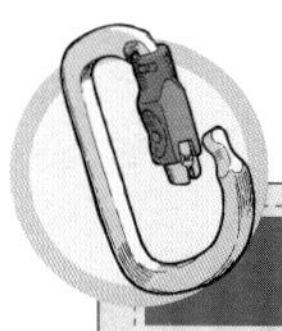

THE FOUR "WALLS" OF CODIT

Reaction Zone

- Up and down (plugged xylem)
- Inward (growth rings)
- Around (rays)

Barrier Zone

- Outward (new wood growth)

Hollow trees that have large cavities aren't always a high risk. A hollow tree can survive for many years because the outer xylem rings (sapwood) continue to conduct water. Like a cylinder or pipe, a hollow tree can be quite strong structurally. However, when decay spreads through the barrier zone into the remaining tissues, the tree may decline in health and become structurally weak. Although tree health and stability can affect each other, they are not the same thing. A tree can appear healthy and be structurally unsound, or a tree can be dying but still be very stable structurally.

PALMS

In some geographic areas, arborists may be asked to care for palms. Many people do not consider palms to be true trees because they differ biologically in many ways. Whereas trees house their vascular system in growth rings, palms have scattered **vascular bundles** throughout their stems. The outer covering is made up of the dried bases of the **fronds**.

A palm's full crown is concentrated around the apical meristem, commonly known as the "palm heart," at the top of the palm trunk and base of the fronds. This is where frond and trunk growth occurs. Having only an apical meristem and no cambium means that the palm does not form branches or woundwood. There are no growth rings, as layers of tissue are not accumulating. CODIT does not apply, as palms do not wall off injuries. This means that externally damaged tissue will remain exposed and susceptible to insects, disease, and decay.

The root system of palms is formed from a root initiation zone that is regularly dying back and forming new roots. Palm roots are concentrated in a dense mass called a **root mat** that is usually quite close to the trunk but can sometimes extend much farther.

TREE HEALTH AND STRESS

The basic factors that promote plant health include sufficient water and air, optimum light and temperatures, and proper nutrition. Too much or too little of any of these factors can cause **stress** in the tree. Stress is a term used to describe any condition that causes the tree to decline in health and vitality.

Early signs of stress might include reduced growth rate, abnormal leaf color or size, vigorous production of **watersprouts** or suckers, early fall color, or

FIGURE 1.13 A girdling root can constrict a tree's vascular system. This can sometimes be a cause of stress. It is common with some tree species.

FIGURE 1.14 General decline in the crown of a tree is often a sign of root stress. Root stress is a common problem in city and suburban sites.

unusual leaf drop. The most common causes of tree stress are related to the site or environment. If the tree is not well suited for the site in which it is growing, it is more likely to suffer stress at some time in the future. Common conditions that can lead to stress responses include inadequate or excess water, soil compaction, **girdling roots**, extreme cold, and mechanical injuries (including improper pruning techniques). These are all examples of **abiotic** factors, meaning they are not caused by living organisms.

Root stress is a common problem in city and suburban sites. Soils are often compacted, dry, and infertile in the city environment. Compaction reduces the pore space, which reduces water and oxygen availability. If root growth and function are inhibited, the tree will decline.

Trees in a state of stress may be more prone to attack by insects and diseases. All too often, arborists identify and treat only these secondary problems. However, to improve the tree's health and vitality, the primary cause of stress must be identified and corrected.

Many plant health problems are caused by **biotic** (living) agents, such as insects, mites, fungi, and bacteria. In general, insects and diseases that affect only the foliage of deciduous trees are not life threatening. Leaves are temporary organs, and more are produced each year. The exception to this rule is when trees are defoliated year after year, causing the tree to rely on stored energy reserves. If these "borrowed" energy reserves are not "repaid" through photosynthesis, the tree will eventually run out of reserves and die.

Insects, diseases, or wounds that affect the vascular system of a tree are much more serious. The tree must be able to conduct water and nutrients in order to survive. Wood-boring insects and **vascular wilt** diseases are examples of problems that are often fatal.

STRESSORS

Examples of Biotic Stressors	Examples of Abiotic Stressors
Insect pests	Too much/little water
Mites	Inadequate nutrition
Other animals	Inadequate sunlight
Fungi	Wrong growing conditions
Bacteria	Physical/mechanical injuries

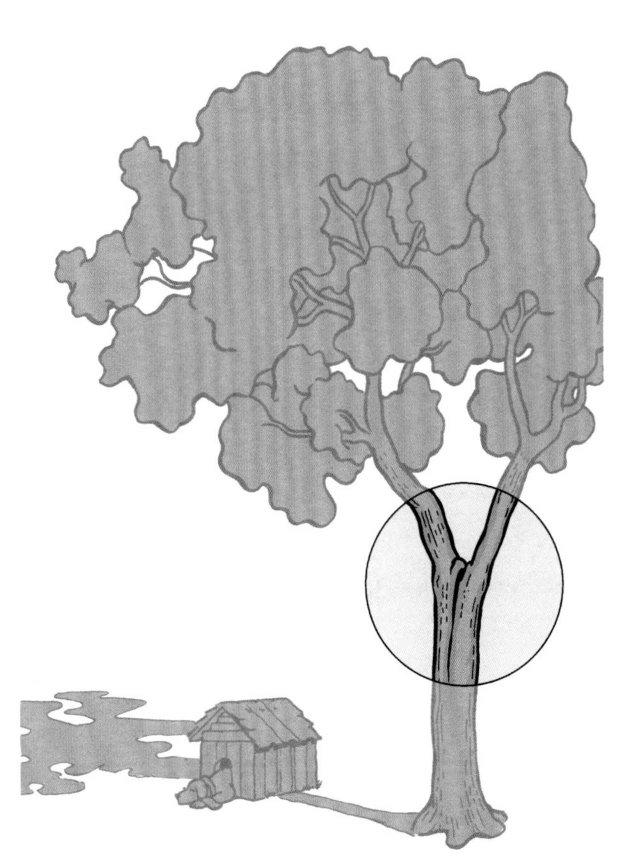

FIGURE 1.15 A split branch union can significantly increase the likelihood of failure.

FIGURE 1.16 Mushrooms are the fruiting bodies of fungi. They can be signs of root rot or root collar decay.

HAZARD RECOGNITION

Before working on any tree, the climber must do an inspection. The tree must be assessed thoroughly for any potential hazards. Some defects and hazards are obvious, such as large dead or hanging branches or major cracks in the wood. Other flaws may not be discovered without a careful search.

One very serious hidden danger is decay at the **root crown (trunk flare)**, the zone where the trunk and roots come together. A number of tree climbers have been injured or killed when the tree they were working in failed at the base. This sort of decay is not always obvious. Decay should always be suspected on dead and severely declining trees. Trees that show a major dieback from the tips are probably suffering from some form of root stress.

FIGURE 1.17 A conk on the outside of a tree is an indication of decay on the inside.

FIGURE 1.18 Frass, a mixture of sawdust and insect excrement, is a sign of insect activity. When frass is observed, a climber should inspect the tree further for decay.

It is important to look around the root zone for indications of dead or decayed roots. Mushrooms, especially if they are growing in a line, can be a sign of root decay. It may be necessary to carefully dig and explore around the trunk flare at the base of the trunk, looking for rotted wood and fungi. Probing around the large **buttress roots** at the trunk flare is helpful to ensure that they are solid.

The climber must inspect the trunk and crown. If there are **conks** on the trunk or branches, there is decay inside. Conks are the **fruiting bodies** of certain decay fungi. Carpenter ants, cavities, and holes are other indications of decay. Other potential hazards include split trunks or branches, branch unions with included bark, dead branches, and soil lifting opposite a lean.

If any of these hazards are identified in a tree, some decisions must be made. Is the tree safe to climb? Does it pose an immediate threat to people or structures in the area? Who should be notified, and what actions should be taken? While the tree climber is not always in a position to make the final decision concerning treatment or possible removal, they still share the responsibility for the evaluation. The safety of the climber and other workers on the crew may depend on the ability of the climber to recognize and communicate concerns related to potential hazards.

PRINCIPLES OF TREE IDENTIFICATION

Identification of the tree is usually the first step in any tree care procedure. The tree worker must be able to identify the various trees on a property in order to perform the work. Accurate identification

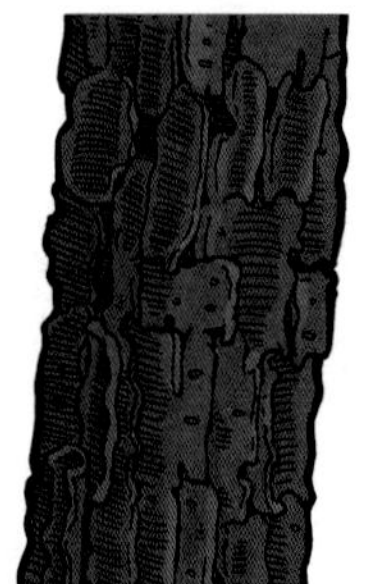

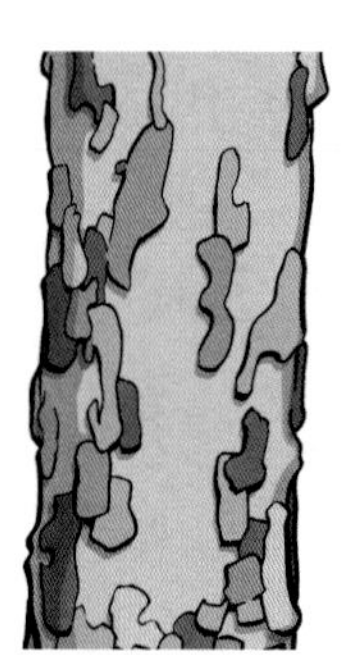
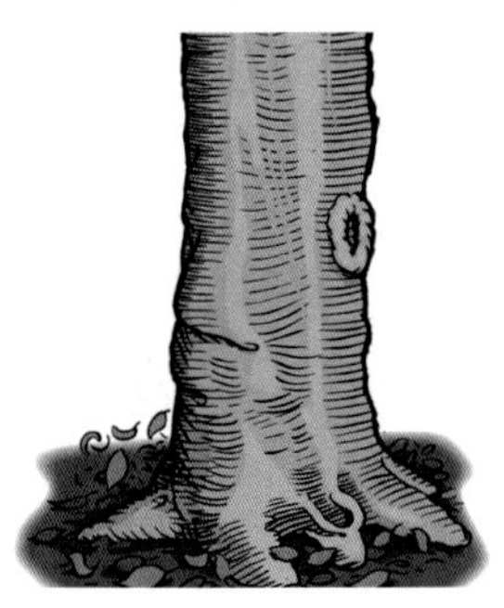

FIGURE 1.19 With or without the leaves, the color and texture of the bark can be used to identify many tree species.

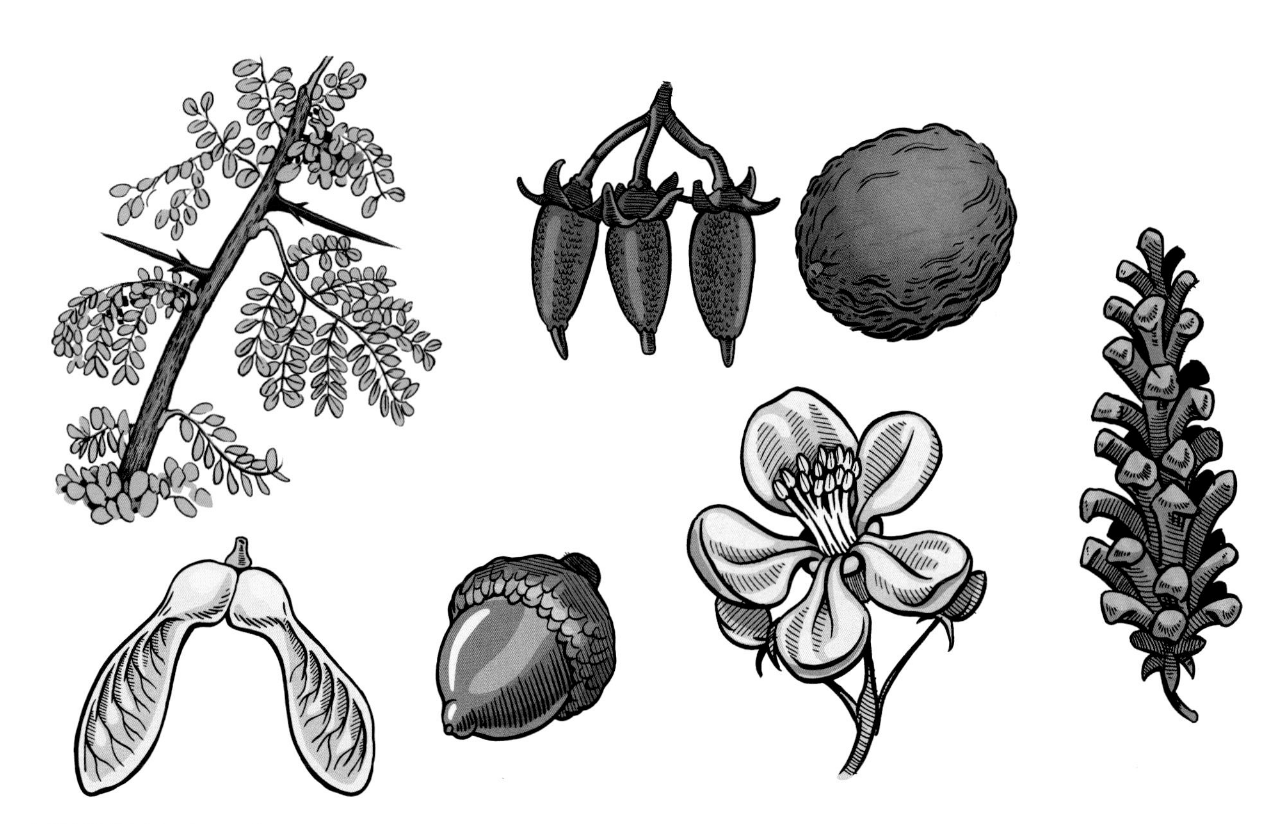

FIGURE 1.20 Other identification characteristics include flowers, thorns, fruits, nuts, and seeds.

requires a combination of knowledge and experience. Once the basic identification skills are learned, proficiency will come with practice and repeated exposure to the trees during different seasons.

Tree identification is based on the size, shape, and appearance of tree parts. Therefore, a fundamental knowledge of tree structure is essential. An informed tree climber learns to identify trees by using a tree's many characteristics. Rather than focusing just on the leaves, it is important to examine the buds, twigs, flowers, fruit, and bark. The size and growth habits of the tree are also key identification characteristics. The arborist who relies solely on the leaves will only be able to identify deciduous trees during half of the year in many regions.

It is wise to use all available information during tree identification. This may require everything from close examination of leaves, twigs, and buds to a broader look at the tree's architecture. Sometimes tree identification is based on more than the visual senses. Smell, and even taste, may be useful to determine the unique characteristics of twigs, leaves, flowers, or fruit.

There are a few basic rules and tricks that can be used in tree identification. In order to use them, a little knowledge of twig anatomy is required. The bud at the end of a twig is called the **terminal bud**. Buds along the twig are called **lateral** or **axillary buds**. These may be leaf or flower buds, or they may develop into twigs. Flower buds are generally larger than leaf buds. The slightly enlarged areas on the stem where leaves or buds arise are called the **nodes**, and the spaces between are known as **internodes**. Marks left on the twig after leaves have fallen are called **leaf scars**. Their unique sizes and shapes can be very helpful in identifying trees. Some twigs have small, visible pores called **lenticels**, which allow

FIGURE 1.21 The growth form of many trees is an identification characteristic.

for the exchange of gases. Prominent lenticels can be used in identification.

An initial step in tree identification is determining the leaf arrangement on the stem. The leaf (or bud) arrangement is the order in which leaves are attached to the stem. If two buds arise across from one another on a stem, the arrangement is called “opposite.” Maples (*Acer*), ashes (*Fraxinus*), most dogwoods (*Cornus*), and buckeyes/horsechestnuts (*Aesculus*) are examples of trees that have an **opposite leaf arrangement**. The majority of deciduous tree species have an **alternate leaf arrangement**, in which leaves and buds arise alternately along the stem. If three or more leaves and buds arise from a single node, the arrangement is called **whorled**. Although this is not common on deciduous trees, it is sometimes found in conifers.

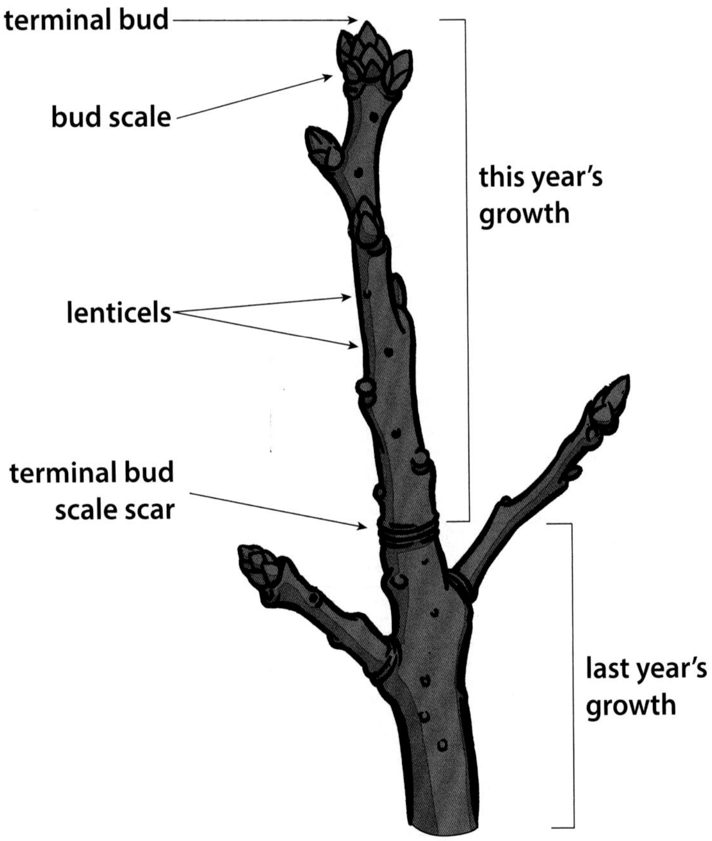

FIGURE 1.22 Twig anatomy showing two years of growth.

TIP!

MAD HORSE

In many parts of the world, most of the trees with an opposite leaf arrangement fall into four groups:

- **M**aple
- **A**sh
- **D**ogwood
- **Horse**chestnut (buckeye)

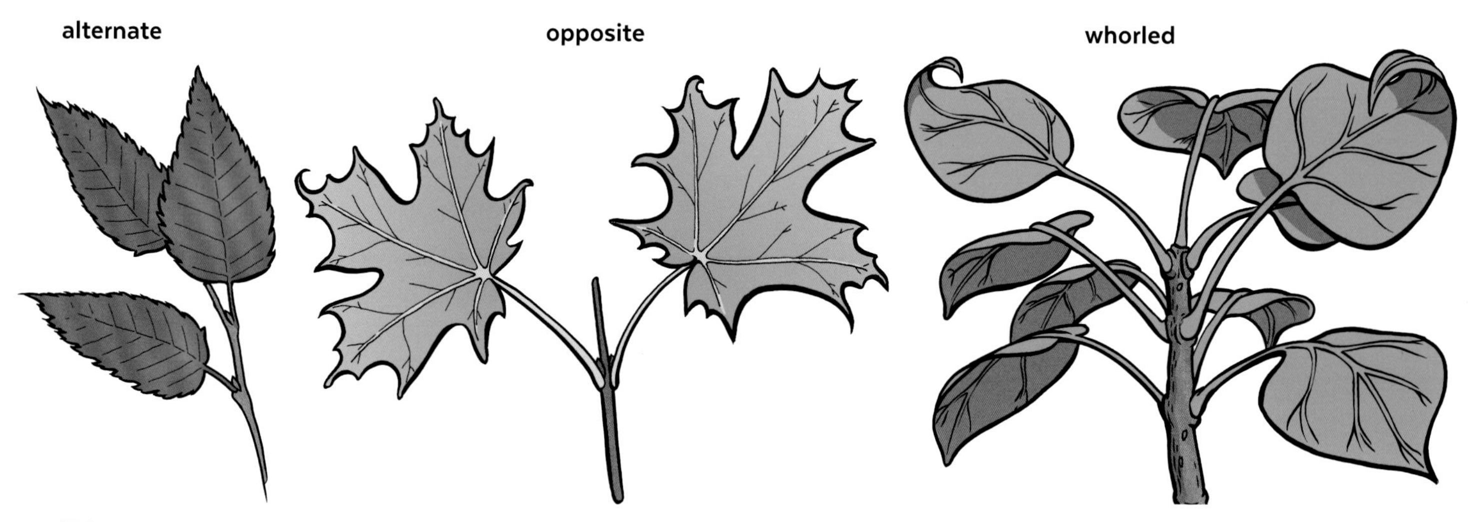

FIGURE 1.23 Leaf arrangements.

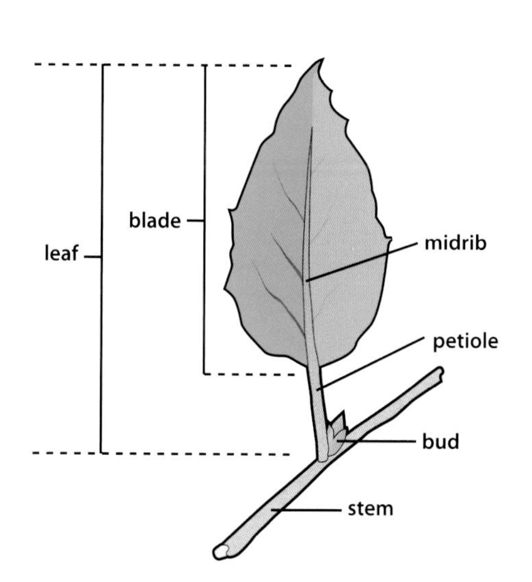

FIGURE 1.24 Anatomy of a simple leaf.

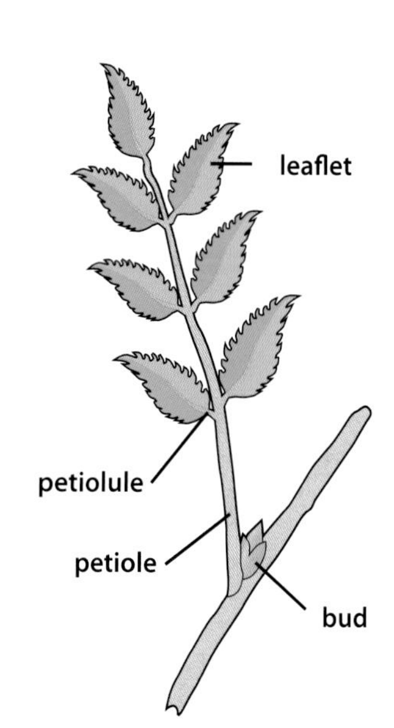

FIGURE 1.25 Anatomy of a compound leaf.

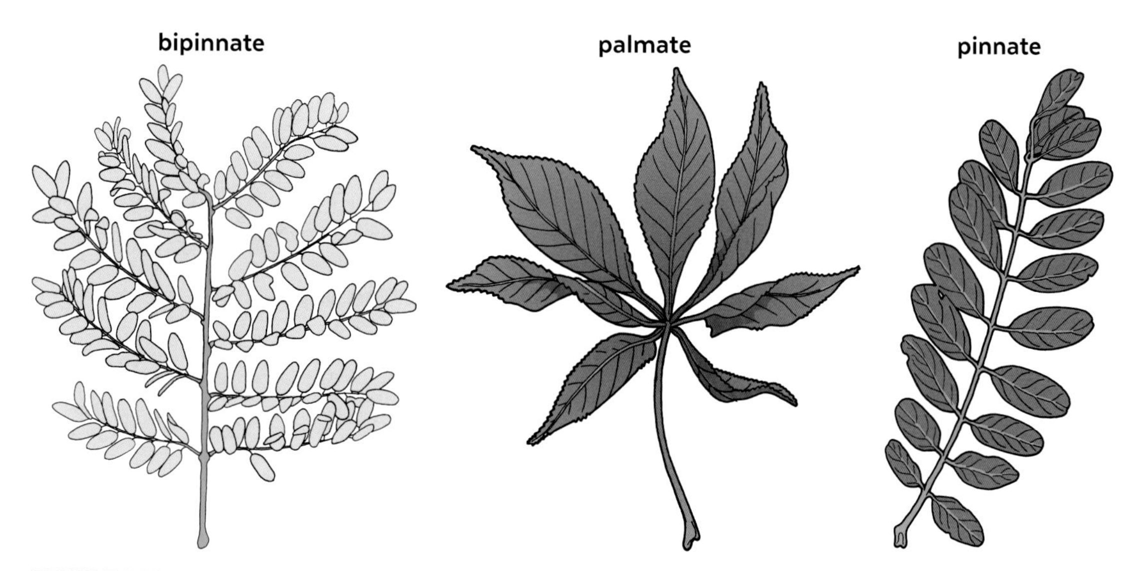

FIGURE 1.26 Arrangement of leaflets on compound leaves.

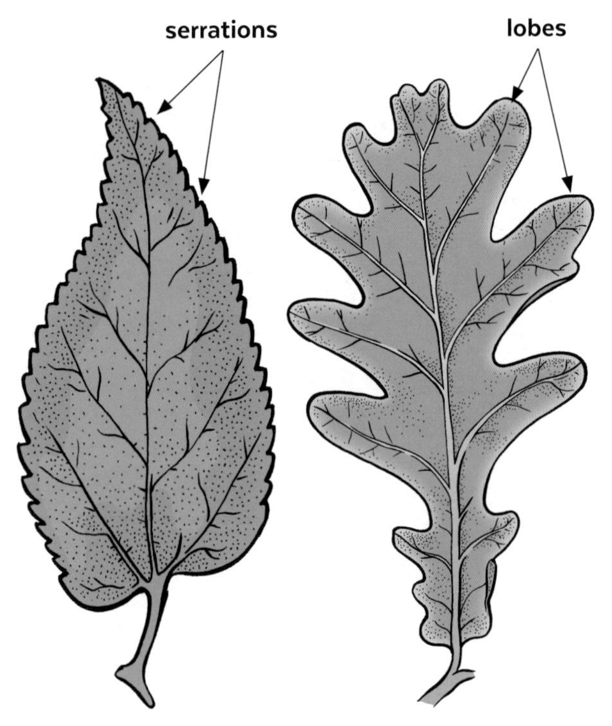

FIGURE 1.27 Other leaf characteristics that can be used for identification are lobes and serrations (teeth along the leaf margin).

The next step is to determine whether the tree has **simple leaves** or **compound leaves**. Simple leaves have one leaf blade and one bud. Compound leaves also have only one bud but branch into multiple **leaflets**. Other leaf characteristics that can be used for identification are **lobes** and **serrations** (teeth along the leaf margin) as shown in Figure 1.27.

In conifers, the size, shape, and arrangement of the needles are important. The needles of spruces (*Picea*), hemlocks (*Tsuga*), yews (*Taxus*), firs (*Abies*), and Douglas-firs (*Pseudotsuga*) arise singly on the stem. Pine tree needles are borne in a **fascicle sheath**, or bundle, of two, three, or five needles. The number of needles in the fascicle sheath is an indication of the species of pine.

The size, shape, and angle of the buds on the twigs are usually good indicators of tree identity,

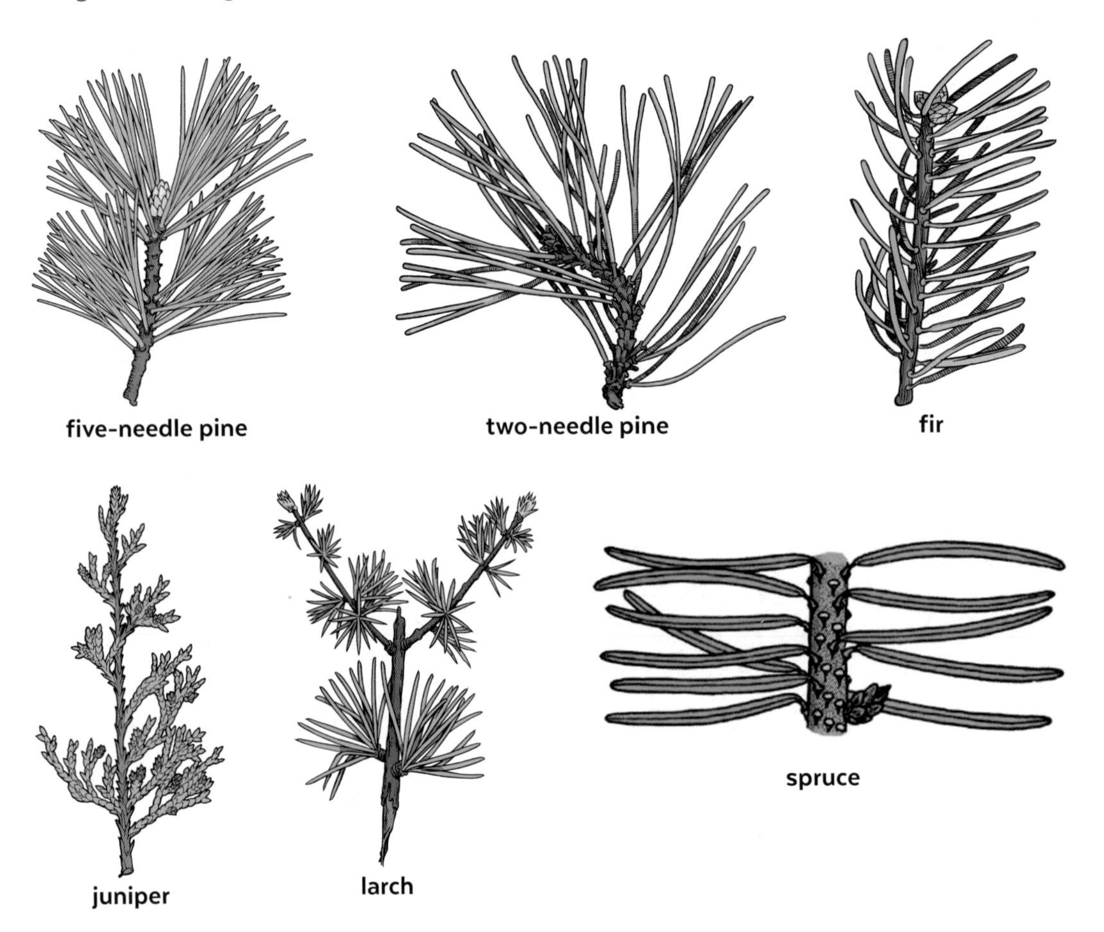

FIGURE 1.28 Conifers can be identified by the characteristics of the needles.

especially in the winter. The leaf scar below the bud can also be helpful. Other characteristics that are often used for tree identification include the bark, fruit, seeds, thorns, stems, spurs, and lenticels.

Many books and apps are available to help with tree identification, and these can be good for learning as well. Even though identification guidelines can be very helpful, there is no substitute for field practice. The more knowledge that can be gained about tree characteristics, the easier the process becomes. Years of experience in observing trees in different settings and at various times of the year can be invaluable.

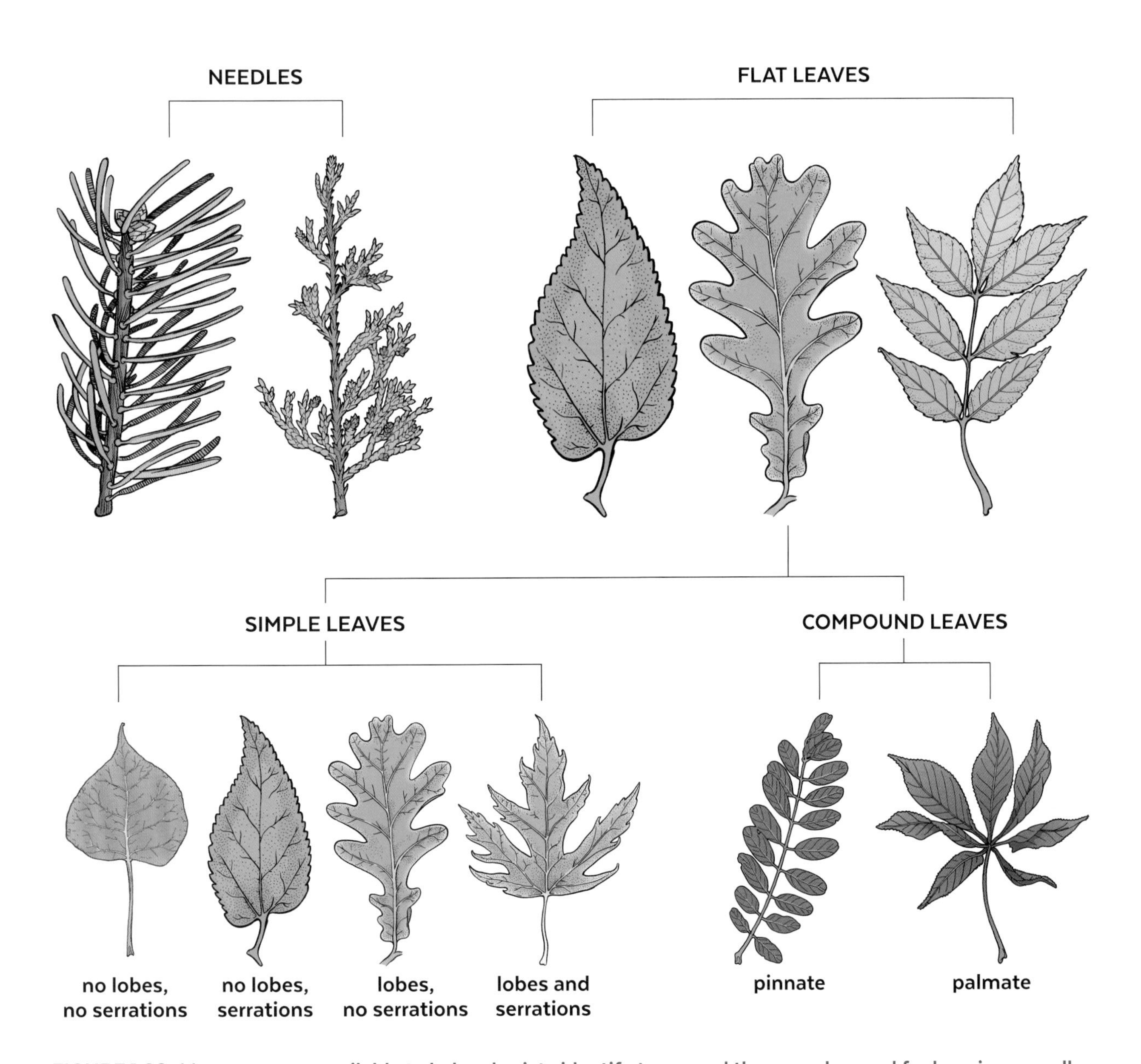

FIGURE 1.29 Many apps are available to help arborists identify trees, and these can be good for learning as well.

KEY CONCEPTS

1. The leaves are the food factories of trees, where sugar is produced by the process of photosynthesis.
2. The cambium, located just under the bark, is a layer of dividing cells that produces the xylem and phloem. Xylem is on the inside of the cambium layer, composed of both living and dead cells. It is responsible for conduction of water and minerals, storage of starch, defense against decay, and structural support. Phloem is on the outside of the cambium, and carries sugar to other parts of the tree for use or for storage as starch.
3. Tree roots serve four primary functions: anchorage, storage, absorption, and conduction. Most roots will generally grow near the surface, where moisture and oxygen are available and growing conditions are favorable.
4. There are four "walls" of CODIT, which is a model to describe how trees compartmentalize decay, creating boundaries to protect against further spread of decay in the tree.
5. Tree stress can be caused by biotic (living) and abiotic (nonliving) factors. It is essential for the climber to know how these factors can affect a tree's structure and health so that work can be performed safely and effectively.
6. Trees can be identified using many characteristics, including but not limited to leaf and leaflet arrangement, bark, natural shape, and flowers.

WORKBOOK

MATCHING 1

_____ xylem

_____ absorbing roots

_____ included bark

_____ phloem

_____ photosynthesis

_____ cambium

_____ transpiration

_____ deciduous

A. trees that lose all their leaves annually

B. food-conducting tissues

C. water vapor loss through leaves

D. usually in the upper 8 in (20 cm) of soil

E. sugar production by plants

F. carries water up through the tree

G. bark within a branch union

H. zone of diameter growth in trees

TRUE/FALSE

1. T F Small fibrous roots serve to take up water and minerals.
2. T F The root system of a tree looks like a mirror image of the top (crown).
3. T F Roots tend to grow where moisture and oxygen are available.
4. T F Tree roots rarely grow beyond the drip line of the tree.
5. T F Starches are stored throughout the trunk and branches of a tree.
6. T F The cambium is located in the center of the trunk and branches.
7. T F The phloem carries sugar only to the roots.
8. T F The xylem is located directly beneath the bark.
9. T F In most cases, each growth ring represents one year of growth.
10. T F The thickness of the growth rings is often an indication of growing conditions in previous years.
11. T F The heartwood conducts water and minerals up through the tree.
12. T F In most tree species, only the outermost rings of sapwood conduct water.
13. T F Rays are storage sites for starch and play a role in defense against decay.
14. T F The bulge at the base of a branch at the point of attachment to the trunk is called the branch collar.
15. T F Leaves may be considered the "food factories" of a tree.
16. T F A vigorous tree will compartmentalize decay to limit its spread.
17. T F Most of the time, if a tree is stressed, the cause is an insect problem.

18. T F Compaction reduces the pore space in the soil, which reduces water and oxygen availability.

19. T F Generally, with deciduous trees, insects or diseases that affect only the foliage of the tree are not fatal.

20. T F Insects or diseases that affect the vascular system of a tree are usually serious.

21. T F Photosynthesis means "made with light."

22. T F Loss of water evaporating from the leaves helps pull water up from the roots.

23. T F Compound leaves have one bud for each leaflet.

24. T F Trees that lose their leaves for the winter are called deciduous.

25. T F The bud at the end of a twig is known as the axillary bud.

MATCHING 2

_____ conk	A. areas between soil particles
_____ simple leaf	B. teeth along the leaf margin
_____ compound leaf	C. bark pushed up in the branch union
_____ branch bark ridge	D. one blade per leaf
_____ pore spaces	E. bud at the tip of a twig
_____ terminal bud	F. sign of decay within the tree
_____ serration	G. leaf with multiple leaflets

SAMPLE TEST QUESTIONS

1. Most absorbing roots are located

   a. very deep in the soil
   b. along the surface of the tap root
   c. in the upper 8 in (20 cm) of soil
   d. within the drip line of the crown

2. If two buds arise across from one another on a stem, the arrangement is called

   a. alternate
   b. axillary
   c. whorled
   d. opposite

3. Which evergreen trees have needles in bundles?

    a. pines (*Pinus*)
    b. hemlocks (*Tsuga*)
    c. firs (*Abies*)
    d. spruces (*Picea*)

CHAPTER

2

SAFETY

LEARNING OBJECTIVES

The tree worker will be able to:

- Explain what safety regulations apply to the tree care industry.
- List the standard personal protective equipment required for tree care operations.
- Summarize the principles of safety on the worksite.
- Discuss the importance of the job briefing for good communication of safe work practices.
- Describe electrical hazards and safety requirements for working near conductors.
- Explain the hazards associated with chain saws, their reactive forces, and precautions required for their safe use.
- Summarize safe chipper operation procedures.

IMPORTANT TERMS

aerial rescue
ANSI Z133 standards
approved
Canadian Standards Association (CSA)
cardiopulmonary resuscitation (CPR)
chaps
chipper
command-and-response system
direct contact
drop zone
electrical conductor
emergency response
first aid
indirect contact
job briefing
kickback
kickback quadrant
landing zone
leg protection
leglock method
OSHA
palm skirt
personal protective equipment (PPE)
reactive force
shall
should
sloughing
work plan

INTRODUCTION

Working in and around trees can be a very hazardous profession if proper care and safety measures are not followed. Safety must always be the first concern. Safety is more than using special equipment, wearing appropriate gear, or attending occasional meetings. Safety is an attitude. It is an ongoing commitment at every level. Safety requires a conscious recognition of potential hazards and the development of a program designed to prevent accidents. Safety precautions must be built into every task performed by tree workers. A small investment of time in safety training can save a great deal in downtime, insurance, injuries, and damages.

This chapter emphasizes the importance of safe work operations in climbing and other aspects of tree work. Safety standards and regulations are the foundation for building safe work policies and procedures. This chapter introduces many of the basic safe work principles, but should not be considered the complete or ultimate authority. All applicable standards and regulations for the region must be followed.

FIGURE 2.1 Safety training is an important part of accident prevention.

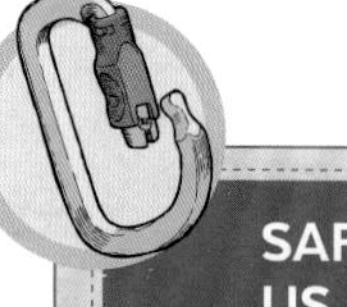

SAFETY REGULATIONS IN THE US, CANADA, AND UK

In the United States, the primary safety laws are administered by the Occupational Safety and Health Administration (**OSHA**). In Canada, the occupational health and safety acts are administered by federal, provincial, and territorial governments, and in the United Kingdom the Health and Safety Executive (HSE) is responsible.

LAWS AND REGULATIONS

In all countries and jurisdictions, employers are subject to the applicable laws, regulations, and safety standards in the region. These regulations may include general safety regulations as well as those specific to tree workers. The purpose of these regulations is to reduce occupational injury, illness, and death through the establishment and enforcement of safety standards and regulations and the provision for mandatory training. In addition to national laws and standards, many states and provinces also have occupational safety and health laws.

Supplementing applicable laws, many countries also have national safety standards. **ANSI Z133** is the safety standard for arboricultural operations in the United States. It is published by the International Society of Arboriculture under the requirements of the American National Standards Institute (ANSI). It is intended to outline safety

FIGURE 2.2 A small investment of time in safety training can save a great deal in downtime, insurance, injuries, and damages.

standards for workers engaged in arboriculture practices, such as pruning, cabling, or removing trees. Workers in Canada must comply with the standards established by the **Canadian Standards Association (CSA)**. State regulations or company policies may be more restrictive.

It is important for all tree care workers to be familiar with and comply with all applicable standards and regulations. It is the responsibility of employers to ensure that all safety regulations and policies are met, but it is the responsibility of all workers to commit to working safely.

Certain terminology is consistent throughout most safety regulations. **Approved** means acceptable to the federal, state, provincial, or local enforcing authority having jurisdiction. In many cases, the word "approved" pertains to certain equipment. For example, the ANSI Z133 standard often references other pertinent standards that regulate certain types of equipment. It is common to see references to these other standards on the labels of various pieces of equipment.

Two additional terms are important to know when reading standards. **Shall** denotes a mandatory requirement; **should** denotes an advisory recommendation.

This text is not a substitute for any safety standard, nor can it reference all of the pertinent standards and regulations for tree work performed in all countries or regions. Workers should familiarize themselves with the standards and regulations pertinent to where they work. Also, the content of standards takes precedence over this and other educational texts.

USE OF "SHALL," "SHOULD," AND "MUST"

Because of inconsistencies between standards in different regions, and for the sake of readability, the use of the terms "shall," "should," and "must" in this text does not necessarily parallel the requirements of ANSI, OSHA, or any specific standards. This text is based primarily on ANSI Z133 standards, although many of the requirements are similar to or the same as those in other standards.

PERSONAL PROTECTIVE EQUIPMENT (PPE)

Tree workers should wear clothing and footwear appropriate for the work conditions and weather. Fabrics should be durable yet allow for free movement. Loose-fitting clothing may catch in machinery and become a hazard. Jewelry should not be worn because it may catch on equipment.

FIGURE 2.3 Head and eye protection must be worn by tree workers at all times.

A worker's safety gear is called **personal protective equipment (PPE)**. This equipment includes head, eye, face, hearing, and foot protection. It also includes apparel specifically designed to prevent chain saw cuts from occurring, often in the form of chain saw pants or chaps. In many regions, PPE also refers to fall protection, including harnesses, hardware, and ropes. For the purposes of this publication, PPE refers to the protective wear on the body. Wearing the required PPE is a "shall" requirement in almost all jurisdictions of the world.

All tree workers must wear head protection (hard hats or climbing-style helmets) to comply with applicable impact, penetration, and electrical requirements. Equipment manufacturers have developed a wide variety of lightweight, comfortable climbing helmets that have many features, such as ventilation and incorporated face and/or hearing protection. Some climbing helmets incorporate equipment for communicating with ground personnel.

Eye protection must be worn when performing tree work. If a worker is poked in the eye by even a small twig, irreparable damage may be done to the eye. Sawdust and wood chips from chain saws and **chippers** pose a significant threat to a worker's eyes. Tree workers must wear protective glasses or goggles. Some protect against ultraviolet (UV) rays as well. Prescription safety glasses are also available and can be worn by workers needing corrective lenses. Some workers also prefer to wear face shields or visors, such as those attached to some hard hats. These face

FIGURE 2.4 Modern climbing helmets are designed for side and rear protection and comfort while working. Some climbing helmets incorporate equipment for communicating with ground personnel.

FIGURE 2.5 Prescription safety glasses can be worn by workers needing corrective lenses.

FIGURE 2.6 A face shield provides added protection against flying debris, but may not be a substitute for protective glasses.

FIGURE 2.7 Hearing protection must be worn by workers using chain saws or chippers. Prolonged exposure to loud equipment can result in permanent hearing damage.

FIGURE 2.8 Leg protection is required by ANSI Z133 for chain saw use on the ground, and is required for all chain saw use in some countries.

shields offer additional protection to the face, but may not be considered a substitute for protective glasses. In the US, workers should look for an ANSI Z87.1 marking to see if the face shield is approved for use as eye protection.

Prolonged exposure to the noise of chain saws and brush chippers can cause permanent hearing loss. Hearing protection is required for workers who are exposed to loud equipment for prolonged periods of time. Because tree workers use chain saws and chippers frequently, hearing protection must be used whenever this equipment is operated. Workers may choose to use either earmuff- or earplug-type hearing protection equipment, provided the devices chosen meet appropriate standards.

Leg protection should be worn when operating chain saws. In the United States, this is only mandatory for chain saw use on the ground, but many countries require leg protection any time a chain saw is used. Leg protection may be in the form of **chaps** or chain saw pants. The fabric of the leg protection apparel is designed to jam the sprocket and slow the cutters of the saw chain if contact is made. Leg protection has been shown to reduce the occurrence and severity of chain saw injuries. Newer designs of chain saw pants are lightweight and less bulky than early models. Other work clothing has been developed with chain saw protection incorporated into the fabric. Examples include shirts, jackets, gloves, boots/shoes, and bib-style pants. Some countries may require that cut-resistant clothing be worn when working with chain saws.

All tree workers should wear sturdy work boots to provide good support, traction, and protection for the feet. Boots should offer ankle protection to minimize injuries due to slips, trips, and falls. Many styles and types of approved work boots are available. Some newer designs have chain saw protection. If climbing spurs are used frequently,

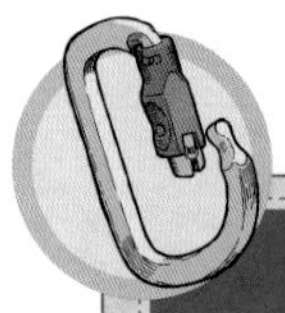

PPE FOR TREE CLIMBERS

- Climbing helmet or hard hat
- Eye protection
- Hearing protection for chain saw or chipper operation
- Leg protection for chain saw operation, where required
- Foot protection
- Gloves

climbers might choose boots with a deep, square heel to brace the stirrup of the climbing spur, and a steel or polymer shank for arch support and comfort. Other boots are designed with flat, rubberized soles to facilitate better contact with tree bark and climbing lines. A stiffer toe box may be preferred by climbers using ascenders or other devices that attach to the boot. Workers should check their local and regional regulations for requirements for the use of steel-toed boots.

FIGURE 2.9 Good communication among workers is an integral part of working safely.

Regulations requiring the use of gloves in tree care operations vary. Some regulations require gloves for tree workers. Gloves are strongly recommended for certain operations, such as sharpening saw chains, handling rigging lines, and chipping brush. Workers must not wear gauntlet-type gloves while chipping brush, however, because these gloves may get caught up in the brush. If gloves are to be worn when climbing trees, they should be a type that provides a good grip to prevent the climber's hands from slipping. For use with rigging lines, a leather-type glove may be preferred.

GOOD COMMUNICATION

Good communication among workers is an integral part of working safely. Workers must coordinate operations on the ground and aloft in the trees, and there is little margin for error. Each worker on the crew must always be aware of what the others are doing, and each must take conscious precautionary measures to prevent accidents.

There must be a clear and efficient means of communication between climbers and ground workers so that each know when it is safe for a ground worker to enter the work zone, including the **landing zone** or **drop zone**, where branches are being dropped or lowered to the ground.

The voice **command-and-response system** ensures that warning signals are heard, acknowledged, and acted upon. Various warning words can be used, but the entire crew must agree on a communication system. For example, the climber commands loudly, "Stand clear," but does not proceed until hearing the acknowledgment, "Clear." When there are multiple workers on the job, confusion can be reduced by assigning one person to respond to the climber after ensuring that the area is clear and safe. Some companies have instituted a 3-step communication system to include cross acknowledgment of commands. Communication should be loud and clear, allowing no room for uncertainty.

There are times when it may be difficult for workers to hear each other. In these cases, hand signals can be used as well. Technology presents some even better solutions, with radios incorporated into headgear. Bluetooth systems are being used as well, and may be incorporated into an existing earmuff setup.

FIGURE 2.10 **Workers must know when it is safe to enter a work zone. The voice command-and-response system is a good way to maintain safety.**

JOB BRIEFING

Each job should begin with a job briefing, which explains and coordinates the activities of every worker. The **job briefing** summarizes what has to be done and who will be doing each task; the potential hazards and how to prevent or minimize them; and what special PPE may be required.

The job briefing should, at a minimum, communicate the following:

- Work to be done and the work procedures
- Communication protocols
- Hazards associated with the job, including electrical hazards
- Precautions and mitigation measures for dealing with hazards
- Work assignments (who does what)
- Personal protective equipment
- Emergency procedures

All workers must have a clear understanding of the communication system that will be used. The onsite supervisor should formulate and communicate the **work plan**. There should be no question about assignments so that the work is well coordinated. Teamwork is essential on a tree crew. This is also a good time to check for cell service or to locate landlines that may be used in case of an emergency.

GENERAL SAFETY

General safety at the worksite begins with proper training. All workers must be adequately trained for their work requirements. Workers should be aware of all applicable safety regulations, and employers must ensure that all workers understand the safety requirements. Safe work procedures must be established. Employers must instruct their employees in the proper use of all equipment and require that all safe working practices be followed. It is also important to train all workers to recognize and reduce or eliminate hazards related to each task they must perform. Employers must document the training.

FIGURE 2.11 Every crew must carry an approved and adequately stocked first-aid kit.

Emergency Response

It is recommended, and required in some regions, that all tree workers receive training in **first aid** and **cardiopulmonary resuscitation (CPR)**. Most companies require that at least two members of each crew have this training. In addition, an approved and adequately stocked first-aid kit must be provided on each truck. The first-aid kit and emergency rescue kit should be taken off the truck at the start of each job so that they are available even if the truck leaves the site to empty the load. All employees must be instructed in the use of first-aid kits and in emergency procedures. Emergency phone numbers should be programmed into cell phones and posted in the truck. All workers must be able to provide the worksite address/location to emergency personnel on the phone.

All crew members must be trained in **emergency response** procedures. Each individual must know what to do in an emergency situation. All climbers should be trained and capable of carrying out an **aerial rescue**. Whenever there is a climber in a tree, there should be a second worker on site and within earshot who is capable of performing an aerial rescue if necessary. Many companies practice emergency response and aerial rescue procedures on a regular basis. Practice will improve efficiency and skills and will reduce the chance of panic or a second incident in the event of an actual emergency. More detailed information about emergency response and aerial rescue can be found in Chapter 5.

"LOW AND SLOW"

Tree climbers often use the expression "low and slow." This refers to the principle that new equipment, knots, and techniques should always be introduced in a low-risk environment—low to the ground and tried out slowly.

The same concept can apply to most aspects of tree work. It is best to avoid combining multiple new processes in a work environment in which the consequences of a mistake are severe.

Poisonous Plants and Biting Insects and Animals

All employees must be instructed in the identification of common poisonous plants, such as poison ivy, poison oak, and wild parsnip. Training should include preventive measures as well as treatment following exposure. Workers must also be trained in techniques for dealing with stinging or biting insects and with other animals that could be encountered in trees.

FIGURE 2.12 All tree workers must be instructed in the identification and treatment of common poisonous plants.

FIGURE 2.13 Gas must be dispensed into approved containers only.

Extreme Weather

Worker training should include guidance for working in extreme weather conditions such as heat, cold, snow, and strong winds. The first consideration is selecting and wearing appropriate attire for the weather. It is also important for workers to stay well hydrated. Workers must be trained to recognize signs and symptoms of heat stress, frostbite, and other weather-related ailments.

Fire Prevention

Trucks should be equipped with a fire extinguisher, and all employees should be trained in its use. Gasoline-powered equipment must be refueled only after the engine has been stopped. Any spilled fuel should be removed before starting. Equipment should not be started or operated within 10 ft (3 m) of the refueling site. Smoking is prohibited when handling or working around any flammable liquid. Flammable liquids must be stored in, handled with, and dispensed from approved safety containers and kept separate from all ropes and equipment. Gas cans must always be placed on the ground before they are filled; otherwise, static electricity can create an arc, starting a fire or explosion.

Traffic Control

A very important safety consideration is traffic control. Effective means for control of pedestrian and vehicular traffic must be instituted on every jobsite. This may include safety cones, warning signs, barriers, and flags. It is the legal responsibility of work crews to "secure the work zone" to make sure that no individuals or vehicles pass under trees where tree work is in progress and to ensure the safety of the workers. All crew members should be trained in the steps involved with setting up the worksite. Traffic control devices used in tree operations must conform to the applicable federal, state, or provincial regulations. Traffic control procedures must follow applicable standards and guidelines.

FIGURE 2.14 **Protecting vehicles and pedestrians is an important part of worksite safety.**

Work Zone/Drop Zone

The crew must also establish the work zone and clarify as part of the job briefing what will happen where on the jobsite. An important part of the work zone is the drop zone, where climbers will be dropping or lowering cut portions of the tree. The drop zone is an area in which the ground workers must take great care, and a good communication system between climbers and ground workers is essential.

ELECTRICAL HAZARDS

Before performing tree work on any site, an inspection must be made to determine whether any electrical hazards exist. An electrical hazard exists when there is a risk of injury or death associated with direct or indirect contact with an electrical conductor. Workers must receive adequate and documented training in electrical hazard tree work procedures to perform tree work in proximity to electrical conductors. Employers are required to certify this training.

An **electrical conductor** is defined as any overhead or underground electrical device, including communication wires and cables, power lines, and related components and facilities. All such lines and cables must be considered energized with potentially fatal voltages.

Every tree worker shall be instructed that a **direct contact** is made when any part of the body contacts an energized conductor or other energized electrical fixture or apparatus. An **indirect contact** is made when any part of the body touches any conductive object in contact with an energized conductor. An indirect contact can be made through conductive tools, tree branches, trucks, equipment, or other conductive objects, or as a result of communication wires or cables, fences, or guy wires becoming energized. When working around energized lines, it is essential to use nonconductive tools.

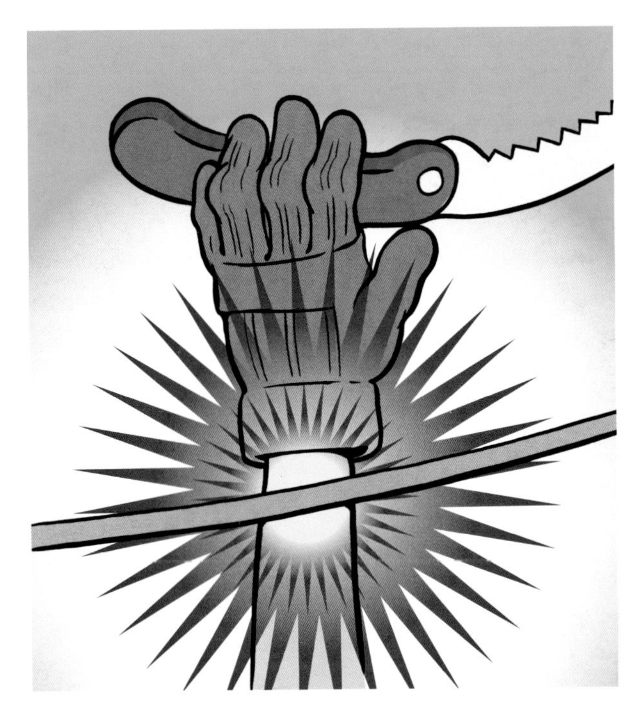

FIGURE 2.15 Direct contact with an energized conductor could be fatal.

FIGURE 2.16 Indirect contact can be made through conductive tools. Only those workers trained and approved can work near conductors, and only non-conductive tools can be used.

Electric shock occurs when a tree worker, by either direct or indirect contact with an energized

FIGURE 2.17 When an aerial lift truck is in use and the platform is near electrical conductors, the truck could become energized.

conductor, tree limb, tool, piece of equipment, or other object, provides a path for the flow of electricity from a conductor to a grounded object or to the ground itself. Simultaneous contact with two energized conductors may result in serious injury or electrocution.

When an aerial lift is in use and the platform is near electrical conductors, workers should be instructed about the possibility of the truck becoming energized. If the truck also has a chip body, workers should stop chipping whenever the lift is in proximity to electrical conductors.

Powered hand tools (except those with a self-contained power source) must never be used in trees near an energized electrical conductor when there is a possibility of the power cord contacting the conductor. Tool operators must use tools in accordance with the manufacturers' instructions. When tools are used aloft, an independent line or lanyard should be used to prevent the tool from falling. Operators should prevent cords from becoming entangled or coming in contact with water.

Footwear, including those with nonconductive soles and dielectric overshoes, should not be considered as providing any measure of protection from electrical hazards. Rubber gloves, with or without leather or other protective covering, must not be considered as providing any measure of protection from electrical hazards.

CHAIN SAW SAFETY

The chain saw has been ranked as one of the most hazardous pieces of equipment in the industry today. It is also one of the most commonly used.

FIGURE 2.18 Safe starting position.

Using a chain saw to prune or remove a tree can greatly reduce the time and effort involved, but care must be taken to ensure the safety of the climber and the ground workers. Careless use of a chain saw in a tree can cause considerable damage to the tree and serious risk of injury to the workers. Safe operation on the ground and in the tree requires proper training and adherence to safety procedures.

Chain saw operators should follow the manufacturer's operating and maintenance instructions. Personal protective equipment that must be worn by chain saw operators includes head protection, work boots, eye protection, and hearing protection. Regulations vary in different countries regarding leg protection. In the United States, leg protection is required when operating a chain saw on the ground.

The operator must have a secure footing when starting a saw. The immediate area should be clear of debris. The chain brake should always be engaged before

FIGURE 2.19 The chain saw should be firmly gripped with both hands. Keeping the left arm straight helps to control the saw.

a chain saw is started. Drop starting (the act of pulling the starter cord while simultaneously directing the saw bar away from the body) is a potentially hazardous technique and is against many regulations. Larger saws should be started on the ground, while firmly braced, with the chain brake engaged. The alternate method is to start the saw using the **leglock method**, with the saw braced behind the right knee.

The saw should be gripped with both hands. No worker should ever operate a chain saw with one hand. Both handles should be gripped firmly with the thumbs wrapped around the handle. When cutting on the ground, it is best to operate the saw to the right of the body with the left arm straight and the right arm bent. Keeping the chain saw engine close to the body increases control and reduces operator fatigue.

The chain brake must be engaged any time the operator takes a hand off the running saw, when the chain saw is set down, or when the operator takes more than two steps. If the operator is moving between cuts, the chain brake should be engaged, and the operator's hand should be off the throttle lever. The engine must be stopped for all cleaning, refueling, and adjustments except where the manufacturer's procedures require otherwise.

The chain saw operator must be aware of the presence and activity of other workers in the vicinity. Workers should never approach a chain saw operator from the rear. If two workers are operating chain saws simultaneously, they should be at least 10 ft (3 m) apart.

Chain saw operators should understand the **reactive forces** of the saw. When cutting with the bottom of the bar, the saw has a tendency to pull the saw into the cut. When cutting with the top of the bar, the saw pushes back toward the operator.

FIGURE 2.20 The chain saw operator must be aware of the presence and activity of other workers in the vicinity.

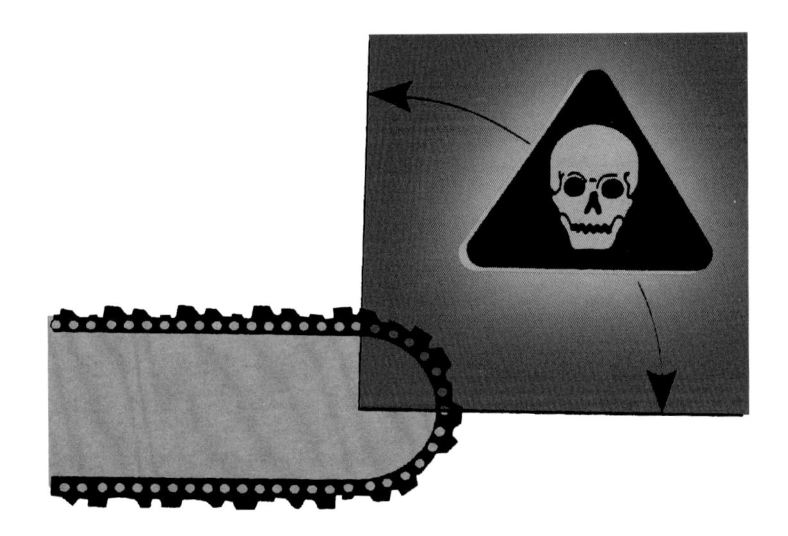

FIGURE 2.21 Kickback occurs when the upper portion of the tip of the guide bar (kickback quadrant) contacts a log or other object.

A common cause of chain saw injury is **kickback**. Kickback occurs when the upper portion of the tip of the guide bar (**kickback quadrant**) contacts a log or other object. Operators must always be aware of where the tip of the guide bar is and should prevent the upper quadrant of

FIGURE 2.22 Operators must always be aware of where the tip of the guide bar is and should prevent the upper quadrant of the guide-bar tip from coming into contact with objects.

FIGURE 2.23 Care must be taken when cutting a limb under pressure.

the guide-bar tip from coming in contact with objects. A firm grip should be maintained with the thumbs wrapped around the handles. Kickback occurs at a speed many times faster than a human can react. The operator must be positioned such that the saw cannot contact any part of the body if it were to kick back. A chain saw should not be operated above shoulder level.

Climbers must take extra precautions when using a chain saw aloft in a tree. Only experienced climbers with proper chain saw training should ever use a chain saw in a tree. The climber must use a second means of being secured in the tree, such as a safety lanyard, before making a chain saw cut. Stable footing and work positioning are important to maintain control. All chain saw safety procedures apply, including the two-hand rule and avoiding making cuts above shoulder level. The climber should climb with a hand saw to make finishing cuts; a hand saw can also be used to aid in the case of a pinched chain saw bar.

Work positioning is an important safety consideration when using a chain saw in a tree. Climbers must be sure they are in a safe, stable position before cutting, usually above or to the side of the limb being cut. This means avoiding being in a position that could cause the climber to be injured in the follow-through from the cut or if the saw kicks back. Climbers must also be aware of the position of the climbing line, safety lanyard, and all other ropes to avoid accidental cutting. Finally, it is important to avoid being in a position of being struck by the limb that is cut.

CHIPPER SAFETY

Brush chippers can be very hazardous machines, and proper training and safe work practices are essential when operating them. Training should

FIGURE 2.24 Climbers must take extra precautions when using a chain saw aloft in a tree. All proper PPE must be worn. The climber must use a second means of being secured in the tree. Two hands must be used at all times to operate a chain saw.

include instruction on daily inspection and maintenance, towing procedures, starting the chipper, feeding in brush, and the potential safety hazards involved with operation. All instructional and warning stickers and labels on the chipper must be in place and legible.

Proper PPE is required. Loose clothing, chain saw chaps, jewelry, climbing harnesses or body belts, and gauntlet-type gloves must not be worn while operating chippers because they could be caught on brush and pull the operator into the chipper. Safety vests, if worn while operating a chipper, should be of the tear-away style. All ropes must be kept well away from the chipper and brush staging areas.

FIGURE 2.25 When using a chain saw in a tree, climbers must be aware of the position of the climbing line and all other ropes to avoid accidental cutting.

SAFE CHIPPER OPERATION

Be mindful of potential hazards that might be inside a tree, such as old cables, nails, concrete, or other nonorganic objects that could become projectiles.

Brush should always be fed from the side of the infeed chute, and the worker feeding the brush should move away after the brush is fed. The larger butt end of each branch should be fed in first. Smaller limbs should be pushed into the chipper with larger limbs. Material should be cut and properly prepared to enter the chipper feed wheels before placing it on the feed table to avoid the need to work and make cuts at the feed table. No part of the operator's body should ever reach beyond the back edge of the infeed chute. The operator should be careful to avoid placing foreign material—such as tools, rocks, wires, or other debris—into the chipper because such material could damage the knives or cause projectiles to be thrown from the machine.

FIGURE 2.26 Brush should always be fed from the side, and the worker feeding the brush should move away after the brush is fed. The larger butt end of each branch should be fed in first. Note the tear-away vest worn by the worker when operating a chipper.

Many accidents have occurred when workers attempted to perform maintenance while the chipper disk or drum was still moving. No person should ever work on a chipper unless the engine is turned off, the ignition key is removed, and the cutter wheel is completely stopped (with lock pin in place, if applicable) and prevented from moving.

PALM SAFETY

Some species of palms retain a full **palm skirt**, consisting of dead fronds that may remain attached and hanging along some or all of the length of the trunk. Birds, rats, raccoons, centipedes, scorpions, and bats are among the species that may nest within the skirt. Large gaps in the skirt can indicate **sloughing**, which is when large sections of frond rings detach and settle on a lower portion of fronds. Sloughing of fronds is a leading cause of fatalities among climbers in palms, as they can pose an asphyxiation risk. A sloughed skirt on a climber is a particularly challenging scenario for a rescue, which is why climbing and pruning under the skirt must be avoided.

Fan palms can contain a significant amount of dry, dead material within these skirts. Arborists should be aware of the potential for a fire hazard. Chain saws used should be properly operated and maintained, and workers should not smoke while working to avoid starting a fire.

Palms require a larger drop zone for pruning or removal operations, as fronds can often glide down, away from the trunk. Precautions should be taken to avoid dropping fronds onto or permitting fronds to blow into electrical lines.

FIGURE 2.27 Proper lifting technique can help prevent back injuries.

LIFTING

The most common injury causing missed work among tree workers is back injury. Before lifting any weight, the tree worker should:

1. Be sure the path is clear if the weight is to be carried from one place to another.
2. Decide exactly how the object should be grasped to avoid sharp edges, slivers, splinters, or other things that might cause injury.
3. Maintain the center of gravity close to the body.
4. Make a preliminary lift to be sure the load can be handled safely.
5. Place feet solidly.
6. Crouch as close to the load as possible with legs bent.
7. Maintain normal back curvature. It is not necessary to attempt to keep the back straight.
8. Lift with the legs, not the back.
9. Get help from a second worker when necessary.

KEY CONCEPTS

1. In the context of a safety standard, "shall" denotes a mandatory requirement, and "should" denotes an advisory recommendation.
2. Personal protective equipment (PPE) is required during tree care operations. Workers must know the required PPE for the task performed.
3. All overhead and underground electrical conductors shall be considered energized with potentially fatal voltages.
4. A documented job briefing should be performed before each job and be reviewed should any conditions change on the jobsite. The job briefing should be completed with all members of the crew present.
5. Chain saws shall always be operated with two hands. Use of chain saw protective clothing varies based on region and work practice.
6. When chipping brush, the brush should always be fed from the side, and no part of the operator's body should ever reach beyond the edge of the infeed chute.

WORKBOOK

MATCHING

_____ shall
_____ approved
_____ CPR
_____ direct contact
_____ should
_____ indirect contact
_____ ANSI Z133
_____ chaps

A. leg protection for chain saw use
B. advisory recommendation
C. cardiopulmonary resuscitation
D. body touches energized conductor
E. US safety standard for tree work
F. mandatory requirement
G. meets applicable safety standards
H. touching an object in contact with an energized conductor

TRUE/FALSE

1. T F Head protection need only be worn while there are climbers in the trees.
2. T F Eye protection is a good idea but is not required for tree work.
3. T F Hearing protection may be in the form of earplugs or earmuff-type devices.
4. T F Workers must not wear gauntlet-type gloves while chipping brush.
5. T F The voice command-and-response system ensures that warning signals are heard, acknowledged, and acted upon.
6. T F The job briefing summarizes, among other things, what has to be done and who will be doing each task; the potential hazards and how to prevent or minimize them; what special PPE may be required; and emergency procedures.
7. T F Employers must instruct their employees in the proper use of all equipment.
8. T F Carrying a first-aid kit on each truck is recommended but optional.
9. T F The first-aid kit should be left on the truck at all times, except when in use.
10. T F Gas-powered equipment should not be started or operated within 10 ft (3 m) of the refueling site.
11. T F All power and communication wires shall be considered charged with potentially fatal voltages.
12. T F An electrical conductor is defined as any overhead or underground electrical device, including wires and cables, power lines, and other such facilities.
13. T F Rubber footwear and gloves provide absolute protection from electrical hazards.

14. T F Drop starting is the recommended method for starting a chain saw.
15. T F On the ground, both hands are required for chain saw operation, but one hand can be used in the tree.
16. T F Chain saw engines must be stopped for refueling.
17. T F Kickback can occur when the upper tip of the chain saw guide bar contacts an object.
18. T F A well-trained climber, in good condition, should be able to dodge the kickback of a chain saw.
19. T F The most common injury causing missed work among tree workers is back injury.
20. T F When chipping brush, you should stand directly behind the chipper infeed chute to feed branches in.

SAMPLE TEST QUESTIONS

1. Which of the following should be considered energized with a potentially fatal voltage?

   a. overhead electric lines
   b. underground electric lines
   c. telephone and cable TV wires
   d. all of the above

2. Head protection is required for tree workers

   a. whenever performing tree care operations
   b. when specified by the supervisor
   c. whenever there are climbers working aloft
   d. only if chain saws or chippers are in use

3. To avoid chain saw kickback, you should

   a. avoid cutting with the top of the bar
   b. never operate a chain saw on its side (cutting horizontally)
   c. not allow the upper tip of the guide bar to contact an object
   d. not allow the lower tip of the guide bar to contact an object

CHAPTER

3 ROPES AND KNOTS

LEARNING OBJECTIVES

The tree worker will be able to:

- Discuss the construction types and materials used for arborists' ropes.
- Define the terminology used to describe the parts of a rope in use.
- List the various knots used in tree care operations.
- Describe the application, advantages, and limitations of various knots used by arborists.

IMPORTANT TERMS

3-strand rope
12-strand rope
16-strand rope
24-strand rope
anchor hitch
bend
bight
Blake's hitch
bowline
butterfly knot
carabiner
climbing hitch
clove + half hitches
clove hitch
cow hitch
directional knot
Distel hitch
double braid
double fisherman's knot
endline knots
fall
figure-8 knot
friction hitch
hitch
hitch cord
hollow braid
kernmantle
knot
lead
Michoacán
midline knot
Prusik hitch
running bowline
Schwabisch
sheet bend
slip knot
spliced eye
standing end
standing part
tautline hitch
timber hitch
***Valdôtain tresse* (Vt)**
working end

INTRODUCTION

Rope may be considered the arborist's most important tool. All tree climbing and rigging operations are dependent on ropes. In fact, a climber's life is quite literally hanging on a rope. Tree workers must learn a great deal about rope types, materials, and construction to be able to select appropriate ropes for each application. It is also essential to learn how to inspect ropes and how to maintain them in good condition, as well as when to retire them.

This chapter provides much of the fundamental information about which ropes are appropriate for various uses. Readers are encouraged to consult manufacturers and suppliers for more detailed information when selecting ropes.

It has been said that a "line" is a "rope" in use. This chapter presents the basic terminology for the parts of a line. This terminology is often used as part of instructions for tying knots, for installing equipment, and for tying into a tree for climbing. Readers are encouraged to become familiar with this terminology.

Ropes are not very useful to an arborist unless they can be connected to trees, equipment, and even themselves. Much of this chapter is devoted to the various knots, bends, and hitches used in tree care operations. Each knot includes information about applications, as well as some of the characteristics, advantages, and limitations. Drawings are provided to help with learning to tie the knots. Hands-on instruction is strongly recommended, as is supervision for using knots until they are mastered.

ROPES USED IN TREE CARE

The characteristics of a rope (strength, stretch, durability, etc.) are the result of the materials and techniques used to make it. Polyester and polyester blends are widely used by arborists, and many commercially available climbing and rigging lines are made from polyester, at least in part. Nylon has high strength, stretch, and energy absorption, but tends to lose strength when wet. Natural fibers are generally not as strong as synthetic fibers and can rot over time. Newer fibers, such as high-modulus polyethylene (HMPE) and aramid, have been introduced for arboricultural applications. HMPE introduces improved rope characteristics, such as UV and chemical resistance, ultra-high strength, low weight, and abrasion resistance. However, its stiffness may not make it practical for all uses. Aramid's flexibility and extremely high melting point make it particularly helpful in high-friction areas, such as with a friction hitch (climbing hitch). In many cases, these fibers are blended.

FIGURE 3.1 A 3-strand rope is constructed with three twisted strands and does not have a core.

Many types of ropes are used in arborist climbing and rigging. A **3-strand rope** has relatively low strength and high elongation, and is inexpensive. It is appropriate to run through natural branch unions for climbing or rigging. A major drawback to 3-strand rope is the twisting, or hockling, that occurs as the line is used.

Most modern ropes have a braided construction; 3-strand is the only rope with twisted construction commonly in use in arboriculture today, and its popularity has decreased. Braided ropes vary in the number of fibers and strands used, the diameter of each, and the method and tightness of the braiding. Some arborist ropes are constructed with an inner core and an outer cover.

Arborists' ropes used for climbing or rigging should be durable, without excessive stretch. Climbers need to use ropes that hold their shape and maintain flexibility. Newer ropes are designed to run smoothly through the various mechanical devices in use today. The characteristics of a rope can make it ideal for some applications, yet inappropriate for others.

Kernmantle ropes are those with a cover and an inner core. Although the broad definition of kernmantle includes either braided- or parallel-core construction, the tree care industry has used kernmantle to more specifically refer to those with a parallel core. Some are designed for the core to bear most of the load and for the cover to serve primarily as a protective sheath. Many of the "static" (low stretch) climbing ropes used by arborists, especially in stationary rope systems (explained in Chapter 7), are kernmantle construction. Kernmantle ropes are the only ropes designed to be used with life-supporting toothed cams, and with some other climbing hardware.

Double-braid ropes are just that: a rope inside a rope. Double-braid ropes fall in the kernmantle family, but they have a braided core. Some double-braid ropes are designed for rigging applications. The core and cover are balanced and share the load almost equally. For this reason, they are not recommended for rigging through natural branch unions, in which the friction of the cover with the tree causes an imbalance in the load taken by the core and cover braids. They are exceptionally strong and low-stretch ropes, but should be run only over the smooth sheaves of a block or pulley or the bollard of a friction device. Generally, the fewer the strands, the better the rope will handle abrasion.

A **12-strand rope** is a braided rope which may be loosely woven, making it hollow in the center. Loosely woven, **hollow-braid**, polyester 12-strand rope is often used for rigging slings, but would not be appropriate as a climbing or rigging line. Tightly woven, solid-braid, polyester-blend 12-strand ropes are sometimes used for climbing and rigging through natural branch unions. The number and diameter of the strands compared to the diameter of the rope determine whether the lines can be spliced. They also determine abrasion resistance and whether the rope remains round when loaded.

A **16-strand rope** has relatively large, braided cover strands for strength and abrasion resistance and a small-diameter core to

FIGURE 3.2 Double-braid rope has both a braided sheath and braided core. Both the sheath and core share the load.

FIGURE 3.3 A 12-strand rope is braided with no core.

FIGURE 3.4 A 16-strand rope has a small-diameter core with the strength mostly in the braided cover.

KEEPING ROPES CLEAN

Most ropes can be washed manually, and some can even be machine washed.

keep the rope round and firm under load. In this construction, the core does not carry much of the load. These ropes are commonly used for climbing and tend to be easy to knot.

The **24-strand rope** was introduced to the arboriculture industry more recently than the 16-strand, but immediately became a popular choice. Like 16-strand ropes, they have a core and cover, and they are primarily designated as climbing lines. These 24-strand climbing ropes tend to be strong with minimal stretch. They are typically double-braid designs.

Many ropes can be purchased with a **spliced eye**—interwoven strands forming a loop in one end for easy connectability to hardware. The ability of a rope to be spliced is another important characteristic for arborists' ropes. When rope constructions do not allow for a spliced eye, another option can be a stitched eye. The stitched eye serves a similar function, allowing for easy connectability to hardware. Eyes should be stitched by professionals and must meet industry standards. Stitched eyes should also have a label on the stitching that identifies the manufacturer, the strength of the eye, and its production date.

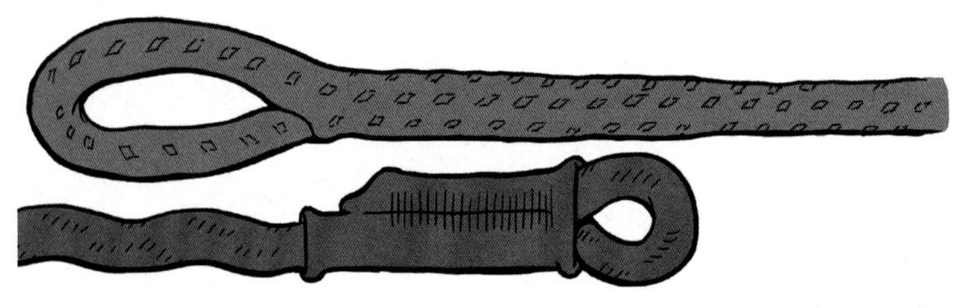

FIGURE 3.5 Hand-spliced eye (top) and stitched eye (bottom).

ROPE INSPECTION

Ropes should be inspected before each use. Dirt can get between fibers and cause abrasion, so keeping ropes as clean as possible is recommended. Most ropes can also be degraded by UV light. The biggest degradation in rope strength comes from the wear and tear of everyday use. Use of knots, bends around hardware, elongations from loads, heat from friction devices, and friction from running over bark all contribute to rope degradation.

When inspecting ropes, tree workers should look for cuts, picks (snags), and frays of the strands. Glazing results from excessive heat, usually from friction, and can significantly reduce a rope's strength. Inconsistencies in the diameter such as bulges, skinny areas, or lumps can indicate significant damage from elongation, debris, or torn inner fibers. If any significant cuts, bulges, or glazing are found, the rope should either be retired or have the affected end cut off. Often, the part that needs to be cut off is near the end, so the rope just becomes a little shorter. Many manufacturers provide excellent inspection information, as well as guidelines for retirement.

BASIC ARBORISTS' KNOTS

All tree workers should be familiar with the knots used in tree work. A climber should know how to tie and untie each of the basic knots and at least two or three **friction hitches (climbing hitches)** used for climbing. Friction hitches are the "climbing knots" used by climbers to position themselves as they move and work in the tree. Although all knots function based on friction, "friction hitches" are so named because they provide the controlled friction needed to hold a climber in place and allow ascent and descent on a line. For this reason, they are also known as "climbing hitches." Some

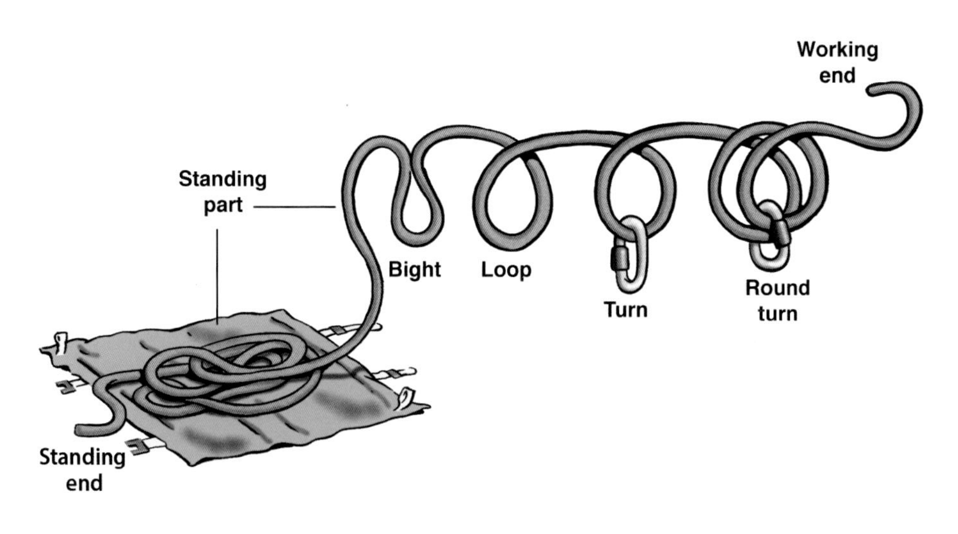

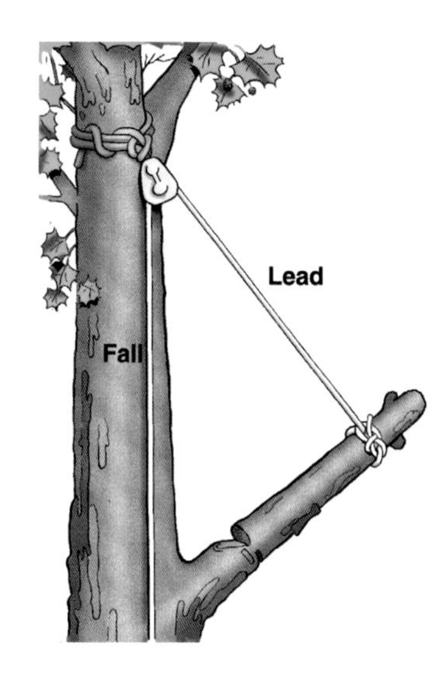

FIGURE 3.6 Parts of a line.

of the same friction hitches used in climbing are also used for other applications, such as in rigging.

A line is a rope in use, usually differentiated by the use: rigging line, climbing line, tagline, etc. A line has a **working end** and a **standing end**, or, the ends in use (usually forming a knot) and not in use, respectively. Figure 3.6 also shows examples of a **bight**, loop, turn, and round turn, and the **lead** and **fall** of a line in use.

"**Knot**" is the general term given for all knots, hitches, and bends. A **hitch** is a type of knot used to secure a rope to an object, another rope, or the **standing part** of the same rope. A **bend** joins two rope ends together. There are several categories of knots, hitches, and bends. Tree climbers use **endline knots** and hitches to secure the climbing line to **carabiners** or rope snaps. Endline knots are also used to tie off branches being rigged.

Some knots are described as being **directional**. A knot is said to be directional if it performs differently when loaded (pulled) from opposite directions or ends. A slip knot, for example, cinches when pulled from one direction but unties when pulled from the opposite direction.

Tree workers should know how each of the common knots is used and the advantages and disadvantages of each.

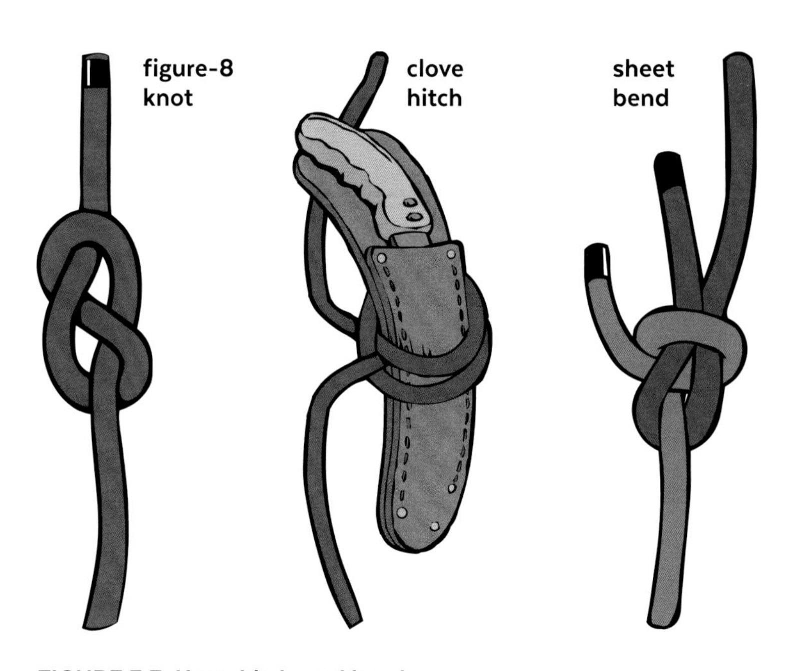

FIGURE 3.7 Knot, hitch, and bend.

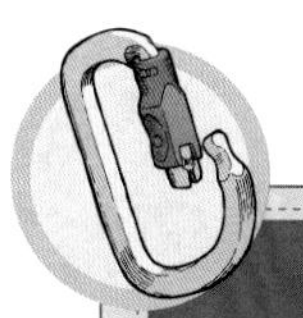

TIE, DRESS, AND SET

Part of knowing how to tie a knot is knowing how to "dress" and "set" the knot properly. To tie a knot, one must first correctly form the knot in the rope. The dressing of the knot is the alignment of the parts; setting it tightens the knot in place.

Figure-8 Knot

- Used as a stopper knot
- Fast and easy-to-tie endline knot

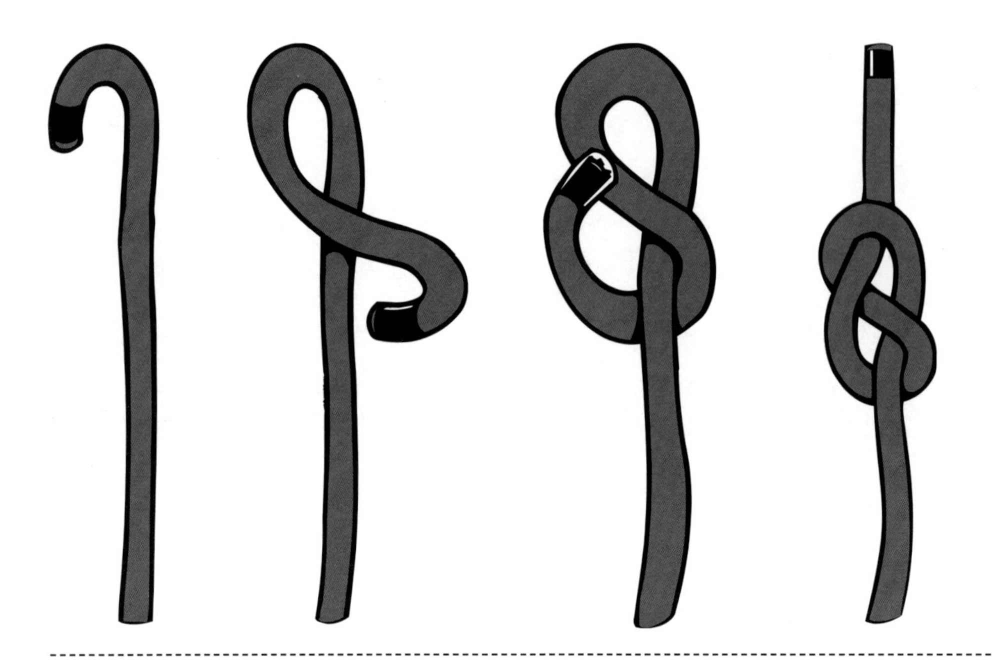

Bowline

- Strong knot for forming a loop
- Easy to untie, even after loading
- The basis for other knots in the "bowline family" (running bowline, bowline on a bight, sheet bend, double bowline)
- The Yosemite finish is shown in orange

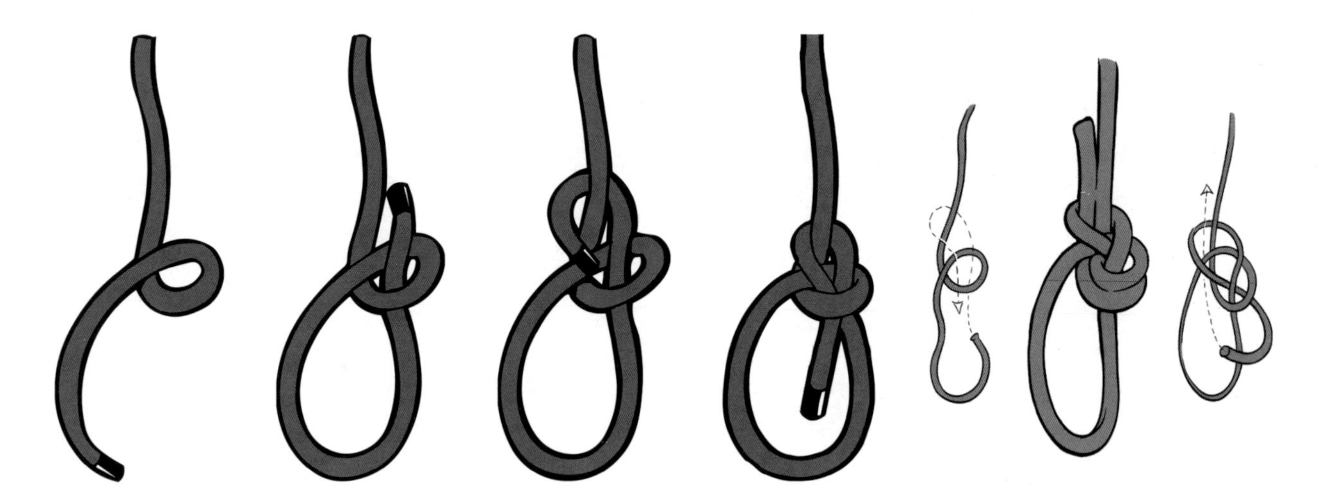

Running Bowline

- Often used in tying off limbs or setting up an anchor in SRS (stationary rope system). When used in any climbing/life support role, should be secured with a Yosemite finish
- Can be tied around something that is far away and "run up" the line and cinched from afar
- Easy to untie after loading
- Cinching functionality is directional

Midline Clove Hitch

- Used to send equipment up to the climber
- Quick to tie as a **midline knot**

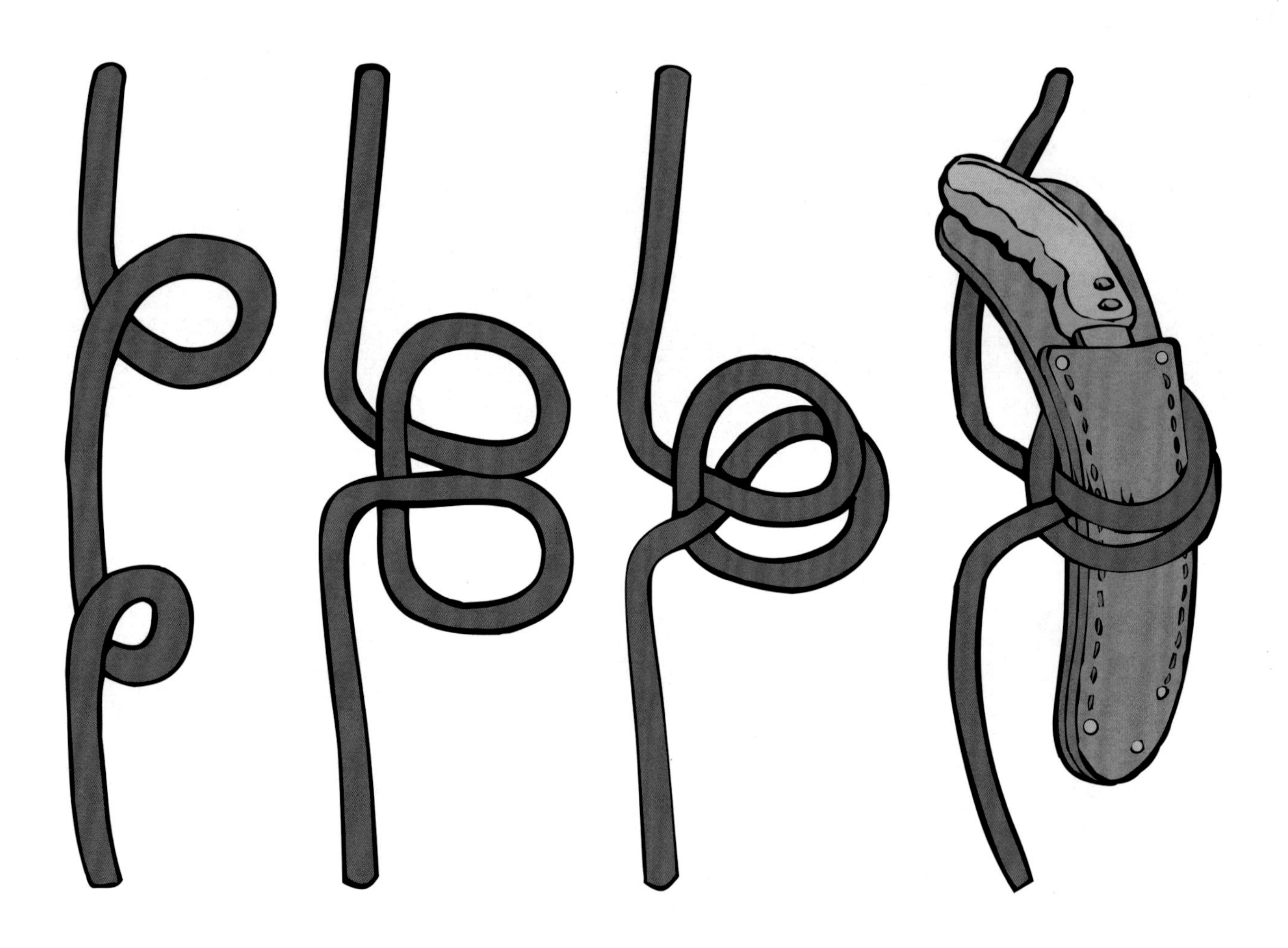

Endline Clove Hitch with Two Half Hitches

- Used (when backed up with at least two half hitches) to tie off limbs or sections of wood
- Quick and easy to tie

Slip Knot

- Easy to tie, even with one hand
- Experienced climbers find many uses for this knot
- A directional knot—it tightens when loaded one way but spills when pulled from the other side

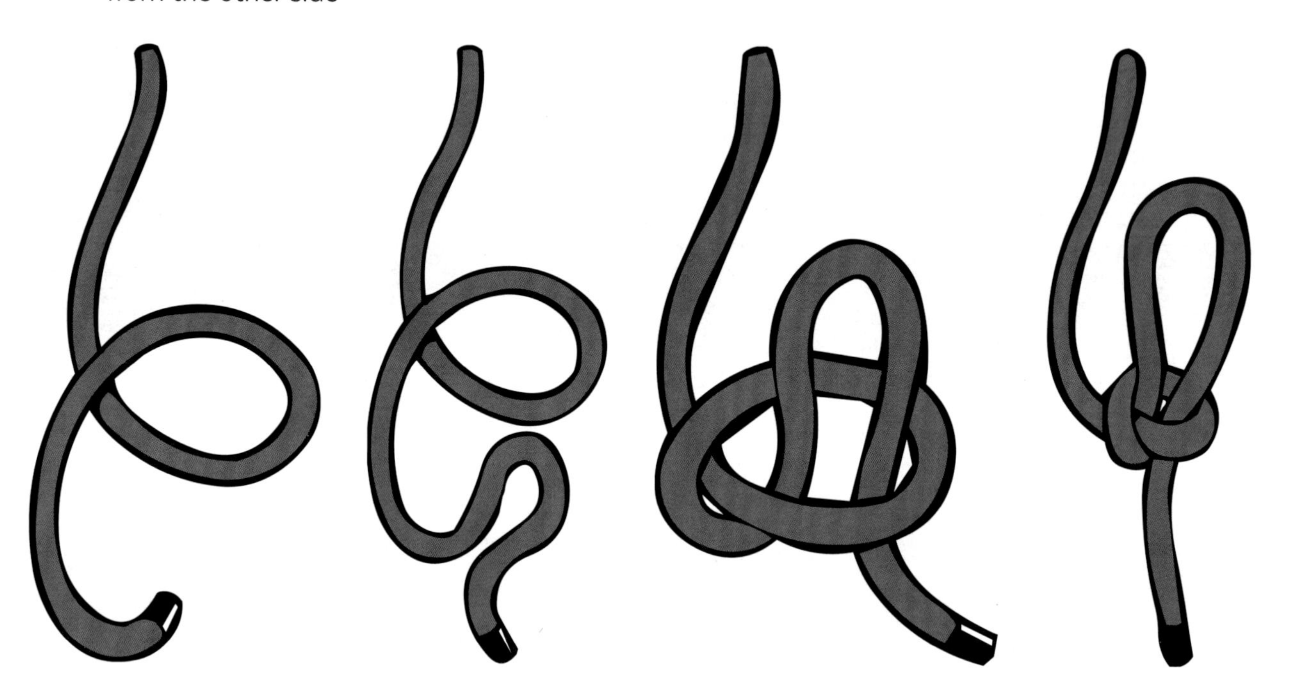

SLIPPED KNOTS

Almost any knot can be “slipped.” Typically this means the final tuck of the working end is replaced by tucking a bight instead, so that the knot can be rapidly untied by pulling on the working end. The knot known as the slip knot is a slipped overhand knot. The bow with which we tie our shoes is a doubly slipped square knot.

Sheet Bend

- Used to join two ropes of different diameters; often used to send a line up to the climber
- The smaller line should be the one tucked under its own standing part
- Essentially, a bowline tied with two ropes

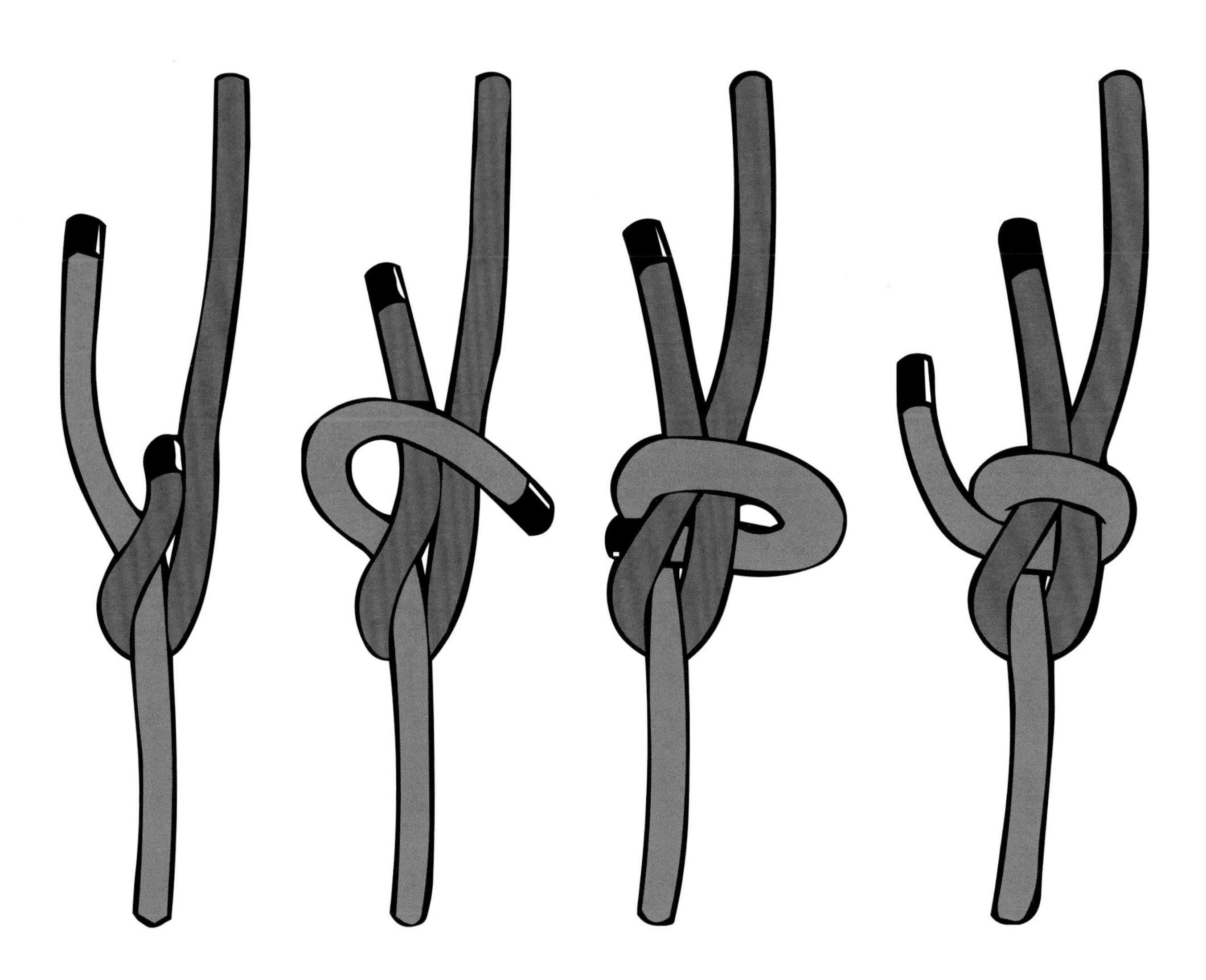

Double Fisherman's Knot

- Used to form a Prusik loop
- Can be used as a termination knot for attachment to hardware (called a scaffold knot, in this application)
- May be difficult to untie after it has been loaded

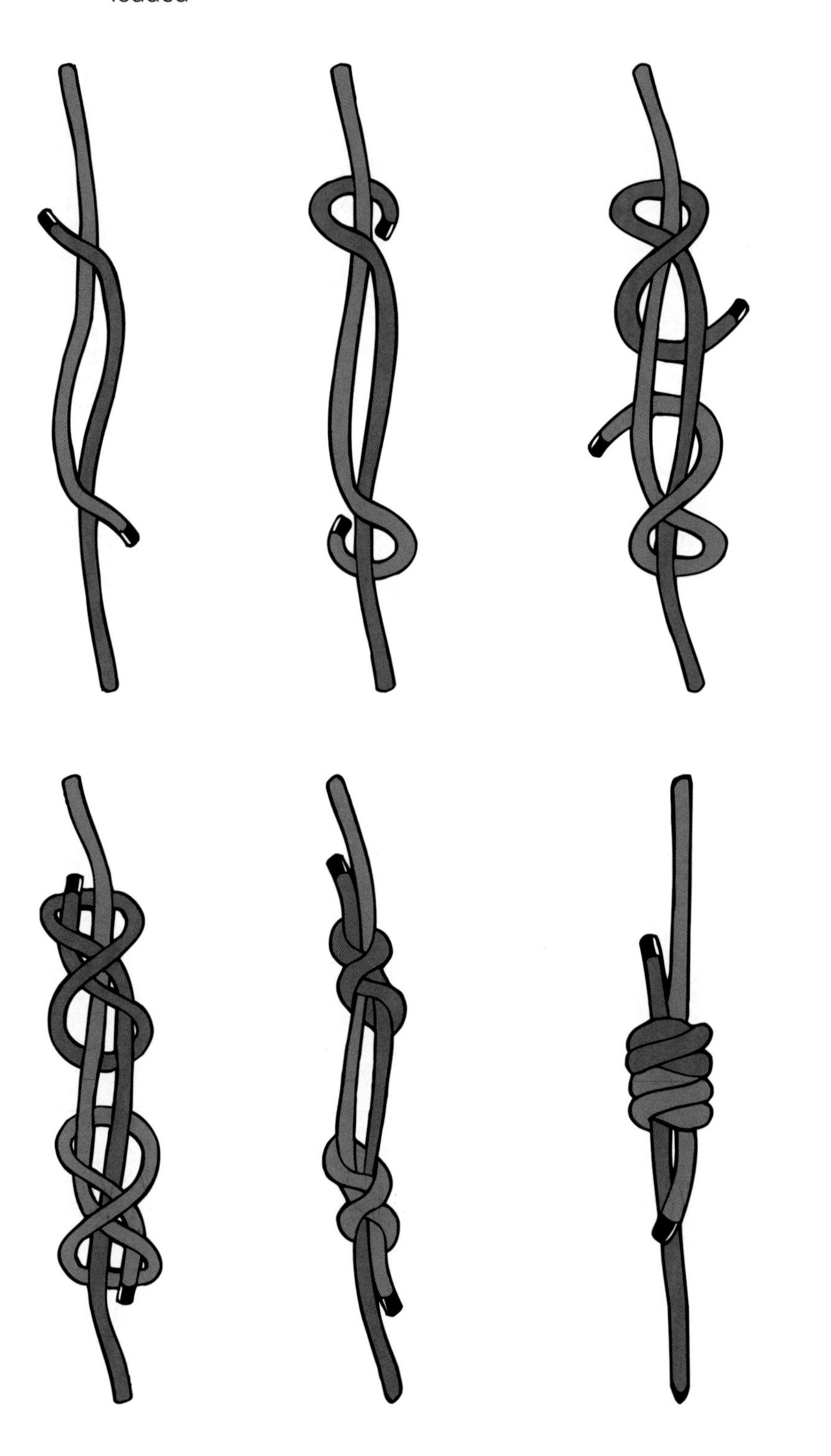

Anchor Hitch

- Used as a termination knot; snugs tightly against a carabiner or other hardware
- Does not loosen when loaded and unloaded repeatedly, though a stopper knot, such as a figure-8, may be added
- Can easily be untied after loading
- Generates two loops around the hardware; may not fit in all hardware
- The loaded side of the knot should be closest to the spine of a carabiner

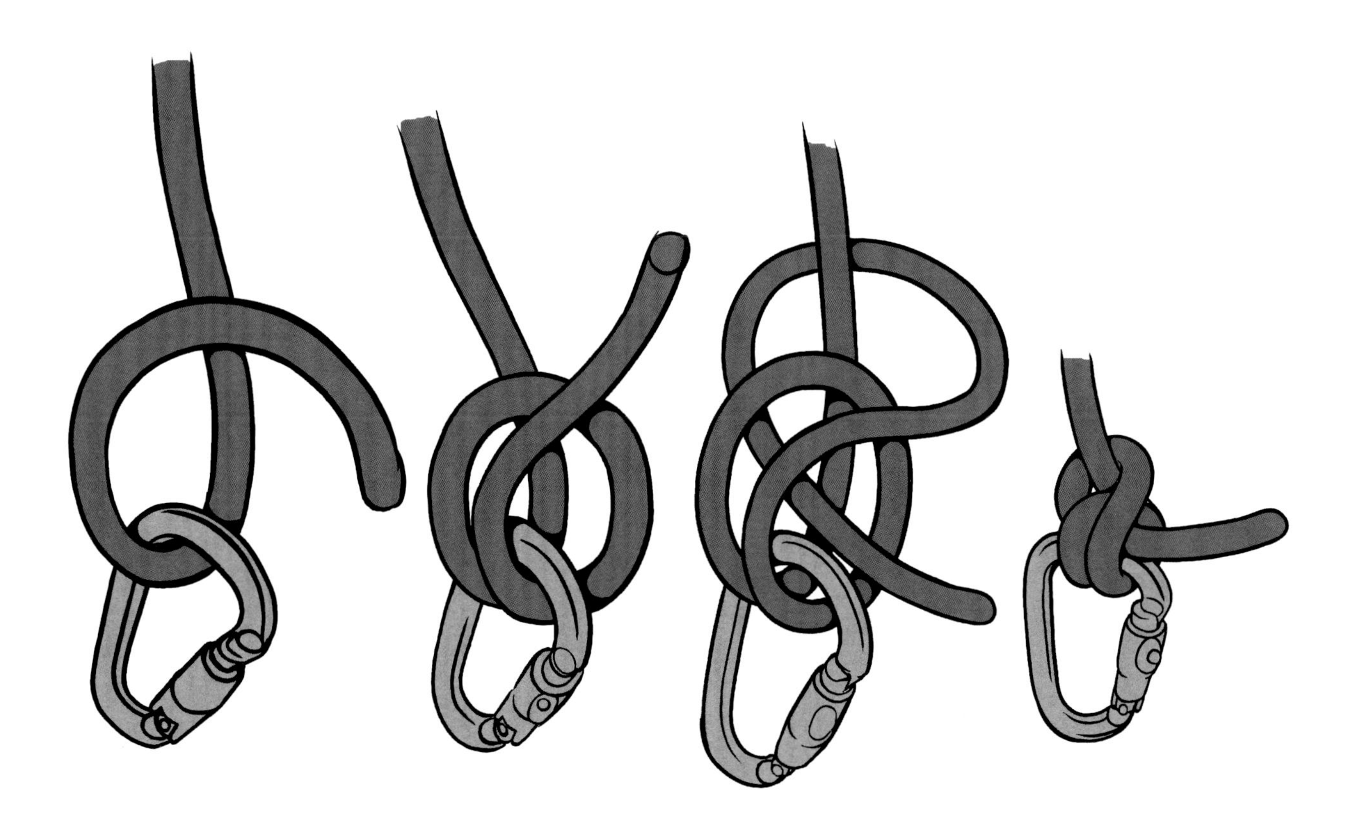

Butterfly

- Primarily used for forming a midline loop
- Symmetrical, without extreme bends; can be loaded in either direction
- May be difficult to untie after it has been heavily loaded

Cow Hitch with Half Hitch

- Tied with a sling and used for securing hardware to a tree
- Variation on a simple girth hitch but formed with a line instead of a loop
- Cinching functionality is directional, though the half hitch minimizes movement

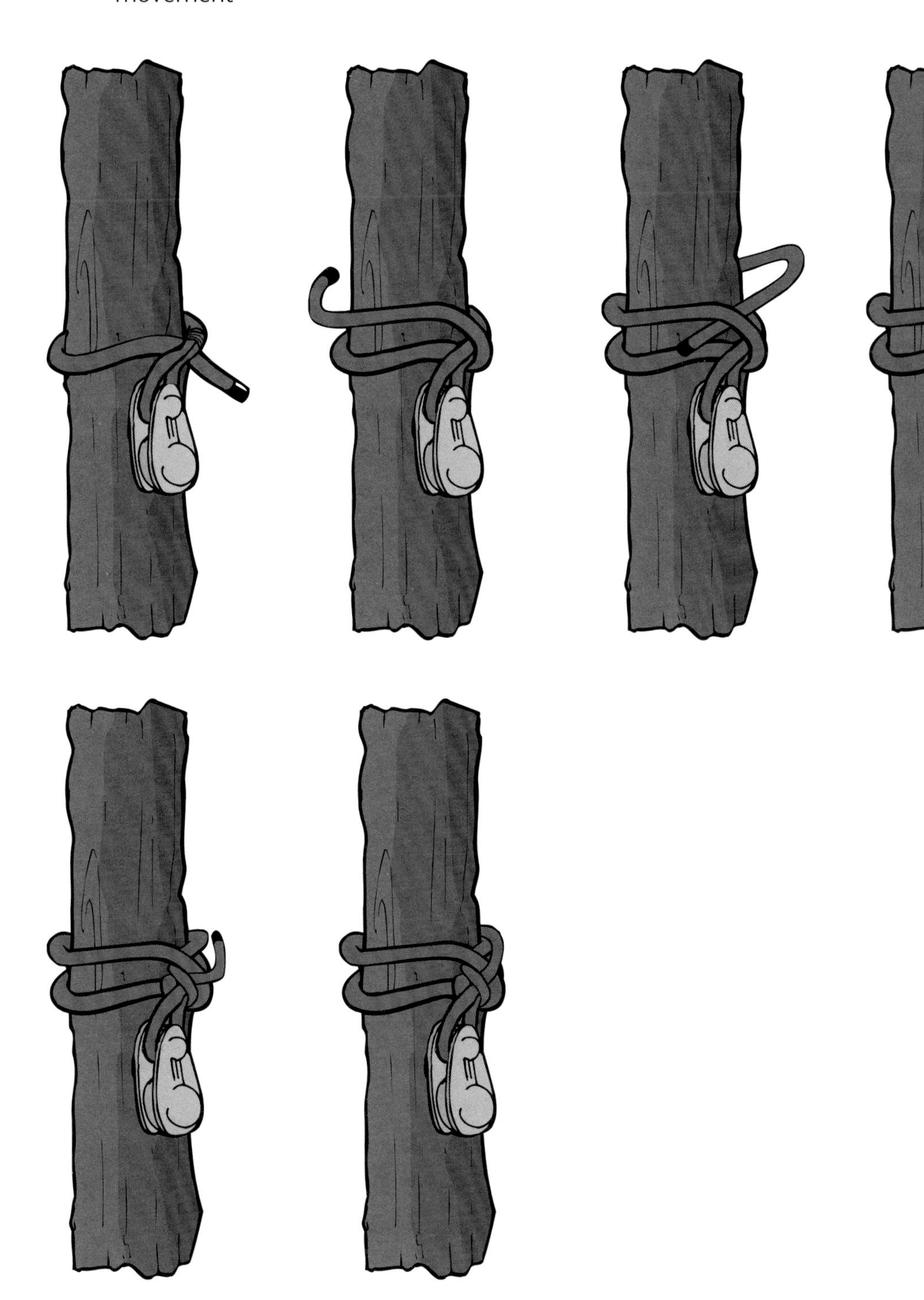

Timber Hitch

- Tied with a sling and used for securing hardware to a tree (especially on large trees when the rope sling is not long enough to tie a cow hitch)
- Always make at least five wraps, spread at least two-thirds of the way around the stem
- This hitch is most secure when tied on larger pieces and when the pull is always against the bight so that it tightens the hitch on the stem. The sling should never be loaded away from the bight because doing so could loosen it
- Cinching functionality is directional

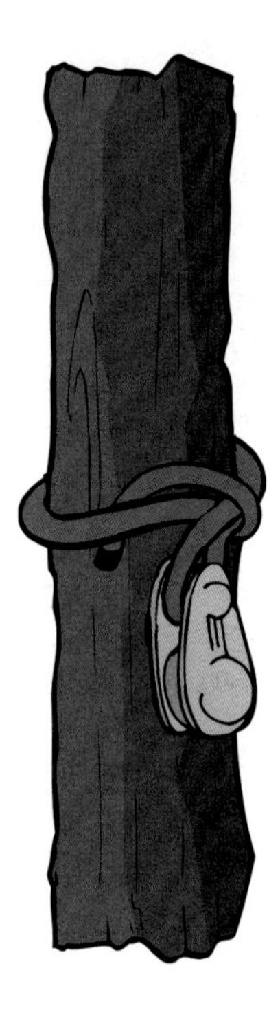
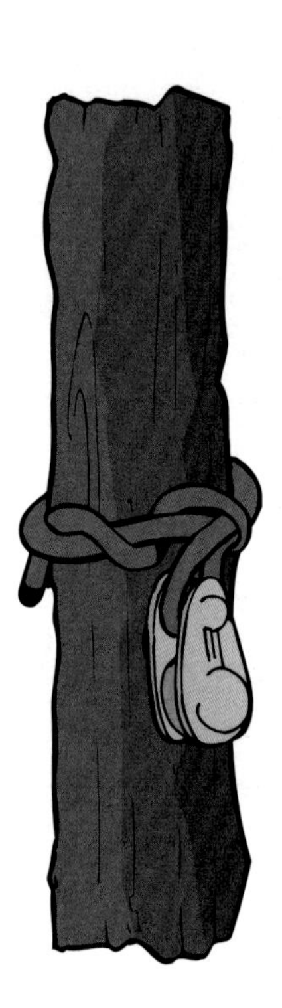

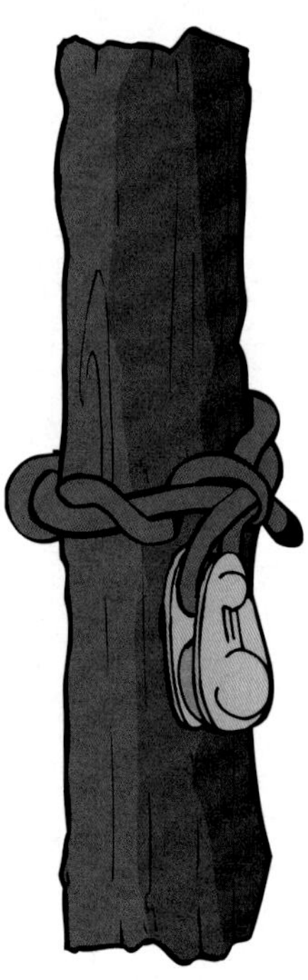

Half Hitch and Running Bowline Tied for Butt-Hitching

- Used to tie off a section when butt-hitching or when there is no secure point for a running bowline alone
- The half hitch shares the load with the running bowline and reduces the chances of the knot slipping off the piece once cut

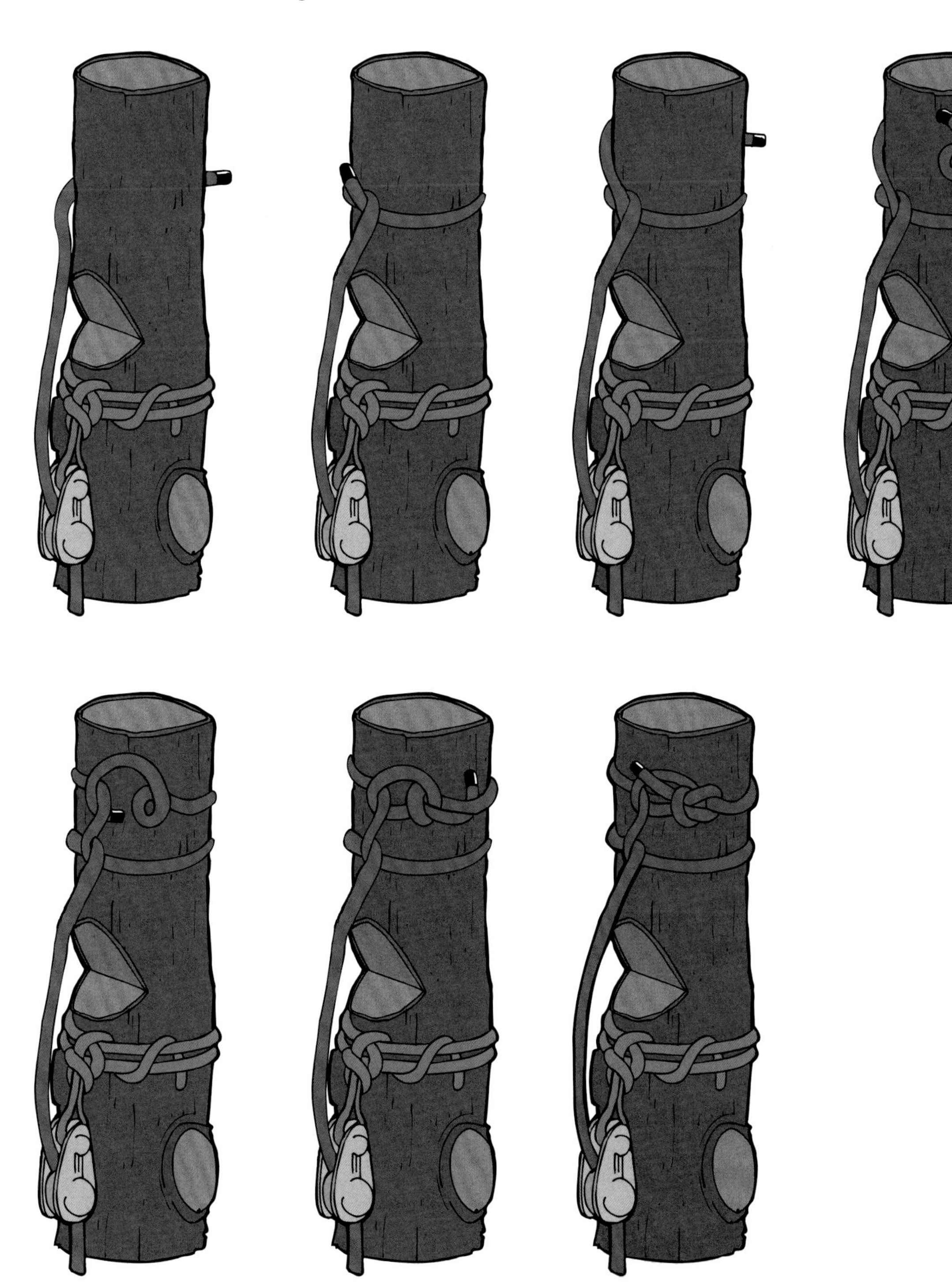

Prusik Hitch

- Friction hitch used in both climbing and rigging applications
- Bidirectional in some applications
- When used as a Prusik loop (as in the secured footlocking technique), a smaller-diameter rope is used to attach the Prusik to a working line. The type of rope affects how the knot will perform

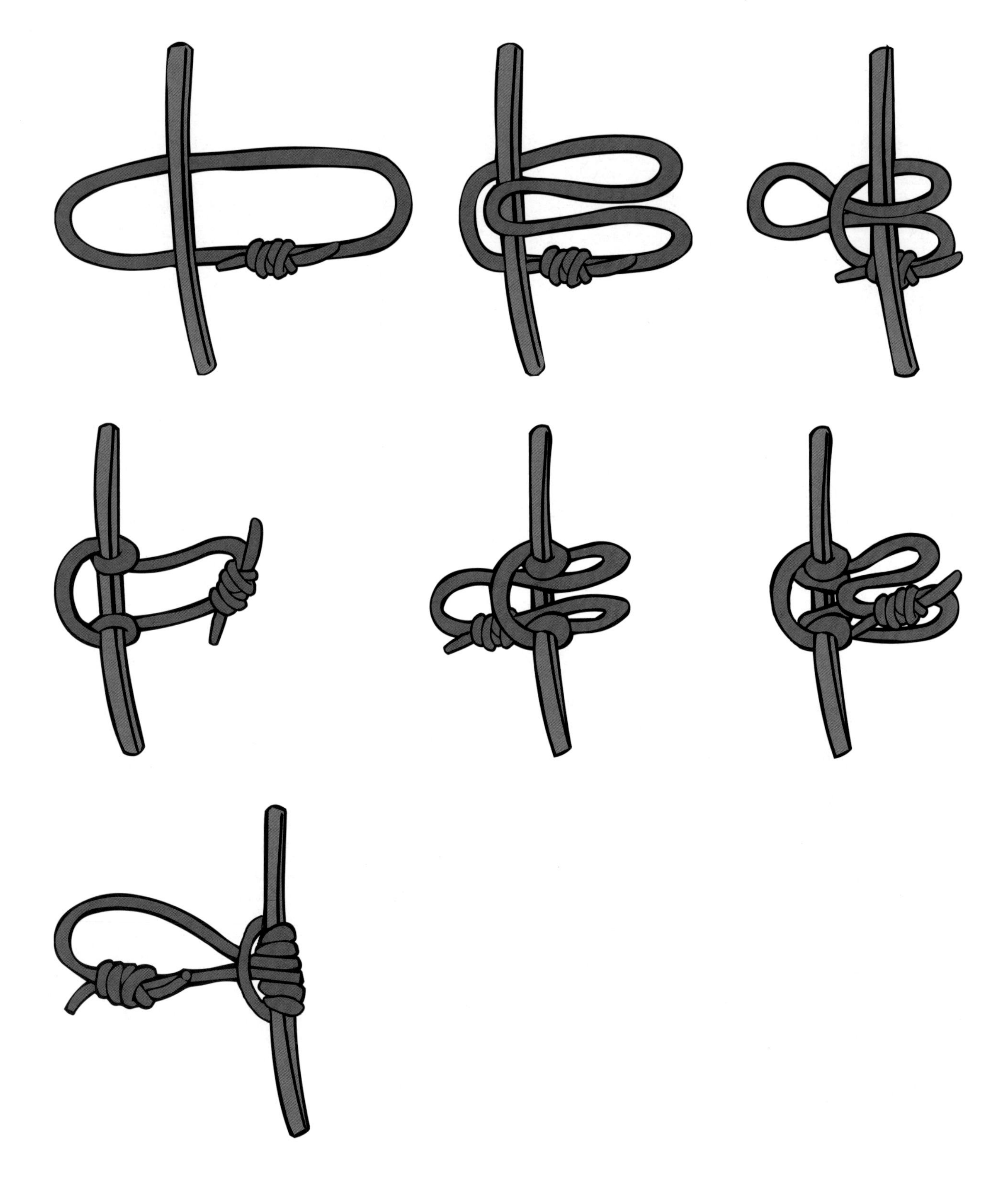

Tautline Hitch

For years, the primary friction hitch used by climbers in the United States was the tautline hitch.

- Used as a friction (climbing) hitch
- Requires a stopper knot (such as a figure-8 knot)
- Has a tendency to roll out
- Must be adjusted (tended) frequently

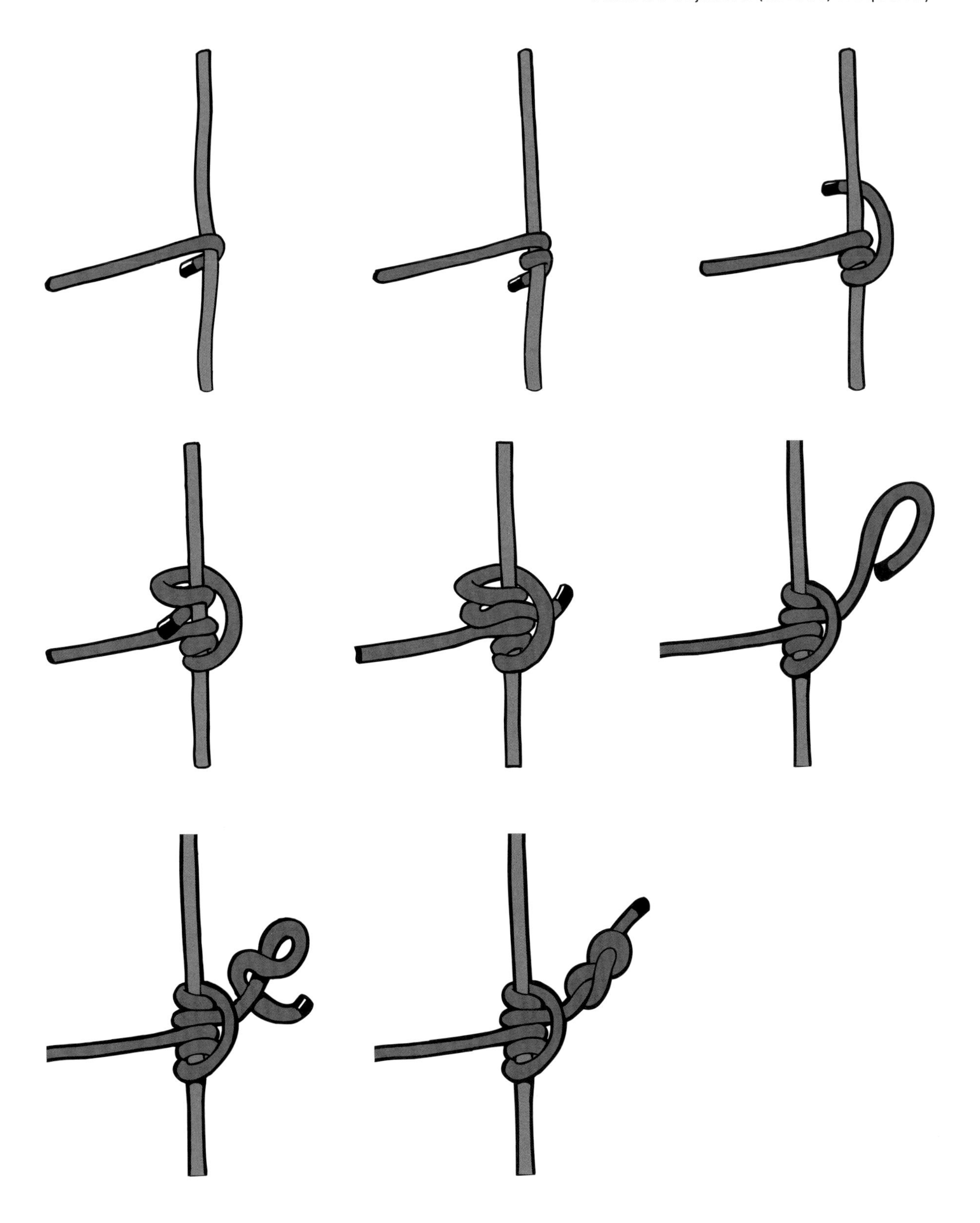

Blake's Hitch

Blake's hitch has largely replaced the tautline hitch because it maintains more uniform friction and does not roll out.

- Climbing (friction) hitch, often preferred over the tautline
- Stays dressed and set, less need to tend
- Doesn't tend to roll out (although a stopper knot is still recommended)
- Higher tendency to glaze on a long or rapid descent

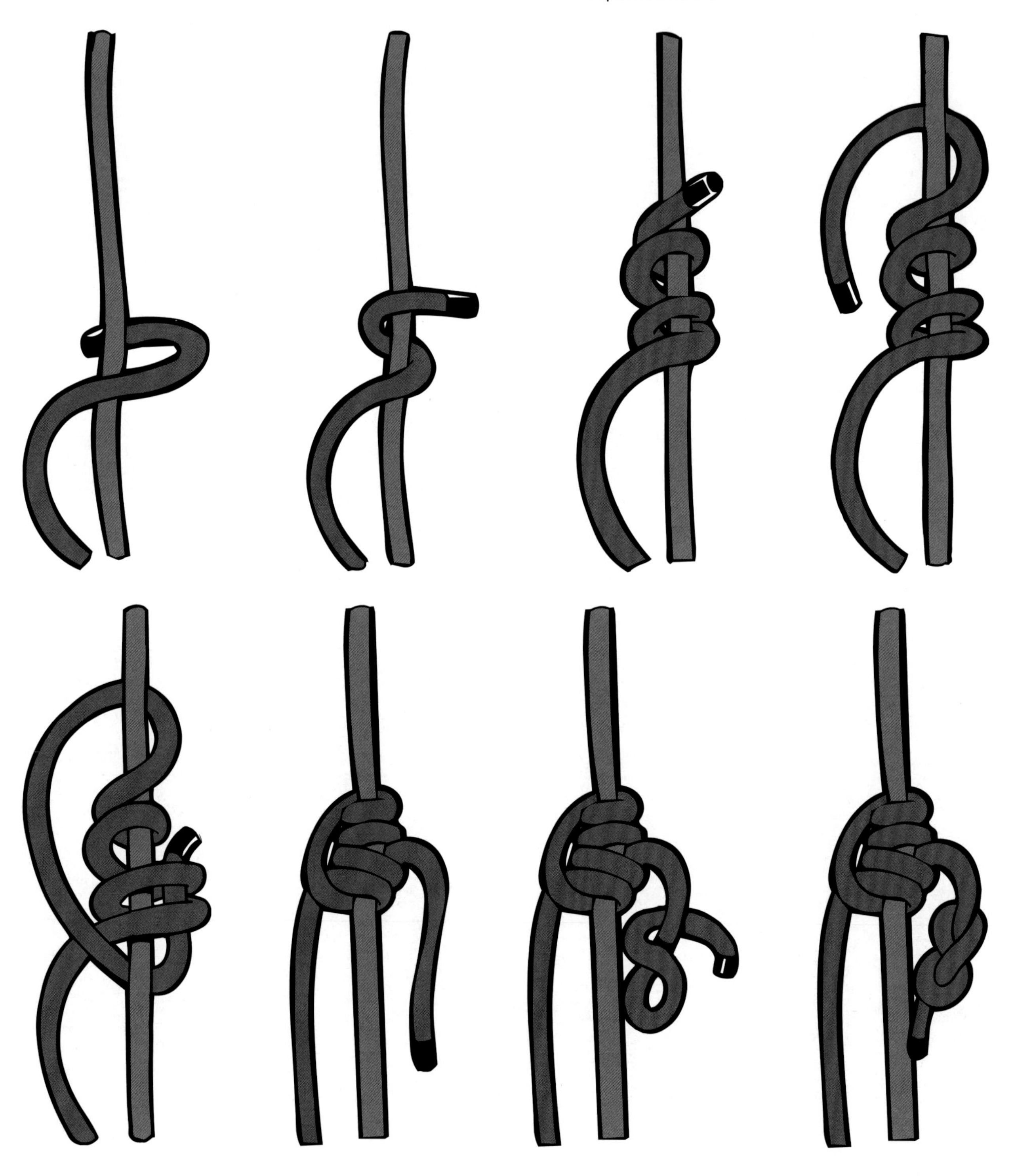

ADVANCED FRICTION (CLIMBING) HITCHES

Climbing equipment and techniques are always changing. The arboriculture profession has benefited from techniques borrowed from related fields such as rock climbing, caving, and rescue applications, as well as from improvements in ropes and cordage.

Often, as improved cordage is introduced, so are more sophisticated friction hitches. Each of these friction hitches is typically tied with a separate **hitch cord** or, in some cases, a loop. The hitch cord must meet strength requirements for climbing lines when configured as used. Usually the hitch cord is used in an eye-and-eye configuration, with the eyes formed either with splices or with double fisherman's knots. The construction, diameter, and length of the split-tail can affect (sometimes dramatically) the performance of the hitch. Even the buried part of the splice can affect how the cord will grip the climbing line.

Most of these friction hitches are used as closed hitches, which means the tail of the hitch is incorporated into the hitch. In an open friction hitch, the tail is not incorporated and usually a stopper knot is required, such as with the tautline and Blake's.

French Prusik is a name that includes a number of friction hitches, including the *Machard, Machard tresse, Valdôtain,* and *Valdôtain tresse.*

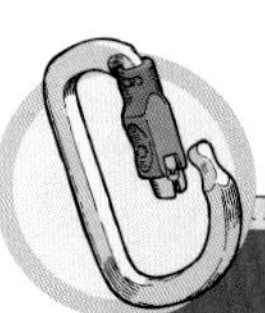

"LOW AND SLOW"

Tree climbers often use the expression "low and slow." This refers to the principle that new equipment, knots, and techniques should always be introduced in a low-risk environment—low to the ground and tried out slowly.

The most commonly known variation is the *Valdôtain tresse.* All of the French Prusiks, as well as the Schwabisch, Distel, and Michoacán, are often considered to be advanced friction hitches. They tend to be fluid and very responsive to quick adjustment, but they can also require close attention. Their behavior on the climbing line is affected by the size and type of cordage, as well as the number of wraps and/or braids. Climbers sometimes experiment to find the best combination to suit their individual climbing style, cordage, and equipment.

These hitches should be used only after proper qualified instruction. As with all climbing techniques and equipment, adopting a new friction hitch should start low and slow. That is, the climber should experiment carefully, low to the ground, and in a situation where there is no risk of falling.

Valdôtain Tresse (Vt)

- Probably the most commonly used of the variations of the French Prusik
- Tied with a length of cord (eye-and-eye split-tail) that is smaller in diameter than the line on which it is tied
- Holds securely and releases easily
- Also used in rigging applications

Schwabisch

- Essentially an asymmetric Prusik hitch
- Holds securely, but can bind
- Neither as fluid nor as temperamental as a French Prusik; grips the line more consistently

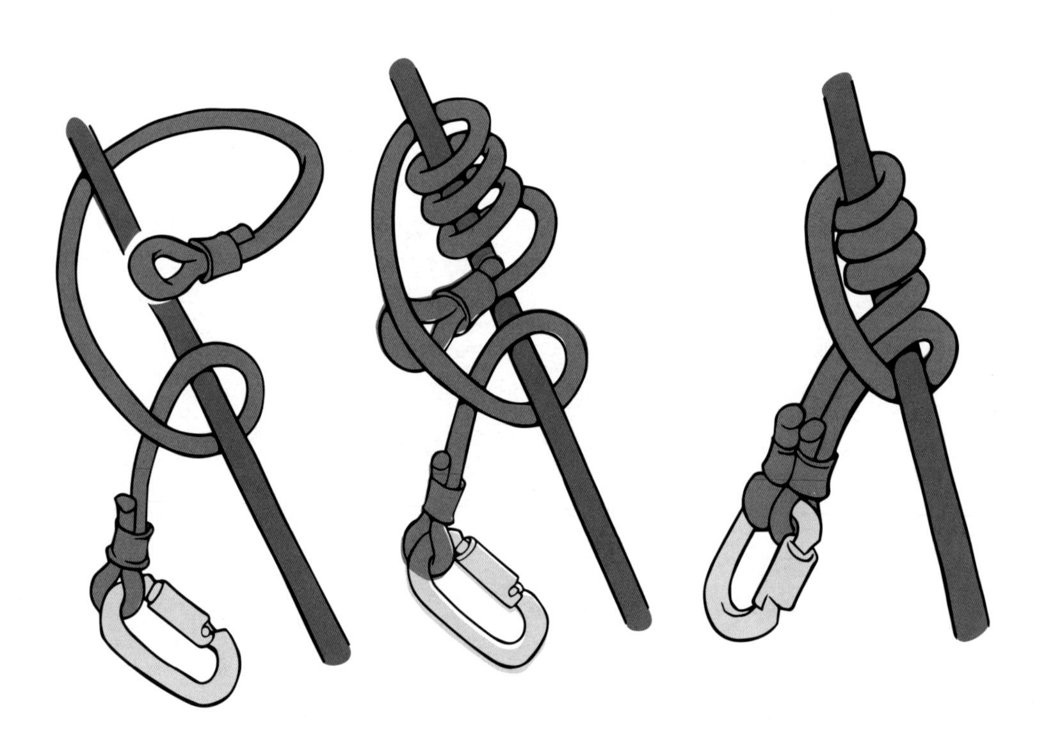

Distel

- Tied similarly to the tautline hitch but performs differently because it is used as a closed hitch
- Used as a closed friction hitch, with both legs of the split-tail attaching to a carabiner
- Neither as fluid nor as temperamental as a French Prusik; grips the line more consistently

Michoacán

- Essentially Blake's hitch tied with an eye-and-eye split-tail
- Holds securely
- Grabs quickly but releases easily

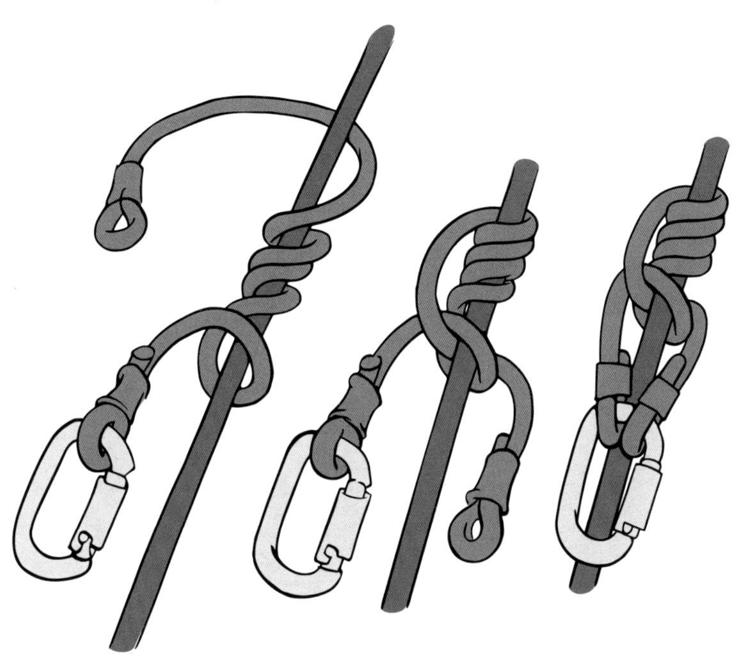

KEY CONCEPTS

1. The characteristics of a rope (strength, stretch, durability, etc.) are the result of the materials and techniques used to make it. These characteristics can make a rope ideal for some applications, yet inappropriate for others.
2. Ropes should be inspected before each use. Use of knots, bends around hardware, elongations from loads, and friction from running over bark all contribute to rope degradation. If any significant cuts, bulges, or glazing are found, the rope should either be retired or should have the affected end cut off.
3. All tree workers should be familiar with the knots used in tree work. A climber should know how to tie and untie each of the basic knots and at least two or three friction hitches (climbing hitches) used for climbing.
4. As with all climbing techniques and equipment, adopting a new friction hitch should start low and slow. That is, the climber should experiment carefully, low to the ground, and in a situation where there is no risk of falling.

WORKBOOK

MATCHING

_____ braided rope
_____ working end
_____ butterfly knot
_____ cow hitch
_____ figure-8 knot
_____ double braid
_____ friction hitch
_____ bight

A. curve or arc in a rope
B. also known as a climbing hitch
C. used to secure hardware to a tree
D. core and cover share the load
E. rope construction commonly used for tree climbing
F. the end of a rope in use
G. used as a stopper knot
H. often used to form a midline loop

TRUE/FALSE

1. T F Polyester and polyester blends are the materials most commonly used for arborists' ropes.
2. T F A 3-strand rope is known for its high strength, high price, and resistance to twisting and hockling.
3. T F Double-braid lines are recommended for rigging through natural branch unions.
4. T F A line has a working end and a standing end, or the ends in use (usually forming a knot) and not in use, respectively.
5. T F "Knot" is the general term given for all knots, hitches, and bends.
6. T F A hitch is a type of knot used to secure a rope to an object, another rope, or the standing part of the same rope.
7. T F "Dressing" a knot aligns the parts; "setting" it tightens the knot in place.
8. T F Most of the "advanced" friction hitches are tied with a separate hitch cord.
9. T F One limitation of Blake's hitch is a tendency to glaze on a long or rapid descent.
10. T F An advantage to using the running bowline to tie off limbs is that it is easy to untie after loading.
11. T F The standard figure-8 knot is a good example of a "slipped" knot.
12. T F A midline clove hitch is commonly used to send equipment up to a climber.
13. T F When using an endline clove hitch to tie off limbs, it should be backed up by at least two half hitches.
14. T F There are very few knots that can be "slipped."

15. T F The knot known as the slip knot is a slipped overhand knot.

16. T F The primary purpose of a sheet bend is to form a Prusik loop.

17. T F A knot is said to be directional if it performs differently when loaded (pulled) from opposite directions or ends.

18. T F When tying a timber hitch in a sling to attach hardware to a tree, you should always make at least five wraps and spread them at least two-thirds of the way around the stem.

19. T F A sheet bend is used to join two ropes of unequal diameters and is often used to send a line up to a climber.

20. T F Natural fibers are generally not as strong as the new, synthetic fibers and can rot over time.

SAMPLE TEST QUESTIONS

1. A type of knot used to secure a rope to an object, another rope, or the standing part of the same rope is a

    a. bend
    b. bight
    c. hitch
    d. slip

2. A common, easy-to-untie knot for forming a loop is a

    a. bowline
    b. clove hitch
    c. tautline hitch
    d. sheet bend

3. Which of the following can be used to join two ropes of unequal diameter?

    a. clove hitch
    b. sheet bend
    c. running bowline
    d. butterfly

CHAPTER

CLIMBING EQUIPMENT

LEARNING OBJECTIVES

The tree worker will be able to:

- List the components that make up personal protective equipment.
- Identify key pieces of equipment used for tree climbing, including their features and applications.
- Describe the protocol for inspecting climbing equipment.
- Summarize care and storage of climbing equipment.
- Describe appropriate disposal methods when retiring equipment.

IMPORTANT TERMS

ascender
bridge
burr
carabiner
chain saw protective pants
chaps
climbing harness
climbing helmet
climbing line
climbing saddle
climbing spikes (spurs)
connecting link
cordage
crazing
daily inspection
D-ring
friction-saving device
hard hat
hitch cord
lanyard
life-support equipment
mechanical friction device
micropulley
periodic inspection
personal protective equipment (PPE)
post-incident inspection
Prusik loop
quick link
rescue pulley
rope snap
self-double locking
sling
split-tail
stationary rope system (SRS)
swivel
tensile strength
tether
throwline
tie-in point
triple-action carabiner
webbing
work-positioning lanyard

INTRODUCTION

Tree care is a skilled profession that requires a wide range of equipment and gear. Part of being a skilled professional is knowing the many tools available to perform the work. These tools include the machinery used to facilitate tree care operations, such as vehicles, chain saws, and brush chippers. It also includes safety gear, such as harnesses, helmets, and ropes.

Tree climbers' safety depends on the reliability of their gear. A climber must be able to select, inspect, and use these tools correctly. Just as important as the selection and use is knowing when it's time to retire a piece of gear. All equipment used by tree workers, including climbing gear and tools, must conform to applicable safety standards and should not be altered. Equipment should be inspected according to manufacturers' guidelines. This chapter provides general guidance on the types of gear used to climb safely. For most equipment, there are multiple options available. If possible, it is good to test various options of equipment prior to purchasing.

This book is not a substitute for reading and following the manufacturers' user manuals. Each piece of equipment has its own set of individual components that require proper use and inspection. Inspections will typically include both a visual inspection and a function test. It is important to consult with the product's inspection protocol first to ensure that use and inspection follow manufacturers' recommendations.

TIP!

TRY OUT AND LEARN ABOUT CLIMBING GEAR

One way to learn more about climbing gear is to attend industry trade shows and talk with experts about the many choices. In some cases, it is possible to try out some gear on the trade show floor. Another way to learn more is by talking with experts at official tree climbing competitions through the International Society of Arboriculture.

EQUIPMENT SELECTION

The range of climbing gear and equipment available is vast. Climbing ropes alone are available in dozens of options, with variations in construction, material, color, and size. Some gear is appropriate for many styles of climbing, while other gear is specific for certain climbing techniques. It takes a great deal of training and experience to become familiar with the many choices of climbing equipment. Moreover, some components may not be compatible with others, creating a dysfunction in the system. Knowing the advantages and disadvantages or limitations of each can be daunting.

Caution is required when purchasing tree climbing gear. Unfortunately, it is possible to buy gear that does not meet the standards or regulations for tree climbing gear. Using unapproved gear or gear that does not meet standards could result in equipment failure, leading to accidents and injury or death. It is essential to ensure that all climbing gear employed meets applicable standards, is used according to manufacturers' recommendations, and is maintained in good working order. Purchasing equipment from reputable arboriculture equipment suppliers is strongly recommended.

This chapter highlights key components of equipment used for climbing, variations of that equipment, and inspection protocols. The inspection protocols outlined here are intended to guide climbers through an inspection and should not replace the inspection protocol outlined by the manufacturer. This section does not serve as an exhaustive list of options available. It graphically represents equipment that is approved for use in tree care at the time of publication. However, as industry standards change and continue to improve, approval of equipment may change. It is essential to refer to the latest manufacturer notices and industry safety standards to ensure the most current information is used.

PERSONAL PROTECTIVE EQUIPMENT

A worker's safety gear is called **personal protective equipment (PPE)**. This equipment includes head, eye, face, hearing, and foot protection. It also includes apparel specifically designed to stop chain saw cuts from occurring, often in the form of chain saw protective pants or chaps. In many regions, PPE also refers to fall protection, including harnesses, hardware, and ropes. For the purposes of this publication, PPE refers to the protective wear on the body.

Climbing-Style Helmets/Hard Hats

Head protection must be worn at all times during arboricultural operations. **Hard hats** that meet the applicable standards can be worn for climbing, but arborist **climbing helmets** are more comfortable and better-fitted, offer additional impact protection, and stay in place much better than standard hard hats.

FIGURE 4.1 Climbing-style helmet/hard hat.

Purchasing Options

- Climbing-style helmets will include a rated chin strap. Hard hats without a chin strap are intended for ground work only
- Full brim, front brim, or no brim
- Suspension system and/or foam interior
- Attachment point for a face shield or visor
- Attachment points for earmuffs
- Vents (helmets with vents are not acceptable for use when working in proximity to electrical conductors)

Inspection Protocol

- Check shell for cracks, warps, bubbling, and **crazing**
- Check suspension for cuts and damage
- Check padding for cracks, fit, missing components, and attachment to the shell
- Perform function test on the chin strap
- Perform function test on cinching mechanism
- Check expiration dates
- Note: Stickers and other adhesive can hide cracks or attract dust and debris. Stickers made with chemical-based adhesive can damage plastic components. Some stickers can affect conductivity and could make helmets fail standards for working in proximity to electrical conductors

Safety Glasses

Eye protection must be worn at all times during arboricultural operations. A variety of safety glasses/goggles are available, and some can incorporate prescription lenses.

FIGURE 4.2 Safety glasses.

Purchasing Options

- Tinted, reflective, polarized, prescription lenses
- Visor attachments on helmets (may not meet eye protection standards)
- Mesh instead of plastic to eliminate fogging (may not meet eye protection standards)
- Rubber tips to help hold in place

Inspection Protocol

- Look for cracks or scratches
- Excessive scratches can impair vision, causing increased risk of injury

Hearing Protection

Hearing protection should be worn at all times while operating loud machinery, such as chain saws and chippers. The two main categories are earplugs and earmuff-type hearing protection.

FIGURE 4.3
Hearing protection.

Purchasing Options

- Foam or silicone earplugs
- Helmet-mounted earmuffs
- Replacement pads and foam
- Earmuffs can be retrofitted with a Bluetooth communication system

Inspection Protocol

- Disposable earplugs should be replaced regularly to reduce the chance of ear infection
- Check earmuffs for excessive wear or missing foam. Function check the fit of earmuffs

Leg Protection

Leg protection protects the legs of chain saw operators from accidental cutting. Chain saw **chaps** can be worn over the top of clothing, or **chain saw protective pants** can be worn. Chain saw protective clothing must meet industry requirements for chain saw cut protection.

FIGURE 4.4
Leg protection.

Use

- During chain saw operations

Purchasing Options

- Pants or chaps. Some chaps have wraparound ankle/calf protection
- High-visibility
- Cold-weather pants or lightweight, vented pants
- Different sizes to accommodate height and waist of saw operator

Inspection Protocol

- Check for any nicks or burns. If the material has been compromised, it must be replaced

FALL PROTECTION AND WORK POSITIONING

Fall protection includes any components that keep a climber safely positioned above the ground. These components are sometimes referred to as **life-support equipment**. Many components of a climber's gear are for work positioning, to facilitate working safely in trees. This section includes climbing harnesses, connecting links, climbing lines, lanyards, split-tails and hitch cords, and various climbing devices.

Climbing Harnesses

Most modern **climbing harnesses** (sometimes referred to as **climbing saddles**) are constructed with independent leg straps, although butt-strap (seat-type) harnesses are available. Some are full-body types. There is a range of designs of suspension and support points, including traditional **D-ring** attachments as well as O-ring attachments. Many modern harnesses incorporate a suspension attachment point on the **bridge** that allows for sliding attachment of a connecting link for tie-in. Harnesses also include a variety of attachment loops and accessory options. As long as the harness meets the applicable standards, choice of style is mostly a matter of preference. Some types are more compatible with **stationary rope system** (discussed in Chapter 7) climbing than others.

Use

- Suspend a climber on a climbing line and provide attachment points for work-positioning equipment

Purchasing Options

- Sizes can run XS to XL. Size based on hips. Full-body harnesses also use height
- Bosun seat or leg loops
- Additional lumbar support, accessory loops, and comfort pieces
- Attachment points: ventral, sternal, dorsal; positioning of side D-rings for lanyard attachment
- Variable suspension attachments: fixed Ds, sliding Ds, floating bridge, dual bridge, rope bridge, stitched loops
- SRS compatible

Inspection Protocol

- Check for excessive wear on load-bearing stitching and rivets, including enlarged holes on webbing
- Check for cuts, pulls, discoloration, or unraveling of textile components
- Check for corrosion, cracks, **burrs**, or disfiguration of metal components
- Check attachment points carefully, including bridge, D-rings, O-rings, and other attachment points. The bridge often

FIGURE 4.5 Climbing harnesses.

- receives rigorous wear, requiring careful inspection and replacement when worn
- Check expiration date(s)
- Check for cracks or crazing in plastic components
- Function test any buckles

Rope Snaps

Rope snaps are a type of **connecting link**. Other connecting links used in climbing are carabiners and **quick links**. Rope snaps used in securing the **climbing line** or **work-positioning lanyard** must be self-closing and self-locking.

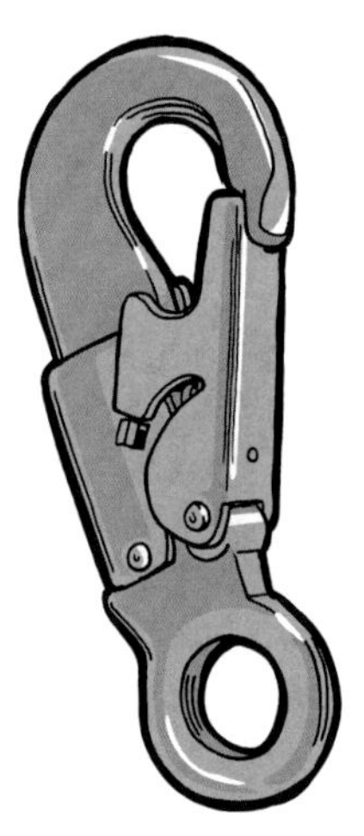

FIGURE 4.6
Rope snap.

Use

- Connecting link, usually from a climbing line or work-positioning lanyard to a harness

Purchasing Options

- Steel or aluminum
- Single- or double-action for locking; be aware of standards for approved use for climbing gear

Inspection Protocol

- Check for deformation of body or enlargement of attachment points
- Check metal for wear, corrosion, flaking, rust, and cracks
- Function test gate for operation and closure

Carabiners

Carabiners are available in a wide variety of shapes, sizes, and constructions, with several types of locking mechanisms. Carabiners used for climbing must be self-closing and **self-double locking (triple-action)**. Both carabiners and rope snaps must have a minimum **tensile strength** of 5,000 lb (23 kN). Carabiners must only be loaded along the major axis.

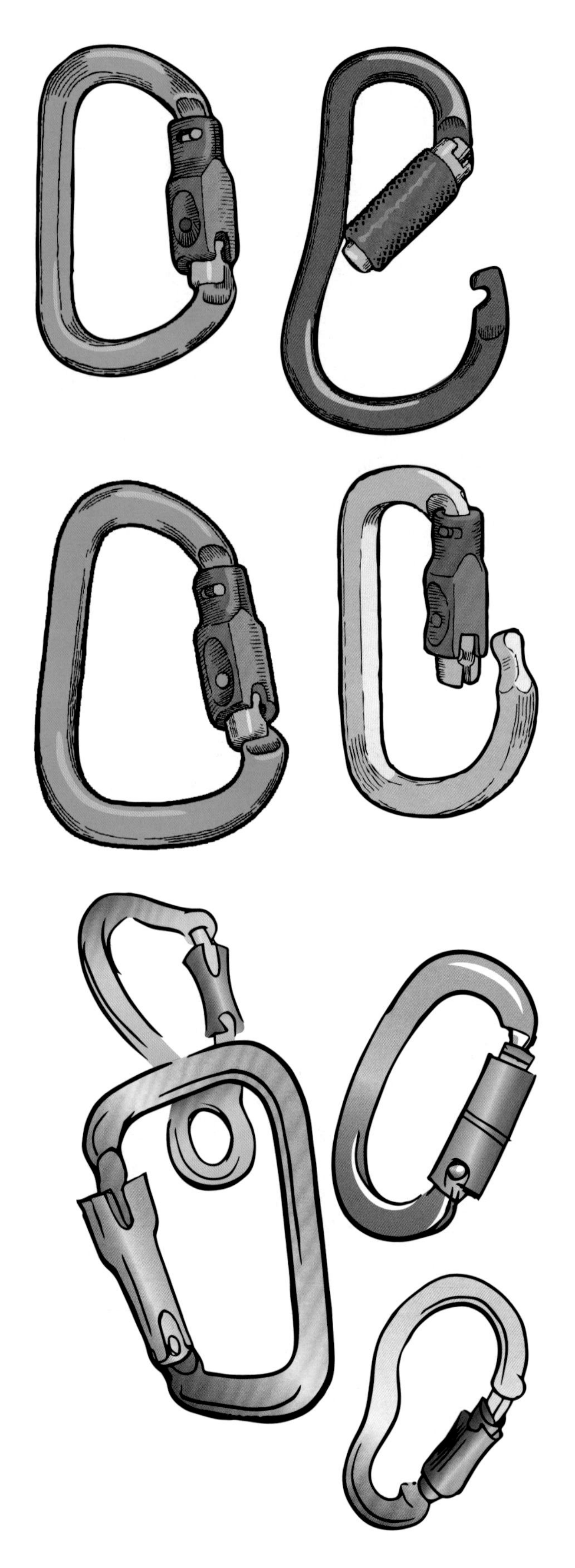

FIGURE 4.7 Carabiners.

Use

- Removable connecting link

Purchasing Options

- Steel or aluminum
- Shapes: oval, HMS, pear, D, captive eye
- Triple- or quadruple-action for locking

Inspection Protocol

- Check for deformation of body, including spine, gate, and major axis points
- Check metal for wear, corrosion, flaking, rust, and cracks
- Check for grooves
- Three-part function test: move gate to unlock position, open gate to half, open gate fully. At all three positions, release gate and check for sticking, delays, and misalignment
- Ensure closure in locked position

Quick Links

Use

- Semi-permanent connecting link; should be tightened with a wrench (because quick links must be mechanically tightened, carabiners and rope snaps are preferred for most fall-protection systems)

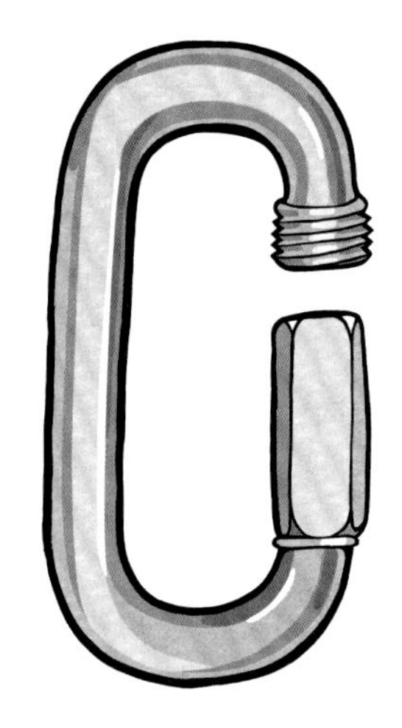

FIGURE 4.8 Quick link.

Purchasing Options

- Various sizes and shapes
- Usually steel construction, some with zinc plating

Inspection Protocol

- Check for deformation of body, including the screw threads and closing mechanism
- Check metal for corrosion, flaking, rust, and cracks
- Check for grooves
- Function test for proper closing and tightening

Climbing Ropes

In addition to being used to suspend a climber, the climbing line helps a climber to maintain balance in the tree, access branch tips, and keep both hands free for working. Ropes used as climbing lines must be identified by the manufacturer as suitable for tree climbing with adequate strength, wear, and stretch characteristics. ANSI standards in the United States require climbing ropes to be 1/2 in (13 mm) in diameter (with some exceptions), be constructed of synthetic materials, meet elongation (maximum stretch) requirements, and have a minimum tensile strength when new of at least 5,400 lb (24 kN). Old, worn, or cut ropes must be retired from use.

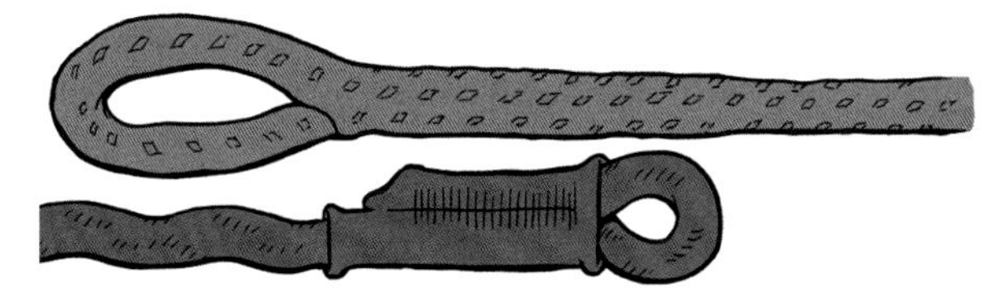

FIGURE 4.9 Climbing lines.

Use

- Suspend a climber aloft; allow for maneuvering in a tree

Purchasing Options

- Commonly purchased in 120, 150, 200 ft (35, 45, 60 m) lengths
- 3-, 12-, 16-, 24-strand; some with double-braid construction or kernmantle
- Low stretch
- Variable ability to hold knots

- 11 to 13 mm diameter
- Stitched or spliced eyes (depending on rope construction)
- EN1891A testing (may be required for compatibility with certain mechanical devices)
- Variable in color and pattern

Inspection Protocol

- Check for cuts, puffs, abrasions, deformation or changes in diameter, discoloration, and glazing of the fibers
- Be sure that rope ends are sealed by taping or whipping
- It is a good idea to alternate the ends of the climbing line, if practical, to the opposite end of the line so that the line wears evenly
- If one end of the climbing line shows signs of excessive wear, it can be cut off
- Inspect for damaged or missing whip stitching on eye-spliced lines. Identify missing protective plastic on stitched eyes

Work-Positioning Lanyards

A **lanyard** is a short length of rope, equipped with carabiners, rope snaps, and/or eye splices, used for work positioning to temporarily secure a climber in place, or to provide additional security when using a chain saw in a tree. A work-positioning lanyard is a component of a climbing system, used for work positioning, consisting of a flexible line of rope or a strap that may incorporate a knot or mechanical device to allow for adjustability. Work-positioning lanyards must meet the same strength requirements for ropes and hardware.

Use

- Holds a climber in place for positive work-positioning
- 2-in-1 style can be used to advance in a tree while remaining secured

Purchasing Options

- One-hand or two-hand adjustments
- Hitch cord or mechanical adjustments
- Variable lengths; extra-long lanyards are often preferred
- Variable rope materials and constructions
- 2-in-1 style with three attachment points
- Snap or carabiner terminations
- Wire-core; should not be used near electrical conductors

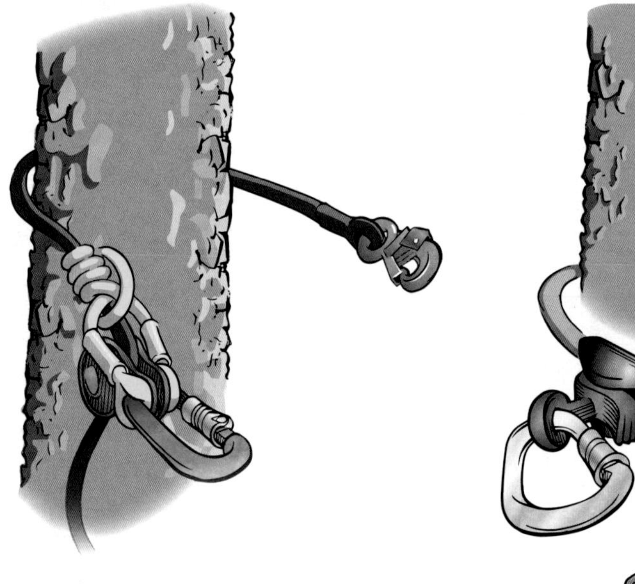
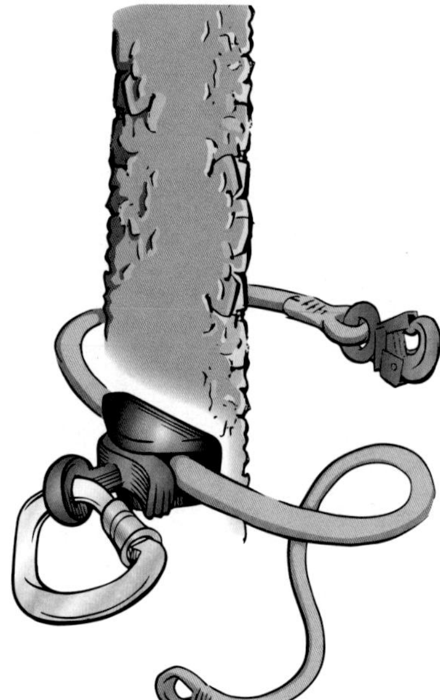

FIGURE 4.10 Work-positioning lanyards.

Inspection Protocol

- Systematically inspect length of rope first, then attachment points, finally adjustment piece
- Look for abrasions, excessive wear, nicks, glazing, discoloration, or changes in diameter
- Check for wires protruding from wire-core lanyard
- Function test carabiners or snaps
- Function test adjustment mechanism; should grab rope under load
- Check expiration dates of individual components; some fibers degrade quickly in UV light

Hitch Cords and Split-Tails

Tree climbers employ various "rope tools" as part of their climbing gear, including **Prusik loops**, **hitch cords**, and **split-tails**. A split-tail is a separate, short length of **cordage** (rope) used to tie a climbing hitch on the climbing line. A Prusik loop is a loop of cordage, formed either with a splice or a double fisherman's bend, used to tie a Prusik knot to the climbing line or the work-positioning lanyard. A Prusik loop may also be used to secure to another line, typically for secured footlocking.

FIGURE 4.11 Hitch cord and split-tail.

Hitch cord is typically a smaller-diameter cordage used to tie the friction hitch. Hitch cords frequently have eyes in both ends, either stitched or spliced. Rope components used in a climbing system must meet the minimum strength standards for climbing lines. Often the hitch cord should be smaller in diameter than the climbing line to which it is attached, and the materials and construction must be compatible for proper functionality.

Use

- Form hitch around climbing line or lanyard, allowing for adjustability of length

Purchasing Options

- 8 to 13 mm diameter
- Variable lengths
- Variable materials and constructions
- Stitched or spliced eyes
- Variable malleability and heat resistance

Inspection Protocol

- Check for cuts, puffs, abrasions, changes in diameter, discoloration, and glazing of the fibers
- Check for changes in the eyes
- Inspect for damaged or missing whip stitching and stitch coverings on sewn and eye-spliced lines. Identify missing protective plastic on stitched eyes
- Check expiration dates of individual components; some fibers degrade quickly in UV light

Mechanical Friction Devices

Mechanical friction devices function in place of, or in addition to, a friction hitch. Many have been introduced to provide the additional friction necessary to secure a climber using a stationary rope system. Each device has a unique design and must be used in a manner that complies with the manufacturer's instructions. Mechanical friction devices must be tested to meet applicable standards to ensure safe use for tree climbing.

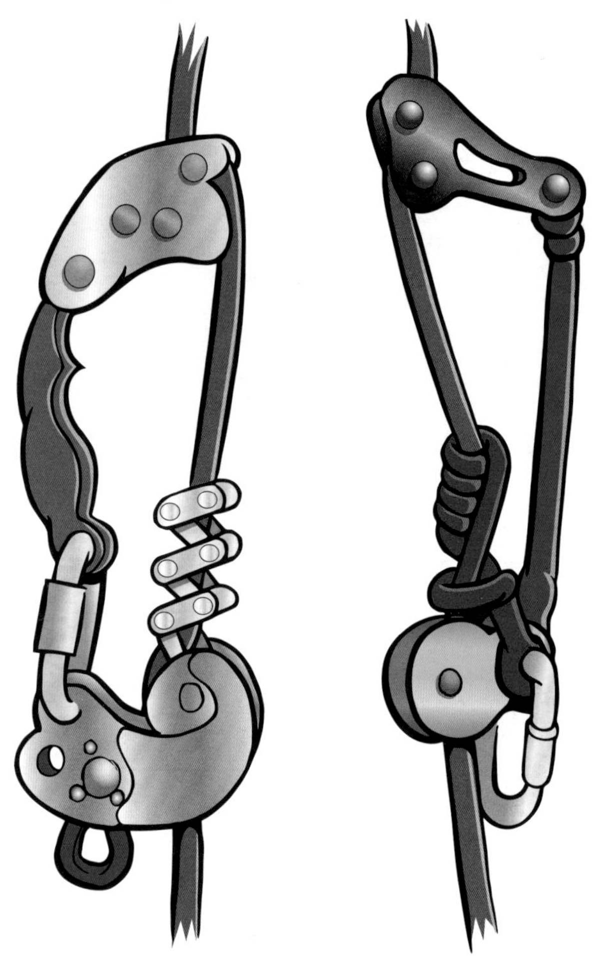

FIGURE 4.12 Mechanical friction devices.

Use

- Provide friction on the climbing line for ascending, descending, and work positioning

Purchasing Options

- Products are widely variable in design and function
- Adjustable friction
- Compatibility with MRS and/or SRS
- Midline or endline rope insertion
- Variable rope diameter tolerances
- Precise application may vary

Inspection Protocol

- Check for deformation of body, including any enlargement of attachment points or wear
- Check metal for corrosion, flaking, rust, and cracks
- Function test for consistent movement of parts and security to the line it is used on

CLIMBING AIDS

Climbing aids may or may not serve as life support, depending on how they are used. They are largely incorporated to create mechanical advantage, to support a more ergonomic body positioning, or to reduce wear and tear on the body, equipment, and tree.

Pulleys/Micropulleys

Two primary types (sizes) of pulleys are sometimes incorporated into climbing systems: **rescue pulleys** and **micropulleys**. A rescue pulley is a light-duty pulley that is sometimes set as part of an in-tree anchor or for establishing mechanical advantage. Micropulleys are smaller, light-duty pulleys, often used to tend slack and assist advancement of the friction hitch.

Use

- Tend slack below a hitch; reduce friction; build mechanical advantage in a system

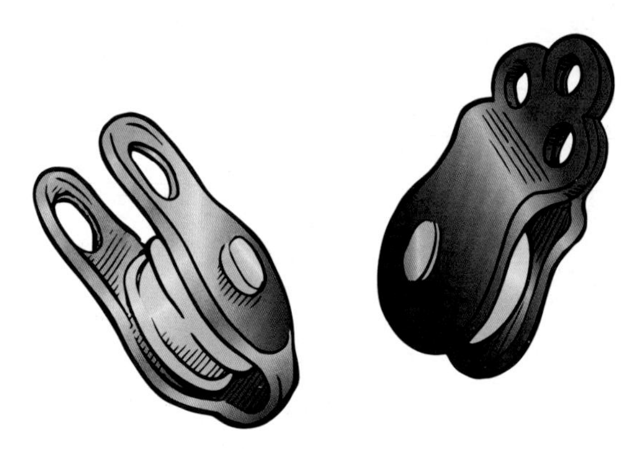

FIGURE 4.13 Pulleys/micropulleys.

Purchasing Options

- One to three attachment points
- Swivel or stationary cheek plates
- With or without a becket attachment point

Inspection Protocol

- Check metal for corrosion, flaking, rust, and cracks
- Check for enlargement of attachment points greater than 1 mm
- Look for deformation and wear on the inside of the plates. Plates should slide easily past each other
- Check for excess wiggle (play) in the plates
- Check for wear and movement of the pulley sheave and axle
- Check sheave for any burrs that may cut rope
- Function test sheave for smooth rotation

Ascenders (Foot, Knee, Handled, Chest)

An **ascender** is a mechanical device that enables a climber to ascend a rope. Attached to the rope, an ascender will grip in one direction (down) and slide in the other (up). Ascenders are used primarily for stationary rope system ascent. They are not designed for working in a tree, for fall arrest, or for descending. Toothed ascenders must only be used on compatible ropes. In most configurations, two attachment points on the rope and/or backup are required.

Use

- Device used for ascending a rope. Grips rope to minimize the need for gripping with the hands or footlocking

Purchasing Options

- Foot ascenders come in left, right, or dual function. Some offer a locking mechanism that keeps the rope from rolling out. Not for life support
- Knee ascenders are adjustable for the climber's height. They can be attached to the foot or shoe (special shoes required). Not for life support
- Handled ascenders come in left, right, or dual function. Different grips may accommodate different hand sizes. Depending on configuration, may be used for life support
- Smooth-cammed ascenders, toothed ascenders

Inspection Protocol

- Check for missing, bent, or otherwise damaged teeth on the cams

FIGURE 4.14 Ascenders: knee, foot, chest, and handled (left to right).

- Check for enlargement of attachment points greater than 1 mm
- Look for warped bodies. Handled ascenders should be able to sit flat on a table without wobbling
- Check that cam catch is not damaged
- Inspect attachment points for wear or burrs
- Check webbing for cuts or excessive wear

Rings/Swivels

Metal rings are incorporated into climbing systems as attachment points on harnesses. **Swivels** are used to prevent lines/attachments from becoming twisted. Swivels rotate to keep gear in alignment.

FIGURE 4.15 Rings/swivels.

Use

- Alternative attachment point on harness
- Swivel helps keep system from over-rotation

Purchasing Options

- Size, number of attachment points, and shape

Inspection Protocol

- Check metal components for cracks, burrs, corrosion, flaking, and rust
- Check for enlargement of attachment points greater than 1 mm
- Function test any moving parts

Friction-Saving Devices

Friction-saving devices, also referred to as cambium savers, are devices of varying design that are installed to reduce friction at the **tie-in point** in the tree. The most common designs employ rope or webbing with rings at either end—double-ring type. Reducing friction reduces wear on both the tree (branch union) and the climbing line and provides more consistent friction (and performance) at the friction hitch. Some designs can be installed to create a tie-in point where there is no branch union, which is very useful for working on spars for removals. Some are capable of being installed and retrieved from the ground.

Use

- Protect a branch union from the friction of a rope; suspend a climbing line below a branch union for a friction-reduced system

Purchasing Options

- Various lengths
- Ring-style (aluminum or steel), fixed or adjustable

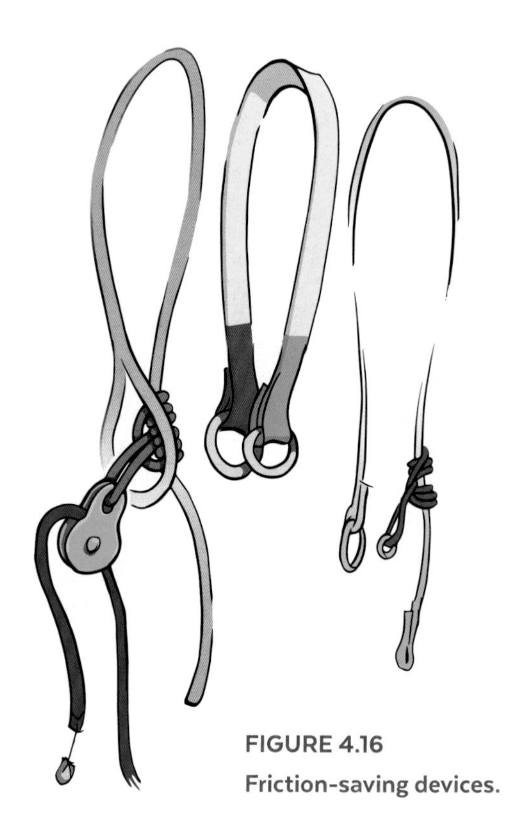

FIGURE 4.16 Friction-saving devices.

- Various hardware options include pulleys
- Sheathing leather, rope, or webbing construction
- Ground-retrievable systems

Inspection Protocol

- Inspection will depend on type of friction-saving device
- Check for enlargement of attachment points greater than 1 mm
- Check metal components for cracks and burrs
- Check webbing for picked or damaged stitching
- Check rope components for changes in diameter, discoloration, and cuts
- Check expiration dates of individual components; some fibers degrade quickly in UV light

FIGURE 4.18 Slings can be used to attach a rigging block or to tie off branches in rigging.

Slings and Tethers

Slings constructed of cordage or **webbing** are often used as redirects or as part of an ascent system. **Tethers** are sometimes incorporated as part of climbing systems, some as specific components of stationary rope climbing systems. Those employed as part of a life-support system must meet their applicable standards for breaking strength.

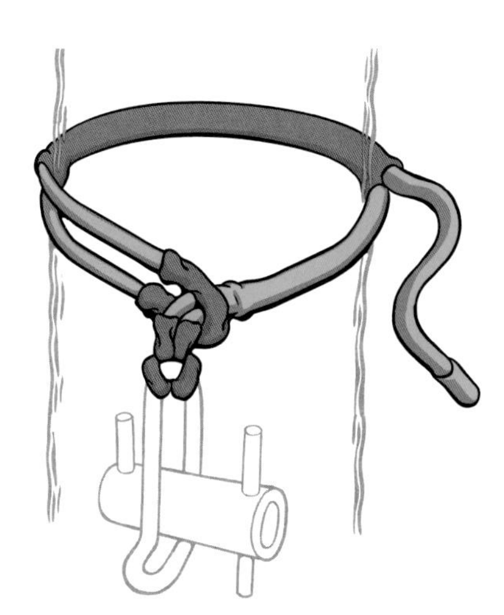

FIGURE 4.17 Whoopie sling with a girth-hitched Port-a-Wrap™.

Use

- Slings are connection devices for installing redirects, rigging equipment, and footloops
- Tethers may be a component of friction devices or used to secure tools while working aloft

Purchasing Options

- Constructed of cordage, webbing, or other materials
- Various sizes and functions

Inspection Protocol

- Inspection will depend on type of sling or tether
- Check for enlargement of attachment points greater than 1 mm
- Check webbing for picked or damaged stitching
- Check rope components for changes in diameter, discoloration, cuts, and excessive wear

Throwlines and Throw Weights

A **throwline** is a thin, lightweight cord with a throw weight (bag) attached to the end(s), used to set climbing or rigging lines in trees. It should never be used in a life-support application.

Use

- Setting a preliminary line in a tree to pull a climbing line through

Purchasing Options

- Various diameters and lengths of cordage, with or without slick coating
- High-visibility colors
- Throw bags in various sizes, weights (6 to 16 oz), and shapes
- Accessories available for storing
- Tools available for launching to greater heights

Inspection Protocol

- Check line for wear and weaknesses
- Check stitching and wear on bag

FIGURE 4.19 Throwline and throw weight.

Spikes/Gaffs/Spurs

Climbing spikes (spurs) are long shanks with sharp spikes (gaffs) on the ends that are attached to the inside of a climber's lower legs to assist in climbing.

Use

- Ascending trees, only for removal or during a rescue

Purchasing Options

- Steel, aluminum, or carbon fiber

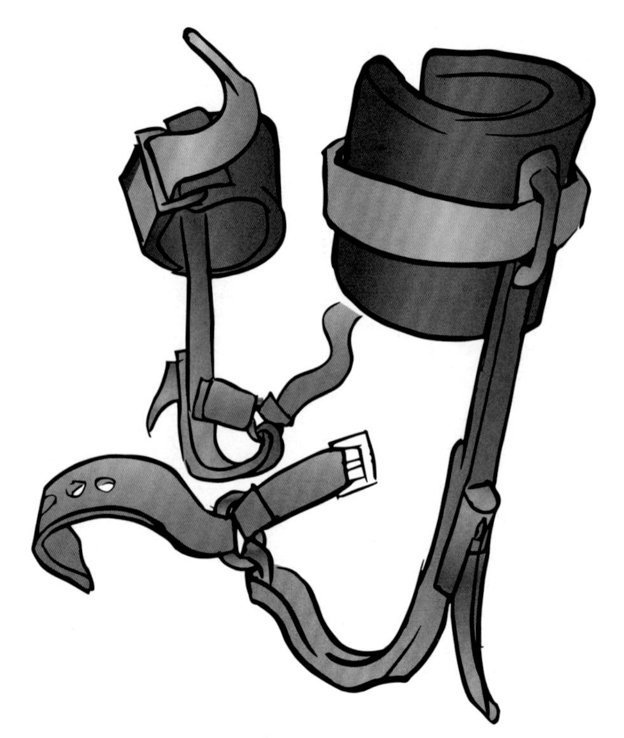

FIGURE 4.20 Spikes/gaffs/spurs.

- Height adjustability
- Straps and/or Velcro® attachments
- Various pad sizes and styles, with or without a solid shank
- Variable gaff size and angle
- Replaceable gaffs

Inspection Protocol

- Check metal components for cracks, burrs, corrosion, flaking, and rust
- Check gaffs for nicks, burrs, or other imperfections; check for sharpness, length, and grind
- Check pads for wear and tear
- Check webbing for cuts, pulls, or other damage

EQUIPMENT INSPECTION

Inspections should be performed in a clean, dry area. It is a good idea to spread a tarp out or find a clean place to inspect. The inspection protocols listed are intended for intermittent inspections.

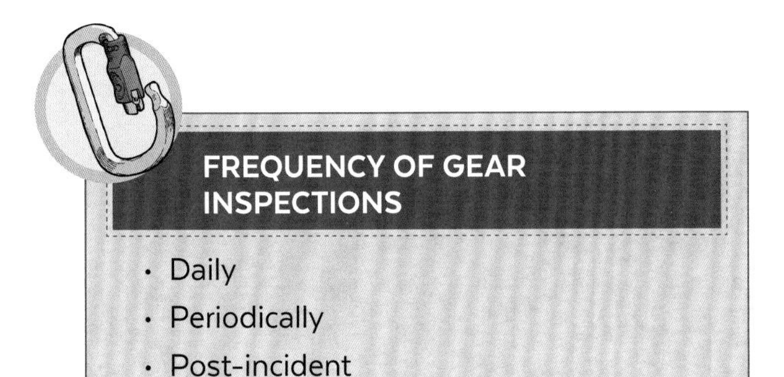

FREQUENCY OF GEAR INSPECTIONS

- Daily
- Periodically
- Post-incident

Employers should develop a protocol for crews, such as a checklist and peer gear inspection. Some standards require documented inspections at specified intervals.

Inspections should be conducted at three main levels: daily, periodically, and post-incident. A **daily inspection** involves a check prior to each use. This is a visual inspection to look for any nicks, deformations, cracks, improperly functioning components, or other major defects that could cause the equipment to fail. Climbing equipment and ropes are examples of gear that should be inspected daily. A **periodic inspection** should be conducted monthly or quarterly, depending on applicable regulations or the extent of use. This inspection includes more thorough visual and function tests. More subtle deformities or defects can be found during this inspection, such as damaged stitching, glazing, or upcoming expiration dates. A **post-incident inspection** occurs following an incident, whether that's an incident on a jobsite or a piece of equipment dropped out of a tree. Particular attention must be given to any indications of acute damage.

EQUIPMENT STORAGE

Proper storage will extend the life of climbing equipment. Ropes may be coiled or flaked into a rope bag. Any textiles, such as rope, slings, and webbing that can easily be nicked, should be stored separately from hand saws (not sheathed in a scabbard), chain saws, and any other sharp objects. All climbing equipment should be stored in a cool, dry area, away from caustic chemicals. If equipment is wet, it should be hung for thorough drying before returning to storage. Plastics, such as helmets, can be damaged by UV rays. Helmets should not be stored on the dashboard of the truck, as this will cause warping of the shell. The better equipment is cared for, the longer it will last.

FIGURE 4.21 Climbers should conduct regular equipment inspections. Employers should develop a protocol for crews, such as a checklist and peer gear inspection.

FIGURE 4.22 Proper storage will extend the life of climbing equipment. The better equipment is cared for, the longer it will last.

EQUIPMENT RETIREMENT

Equipment will wear down at different rates, depending on several factors. Excessive wear, improper storage, incompatible use, extreme weather conditions, and even sweat can contribute to premature wear. Knowing when to retire equipment is crucial. Manufacturers' inspection protocols should be referenced for guidance on retirement indicators. As a general rule, textiles and plastics have a specified shelf life, beginning from the date of manufacture. This is different from the day it was put in the field. This shelf life could be shorter depending on how well the equipment is cared for during its life. Retirement of metal products will depend on wear. Excessive salt from working near a coast or from sweat can cause corrosion. Shock loading, incorrect loading, and excessive loading can warp, damage, crack, or otherwise permanently ruin hardware. Any equipment in need of repair should be tagged and removed from service. Any equipment in need of retirement should be disabled to the extent that it cannot be put back into service, and it should be disposed of appropriately.

KEY CONCEPTS

1. Tree climbers must become competent in the inspection of gear. Inspections include daily (before use), periodic, and post-incident inspections.
2. All personal protective equipment must meet industry safety standards.
3. Climbers should always read user manuals prior to using a new piece of equipment, paying particular attention to the application of that equipment, as well as how to maintain and inspect it.
4. A climber must be able to select, inspect, and use equipment and gear correctly.
5. All equipment used by tree workers, including climbing gear and tools, must conform to applicable safety standards and should not be altered.
6. Metal must be inspected for signs of wear, including burrs, cracks, disfiguration, corrosion, and rust. Ropes and other cordage must be inspected for cuts, puffs, abrasions, changes in diameter, discoloration, and glazing of the fibers.
7. Many types of equipment must be function tested for proper operation and reliable performance.
8. Just as important as the selection and use is knowing when it's time to retire a piece of gear.

WORKBOOK

MATCHING

_____ hitch cord	A. personal protective equipment
_____ friction-saving device	B. weighted cord used to set a line
_____ bridge	C. attachment point on harness
_____ quick link	D. cordage (often smaller diameter) used to tie a friction hitch
_____ PPE	E. connecting link; can be tightened with a wrench
_____ ascender	F. rope-gripping climbing aid
_____ throwline	G. light-duty pulleys, often used to tend slack
_____ micropulley	H. installed to reduce friction at the tie-in point

TRUE/FALSE

1. T F It is possible to buy gear that does not meet standards or regulations for tree climbing gear.
2. T F Advantages to using a friction-saving device when tying in include reduced wear on the climbing line and less chance of damaging the tree.
3. T F If a carabiner is used, it must be loaded only along its major axis.
4. T F Carabiners and snaps used for climbing must have a minimum tensile strength of 5,000 lb (23 kN).
5. T F Old, worn, or cut climbing lines must be used for rigging applications only.
6. T F Work-positioning lanyards must meet the same strength requirements for ropes and hardware.
7. T F Climbing ropes should be inspected daily before use.
8. T F Climbing helmets are more comfortable and better-fitted, offer additional side protection, and stay in place much better than standard hard hats.
9. T F Climbing spurs are acceptable for use in climbing trees whenever the spurs' marks will not be obvious.
10. T F Earmuff-type hearing protection is suitable for tree work, but earplugs do not meet safety standards.
11. T F A throwline can be used to set a climbing line in a tree.
12. T F Because it is used in climbing, a throwline is considered life-support equipment.

13. T F Ropes with spliced eyes cannot be used for tree climbing.

14. T F Gear inspections should be conducted daily, periodically, and after any incident.

15. T F Some friction-saving devices can be installed and retrieved from the ground.

16. T F Mechanical friction devices function in place of, or in addition to, a friction hitch.

17. T F Hitch cords are typically larger in diameter than the climbing line to which they are tied.

18. T F It is a good idea to alternate the ends of the climbing line, if practical, to the opposite end of the line so that the line wears evenly.

19. T F All climbing gear employed must meet applicable standards, be used according to manufacturers' recommendations, and be maintained in good working order.

20. T F As a general rule, textiles and plastics have a specified shelf life, beginning from the date of manufacture.

SAMPLE TEST QUESTIONS

1. All of the following are a requirement of carabiners used for climbing *except*:

   a. be self-closing and self-double locking
   b. have a minimum tensile strength of 5,000 lb (23 kN)
   c. be constructed of stainless steel
   d. only be loaded along the major axis

2. In addition to being a safety device, the climbing line helps a climber to

   a. access branch tips
   b. maintain balance in the tree
   c. keep both hands free for working
   d. all of the above

3. Climbing gear must be inspected

   a. daily before use, visually for wear and defects
   b. periodically, including a functionality test
   c. after any incident in which the gear was involved
   d. all of the above

CHAPTER

5 PREPARING TO CLIMB

LEARNING OBJECTIVES

The tree worker will be able to:

- Describe the elements of a thorough tree and site pre-climb inspection.
- List and describe the different methods used to install a rope in a tree.
- Discuss the safe work procedures for using a ladder to enter a tree.
- Explain the appropriate application of climbing spikes.
- Describe how to execute an efficient rescue plan without endangering other workers.

IMPORTANT TERMS

access line
aerial rescue
arboriculture
arborist
canker
cavity
climbing spikes
conk
crack
dieback
emergency response
friction-saving device
fruiting body
gaff
gaffing out
included bark
isolate
job briefing
mallet
minimum approach distance (MAD)
palm skirt
probe
rescue kit
root crown
sapwood decay
shot pouch
sloughing
spar
spurs
strumming
throw weight
throwing knot
throwline
tie-in point (TIP)
trunk flare
work plan

INTRODUCTION

Tree climbing is a very physical and potentially hazardous aspect of the **arboriculture** profession. However, a well-trained climber who follows all established safety standards and procedures can work safely and efficiently in a tree. Before climbing a tree, a climber should first inspect all safety equipment. Then the site and tree itself must be inspected for hazards. All workers must be made aware of any potential hazards. A good climber plans ahead where to tie in and how to work the tree. Planning can save energy and may prevent accidents.

This chapter begins with the very important step of tree and site inspection. All climbers should be trained to inspect every tree and the area surrounding the tree before climbing. Mitigation of hazards and obstacles must be discussed as part of the job briefing. Because no climber should ascend a ladder or tree without being secured, it is almost always necessary to first install the climbing line. This chapter describes methods of rope installation and ways of ascending into trees. Also discussed are some principles of emergency response and aerial rescue, which should be understood before working in trees. Specific methods of ascent associated with moving rope systems (MRS) and stationary rope systems (SRS) are discussed in Chapters 6 and 7.

FIGURE 5.1 Not all potential hazards and obstacles are immediately visible. A thorough inspection may uncover additional defects or conditions that could pose a risk to the crew. How many can you find in this picture?

INSPECTION OF THE TREE AND SITE

The first inspection of the tree should happen before the crew arrives. Normally, the sales arborist should inspect the tree and surrounding site for hazards and obstacles that will impact the **work plan**. The work plan is how the crew will complete a job, including job assignments and anticipated tools and techniques to be used. Any tree defects or potential hazards communicated to the crew will be used to develop the work plan.

Every job must begin with a **job briefing** that covers the work plan, potential hazards, and all required gear and procedures. Before climbing a tree, a climber must always look carefully and locate any electrical conductors and other utilities. If there are electrical conductors nearby, the climber must develop a work plan to maintain a safe distance so as not to come into contact accidentally. It is important to know and abide by **minimum approach distances (MAD)** for electrical conductors.

Next, the climber and crew should inspect the rest of the surrounding area for other potential hazards and obstacles. Additionally, the site should be checked for signs of recent construction, grade

FIGURE 5.2 Before climbing a tree, a climber must always look carefully and locate any electrical conductors or utility lines. If there are electrical conductors nearby, the climber must develop a work plan to maintain the minimum approach distances (MAD) for electrical conductors.

changes, or root decay that could compromise the root system.

Following a thorough site inspection, the climber can start a systematic inspection of the tree. Signs of decay in the **root crown** (**trunk flare**) could indicate a defect that can lead to whole-tree failure. Snow, vines, debris, soil, and landscaping could hide **conks** or **fruiting bodies** of decay organisms, which indicate decay in the tree. **Dieback** in the top of the tree could indicate root damage. Along the trunk, **included bark**, **cankers**, and other structural defects could result in trunk failure.

A sounding **mallet** can be used along the trunk and root collar. This tool helps the climber listen for hollow spots, which could indicate weakness. A **probe** can also be used to check the depth and extent of a **cavity**. Finally, in the canopy, dead or broken branches, **cracks**, and insects or other animals should be evaluated and considered in the work plan. Cracks, **sapwood decay** in major limbs, substantial dieback, and an unstable root plate should all serve as red flags to the climber. Any problems found may require mitigation measures to reduce or eliminate the risk. The work plan may also need to be changed, including the use of additional equipment or personnel.

A pre-climb inspection should also be used to plan how the tree will be climbed. It is usually a good idea to plan the climbing route while still on the ground and to choose a safe **tie-in point** (TIP) from which the tree can be accessed. An experienced climber will also become familiar with the characteristics of various trees. It is helpful to know how strong or brittle a tree's wood is.

FIGURE 5.3 Climbers must perform a systematic inspection of the tree, starting at the root crown and working up to the top. This pre-climb inspection should take into consideration not only the tree's climbability, but also additional loads that may be placed on the tree during operations.

The pre-climb inspection includes more than just inspecting it for climbability. Depending on the work to be performed, additional loads could be placed on the tree in addition to the climber's weight. Rigging operations and removals can introduce much larger loads than the tree is able to withstand. When planning the work, the climber should not only determine their own climbing route, but also plan the work to be done, as well as where to attach rigging blocks, lowering devices, and other load-bearing equipment to position them at the strongest and most strategic points in the tree. Only once the tree has been deemed stable enough to support the intended operations should work proceed.

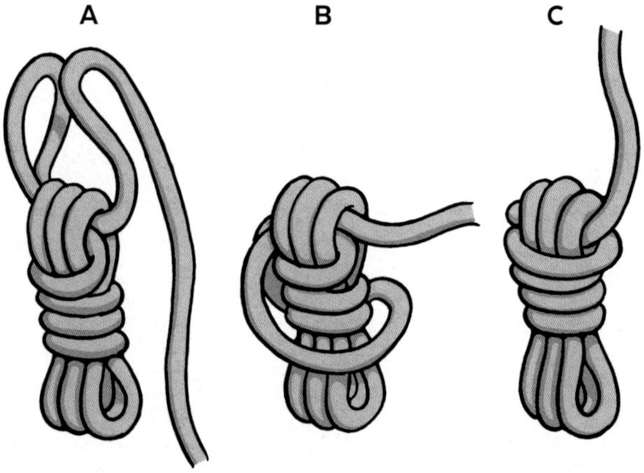

A B C

FIGURE 5.5 The throwing knot is used to provide weight to facilitate throwing. It can be used in an open (A) or closed form (B–C); the closed version will not come undone when the rope is thrown.

ROPE INSTALLATION

Throwing the Climbing Line

Following inspection, the first step to climbing is installing a rope in the tree. There are a number of methods available, depending on the tree and the climber's throwing skills. Sometimes, a climber may throw the climbing line directly into the tree. With short tosses through an open canopy, it may be easiest to simply loop the rope over a low limb. These lower throws can be accomplished with just the rope itself. Simply by gathering a handful of looped rope and tossing it up into the canopy, a low limb can be reached. For trickier throws, those perhaps 20 to 30 ft (6 to 9 m) high, the climber may use a **throwing knot**. A throwing knot is simply a series of wraps that hold the rope together and provide end weight to facilitate throwing. The throwing knot can be used in an open or closed form; the closed version will not come undone when the rope is thrown.

FIGURE 5.4 For trickier throws, the climber may use a throwing knot.

Once in the tree, the climber may advance the climbing line higher by tossing it again while remaining secured with a work-positioning lanyard. Another option is to reset the line using the hook side of a pole saw, taking care to keep the line away from the blade. When advancing the climbing line, it is important to keep it secured to the harness to prevent it from falling to the ground.

Starting low allows a climber to gradually ascend the tree, inspecting the trunk and branches along the way. The limitation is that the ascent will be slow and inefficient, with the climber having to reset their lanyard and advance their tie-in multiple times before reaching a high, central tie-in point.

Using a Throwline

To set a rope higher in the tree, a climber may choose to use a **throwline** instead of throwing the rope. A throwline is thin, slick cordage, roughly 1.75 to 2.5 mm in diameter, with a high breaking strength. A **shot pouch**, or **throw weight**, attached to the end of the throwline can be thrown with amazing accuracy through branch unions 70 ft (20 m) or higher. Shot pouches are available in various weights, ranging from 8 to 16 oz (250 to 500 g). Selection depends on conditions and personal preference. Additional tools that function as a "sling shot" can help with distance and accuracy, as well.

Arborists have developed a number of techniques for throwing, launching, and manipulating throwlines to set them in the specific branch union desired. One option is to use the single-handed approach. A climber will often tie a slip knot in the throwline at around hip height to provide a good grip, then swing the throw weight forward and back, like a pendulum, releasing the throwline when the hand is aligned with the position of the branch union. Once the throwline is installed in the tree, a tug on the line will remove the slip knot. Another method is to pull a bight of throwline through the ring of the throw weight. Using two hands to hold and swing the throwline,

FIGURE 5.6 One option for installing a throwline is the single-handed approach. By holding a slip knot in the throwline at around hip height, the climber can swing the throw weight forward and back, like a pendulum, releasing the throwline when the hand is aligned with the position of the branch union.

FIGURE 5.7 Another method is to pull a bight of throwline through the ring of the throw weight. Using two hands to hold and swing the throwline, the throw weight is suspended between the climber's legs. Using the pendulum method, the climber will release the throwline when their arms are aligned with the branch union.

THROWLINES AND HIGH-FRICTION BARK

An experienced arborist will learn which trees have higher friction bark, such as cottonwood (*Populus deltoides*). For such trees, the arborist may opt to throw a heavier throw bag to counteract the friction. Keeping the throwline free of knots will also help.

the throw weight is suspended between the climber's legs. Using the pendulum method, the climber will release the throwline when their arms are aligned with the branch union.

After the throw weight with the attached throwline passes through the union, it might fall to the ground. Sometimes, however, friction from tree bark can make it challenging to get the throw weight down. In these cases, the climber must manipulate the throwline, such as by **strumming** or pulling on the throwline repeatedly. At times, the climber will need the line to pass over only one branch (referred to as **isolated**), with both of the legs hanging parallel. This can require a bit of manipulation, sometimes by swinging the throw weight into position and letting it drop in the right location. Another strategy is to attach a throw weight to each end of the throwline, which can then be pulled over branches to facilitate isolating the line.

Once down, the throwline can be attached to the climber's line using either a pile hitch or a clove hitch with a half hitch, or simply by attaching a carabiner from the shot pouch ring to a spliced eye. The rope is then pulled up through the branch union.

One limitation to using a throwline to install the climbing line high in the tree is the inability to thoroughly inspect the tie-in point. Using binoculars can help, but most trainers also recommend testing the tie-in point before ascending. This is particularly important if the climber is using a basal anchor for stationary rope systems. More about this added load is explained in Chapter 7.

An additional limitation is the difficulty of installing the throwline around the stem. It takes patience and skill to manipulate the throwline correctly. Finally, worksite cleanliness is vital to maintaining a debris-free throwline. A poorly managed throwline can easily become a rat's nest of tangled string when some loose twigs and leaves get involved. One way to manage this is by proper storage. Something as simple as a bucket can hold the throwline, but the throw weight may still move too freely. A storage device, such as a folding throwline cube, can be a great solution, as it offers pockets to house the throw weight(s) and is a compact storage solution that can be stowed easily in a gear bag.

FIGURE 5.8 Friction from tree bark can make it challenging to get the throw weight down. In this case, the climber must manipulate the throwline, such as by strumming or pulling on the throwline repeatedly.

USING LADDERS

Ladders are an acceptable means of entering a tree if the climber is secured. They offer a simple and quick way to reach lower branches, avoiding the more physically demanding methods of entering a tree. However, their ease of use can be deceiving. Often, people perceive only a low amount of danger when it comes to

FIGURE 5.9 At times, the climber will need the line to pass over only one branch (referred to as isolated), with both of the legs hanging parallel. This can require a bit of manipulation, sometimes by swinging the throw weight into position and letting it drop in the right location.

ladders because there are no moving parts or sharp blades, but that does not mean they come without risk. Ladders can easily shift when not placed on level ground or when loaded unevenly. A climber can also get off balance and fall from a ladder. Falling from even one of the lowest rungs can cause significant and permanent injuries. For these reasons, climbers should be secured from falling when using a ladder to enter a tree, with the climber first installing the climbing line to be tied in while ascending the ladder.

FIGURE 5.10 When the climber is ascending the ladder, a ground worker should hold the ladder steady and remove it from the immediate area once the climber has left the ladder.

The ladder must be set up in a stable position. An extension ladder should have both legs evenly touching the ground, with a comfortable 70 to 75° angle from the ground to the ladder. Some standards use the 4:1 rule: if the ladder height is 20 ft (6 m), the base should be 5 ft (1.5 m) away from the tree or wall it rests against. The climbing system will provide fall protection should the ladder become unstable. When the climber is ascending the ladder, a ground worker should hold the ladder steady and remove it from the immediate area once the climber is in the tree.

CLIMBING WITH SPIKES

Another method of ascending a tree is the use of **climbing spikes (spurs)**. Using climbing spikes to climb trees for pruning is unacceptable and strongly discouraged because it can do irreparable damage to a tree, including to palms. Using

FIGURE 5.11 **Using climbing spikes to climb trees for pruning is unacceptable and strongly discouraged because it can do irreparable damage to a tree, including to palms.**

spurs for tree removal, however, is common and considered a standard technique.

The first consideration is to select the appropriate **gaffs** (spikes) for the tree. Longer gaffs are preferred, if not required, for thick-barked trees; shorter gaffs may be easier to use on thin-barked trees. Either way, the gaffs should be sharpened and the shafts should be properly adjusted for the climber. Dull gaffs or improper technique can lead to **gaffing out**, which is what happens when one or both gaffs come out of the tree, possibly leading to an accident. Straps securing the gaffs to the climber should be adjusted to be snug, but comfortable. Wearing a deep-heeled boot is helpful to hold the shaft of the spike in place.

Beginner climbers using climbing spurs often struggle with the orientation of the spikes and the placement of their feet on the tree. For example, some climbers try to straddle small- to mid-sized stems when climbing. The correct placement of the feet should be at a comfortable, natural-feeling distance apart on the tree, approximately shoulder-distance apart. If the feet are too close together, the chances of the climber accidentally spiking their own leg or their climbing line are increased. Another thing to watch for is the orientation of the gaffs. The gaffs should be pointed downward and more or less toward the center of the tree. Experience is helpful when climbing with spikes, as climbers learn that it is not necessary to stomp to drive the spike into the tree. The knees are generally bent somewhat while ascending, although one or both knees may be locked when working.

Climbers must be secured while ascending and should always carry two means of securing, one of which must be a climbing line. The climbing system must include a method that prevents the line from sliding. Lanyards that cinch are preferred. Some lanyards have a wire core that makes the line more rigid; these wire-core lanyards should not, however, be assumed to provide protection from cutting with a chain saw. Once at the top of the tree, work positioning is important. Using a two-in-one lanyard will allow the climber to remain secured with one end of the lanyard while moving the other end above branches.

Because spikes are worn for tree removals, the climber is often working on a **spar**. A spar is a vertical section of trunk without a top and, often, with no branches below. It is essentially like working on a pole. Working on a spar requires a different tie-in strategy because there may be no way to be tied in above the working area.

The method of tying in is important, especially if securing to remove the top of a tree. The tie-in method must allow the climber to be secured while working, but should also allow for quick and easy descent, if necessary. Also, the lanyard and climbing line must be positioned so that it does not interfere with any rigging or cutting. When removing the top of a tree, it is important for the climber to be secured in a manner that will allow for stable body positioning and ensure that the climber will not be pulled against the tree if the tree were to split.

Gear kits are available for securing to spars, and there are several options available. It is also possible to rig a tie-in point using the climbing line and commonly available gear. One option is to install an adjustable **friction-saving device**. By adjusting the length so the rings are slightly spread apart, friction will hold the climbing system in place. The friction-saving device can be wrapped around the spar twice for additional friction. The climbing line is installed on the friction-saving device, preventing the climber from being pulled into the tree if it splits and allowing for a quick descent. It is important to remember, though, that climbers must not descend on a single, stationary line using only a friction hitch (climbing hitch); additional friction—such as a figure-8 device—is needed.

FIGURE 5.12 Climbers working on a spar should always have two means available for being tied in, one of which includes a climbing line that will reach the ground, facilitating an easier rescue should one be needed.

Climbers working on a spar should always have two means available for being tied in, one of which should be a climbing system that will reach the ground, facilitating an easier rescue should one be needed.

WORKING IN PALMS

Palms must be properly inspected prior to climbing; the elements of an inspection are unique to palms. A strong root system is needed to support an often very tall and slender structure, and climbers should check to ensure that the root mat has not been pruned, damaged, or overly restricted. The trunk should have a regular taper, without significant hourglassing. Injuries from spikes can become pockets for disease. Consistent with a tree inspection, fungal fruiting bodies, excessive, uncorrected lean, cavities, soft spots, and oozing may also be red flags for climbing.

The crown should be inspected for healthy fronds. A leaning crown, or diseased, frizzled, chlorotic, drooping, or excessive necrotic fronds, could be an indicator of an underlying problem. A diseased palm could unexpectedly drop its whole crown under the weight of a climber.

Some species of palms retain a full skirt of dead fronds, which can hide defects and animals that may present a risk. These large skirts are also prone to **sloughing**, which is when large sections of dead, hanging frond rings release and slide down the trunk. Sloughing of fronds is a leading cause of fatalities among climbers in fan palms, as they can pose an asphyxiation risk, which is why climbing and pruning from under the skirt must be avoided.

Setting a Line

The palms that arborists climb are typically a branchless stem with a crown only at the top. This makes them similar to working on a spar. A previously accepted practice, one that is still found in many areas, is the use of spikes to climb palms. It was believed that because the living tissue was not concentrated around the perimeter, it would not negatively impact the palm. This method is fast, relatively easy, and cost-effective as it does not require expensive equipment. However, today, there is more knowledge about the harmful effects of spike wounds to palms. Moreover, now there is specialized equipment that will not damage palm trunks. Additionally, by spiking up a tree, the climber is approaching from under any skirt that may be present. For the safety of the climber, it is best to set a line in the crown of fan palms with skirts.

A throwline can be used to install a climbing line through the center of the crown. It is important for the installation point to be over fronds that will not bend under the weight of the climber, which would cause the system to slide off the crown. The conditions of the crown are not conducive for a rope running through it, so the rope needs to be installed in an SRS configuration, which is described in Chapter 7.

The typical approach for ascending the outside of a palm is by installing a basal anchor either at the base of the tree or at the base of a neighboring tree. The climber can either use the line to ascend using SRS, or pull a moving rope system installed on a pulley up to the crown and ascend using MRS (described in Chapter 6).

Tying In

Regardless of the climbing system used, the climber must always use appropriate fall protection during the ascent. Once at the top of the palm, the climber should install their work-positioning lanyard and reset their tie-in much like they would when working on a spar. Palm trees contain a large concentration of debris in close proximity to the climber's system, making it difficult to see ropes within the fronds. A taut rope could easily be severed with a hand saw. Because of this dense environment, it is best not to work off the basal anchor. When removing **palm skirts**, an adjustable friction-saving device can be cinched just under the crown, much like working off a spar. Climbers should use a rope long enough to allow them to reach the ground without needing to lower the tie-in point.

EMERGENCY RESPONSE

Accidents are prevented through the conscious recognition of potential hazards in the workplace and the effort to avoid them. It takes only one lax moment or unexpected event for an incident to happen. Because of this, every worker on the crew should be trained in first aid, cardiopulmonary resuscitation (CPR), and **emergency response**. **Aerial rescue**, a potential component of emergency response, is the process of safely bringing an injured or unconscious worker to the ground. Aerial rescue requires specialized training.

Emergency response is something that should be trained and practiced. Practicing the response will reduce the likelihood of panic and will reinforce what steps each worker should take. Workers should be trained in effective communication with 911 (or other emergency numbers). This communication includes knowing the necessary information to provide emergency personnel,

FIGURE 5.13 Ground workers should maintain a close watch on climbers and remain in voice contact. Bluetooth capabilities can help with on-site communications. However, a climber could become injured or experience a health emergency and lose consciousness without ever calling for help.

including the location, site, and nature of the emergency. Having an emergency response plan for each job is an essential part of the job briefing. Practicing that emergency response plan is an essential part of saving a life.

There are a number of ways a climber can be injured in a tree. Electric shock, heart attack, heat exhaustion, insect or animal attack, being struck by a swinging limb, or a chain saw–cut could leave a worker dangling helplessly in a tree. Ground workers should maintain a close watch on climbers and remain in voice contact. Bluetooth capabilities can help with on-site communications. However, a climber could get hurt and lose consciousness without ever calling for help.

When a climber is injured or unconscious in a tree, the emergency response procedure should begin immediately. A very quick assessment of the site should take place immediately to identify the victim's situation and potential site hazards. If there is more than one worker in the area, one worker should call or go for help immediately. Most areas have a universal emergency number, such as 911 in the United States, but other numbers, such as the local electrical utility, might be needed as well. It is a good idea to have these numbers programmed into cell phones.

When calling for emergency assistance, the person calling should be prepared to give the exact location of the accident and the nature of the emergency. The operator must be told if it involves a high-angle rescue. The caller should let the emergency personnel obtain all necessary information and let the emergency operator be the first to hang up.

For a two-person crew, the rescuer should first call for assistance, then stay and help the injured worker, if possible. No rescue attempt should be started without first contacting emergency help. If the jobsite is located far into a property, a safety cone or person should be stationed at the road to direct emergency services to the exact site.

The necessary rescue equipment must be in good condition and readily available. Some companies keep a separate **rescue kit** that is not used for routine daily work. This should include a climbing line and harness, a lanyard, a throwline, climbing spurs, and a first-aid kit. The rescue kit should be taken off the truck at the start of each job, as it may not be accessible if the truck were to become energized or if the truck is a long distance from the worksite.

FIGURE 5.14 A rescue kit is not used for routine daily work. It should be taken off the truck at the start of each job, as it may not be accessible if the truck were to become energized. All crew members should be informed as to the location of the rescue kit on the jobsite.

Some companies now advocate that a second line, called an **access line**, be hung when working above 50 ft (15 m), particularly if the tree is difficult to enter or ascend. This can save valuable minutes if an aerial rescue becomes necessary.

Aerial Rescue

In most urban and suburban areas, emergency response professionals can be on site in a very short time. One of their first responsibilities is to secure the area to prevent any more incidents or escalation of the situation. It is likely that they will not allow other tree workers to enter a tree to perform a rescue. Most emergency rescue teams have training and equipment to reduce further injury but are not trained or equipped to rescue victims out of trees. In some cases, emergency personnel will coordinate efforts with a well-trained tree crew to bring a victim to the ground.

There are also times when emergency response crews are more than a few minutes away and it may be necessary to perform an aerial rescue. The cardinal rule of aerial rescue is to not become a second victim. This means that the site must be assessed to determine whether there is an electrical hazard or any other hazard that would make it unsafe to enter the tree. Because the chance of the rescuer becoming a second victim

TIP!

INSPECTING THE RESCUE KIT

Remember to inspect the rescue kit gear when performing periodic inspections. When the time comes to use the rescue kit, the gear must be ready to go.

FIGURE 5.15 An access line can save valuable minutes if an aerial rescue becomes necessary.

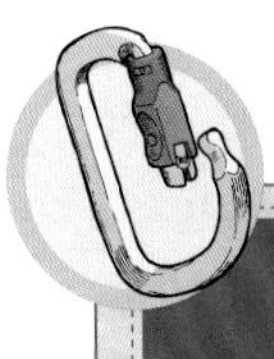

WITH ANY AERIAL RESCUE, A FEW FUNDAMENTAL PRINCIPLES APPLY:

- No rescue should ever be attempted unless it is safe for the rescuer and absolutely necessary.
- The victim should not be moved unless necessary, such as to perform CPR or control serious bleeding.
- Both the victim and the rescuer must remain secured at all times.
- A rescuer must support the victim, if possible, which often requires securing to the victim.

is great when electrical hazards are involved, utility company experts recommend calling the local electric company to avoid any further direct or indirect contact. If the victim has been shocked, there is a good chance that it is not safe to attempt a rescue. A rescuer must never attempt to climb a tree or rope that may be energized or may have the potential of becoming energized.

An important step in assessing the emergency situation is to determine if the climber needs to be rescued. In some cases, the climber may be able to perform a self-rescue. An injured leg, for example, may not inhibit their ability to lower themselves. However, ascent systems that only utilize ascenders will make self-rescue difficult. Ascenders are designed for ascent only. The climber must have a plan (and the necessary equipment) to descend midline should they not make it to a suitable anchor point. A swarm of bees or other hazard may arise requiring an immediate descent.

If there is no electrical hazard and the tree is deemed safe to climb, it is important to get to the victim to assess his or her condition. The rescuer must first assess what may have caused the accident (for example, hanging limbs, insects, or a defect in the tree) before ascending. **The rescuer must never risk becoming a second victim or putting others in danger.** The rescuer should use approved climbing equipment and techniques and must remain secured while climbing to the victim. When practical, the rescuer should use a second climbing line and tie in above the victim. Climbing spurs may be used to reach the victim.

Upon reaching the victim, a quick check should be made to determine the nature of the injury. If the victim appears to have a broken neck or spinal injury and is breathing, no attempt should be made to move the victim. In fact, unless CPR is needed or bleeding is severe, it is better not to move the victim and to await professional emergency response personnel. One of the first tenets of first aid is to avoid moving the victim unless necessary. Although all first-aid procedures can

FIGURE 5.16 Saving a victim from a tree is not about a race to the climber and a swift descent. It is about systematically executing the rescue plan, keeping the safety of both the victim and the rescuer at the forefront.

AERIAL RESCUE PRACTICE

When practicing aerial rescues, a dummy should be used rather than actual climbers. Practice should take place low to the ground, and with the systems most commonly used by the crew.

be performed more effectively on the ground, moving the victim may complicate injuries. In some cases, the best decision may be to await emergency personnel who will have the knowledge and equipment that can prevent further injuries while lowering the victim. The rescuer should ensure that the victim is secure and their equipment is safe for descent, and then wait for emergency help to arrive. However, an injured worker hanging for a prolonged period in the climbing harness could lose consciousness and/or go into shock, so it is important to continue to closely monitor breathing, pulse, and overall condition.

With moving rope systems (MRS), explained in Chapter 6, unless the system has been compromised, the climber can likely be lowered on their own system. The preferred method is for the rescuer and victim to each descend on their own systems; two workers descending on one system adds significant weight and affects how the friction hitch performs.

The rescuer must operate the friction hitch(es) while supporting the victim and minimizing the chances of causing further injury. Usually the victim is secured to the rescuer using one of several possible techniques so that at least one of the rescuer's hands is available to operate the friction hitch.

Some stationary rope systems (SRS) can be configured to allow a victim to be lowered from the ground. Though climbers may set systems to be lowerable, that does not mean the ground crew should automatically lower the climber in an emergency. Proper training in the system and its setup is essential to not cause further damage. Using a basal anchor can make ground rescues possible but can also create additional hazards. A well-meaning but poorly trained crew could cause the victim to drop uncontrolled. The ground workers must be trained in a rescue plan, including how each component of the basal anchor functions. If there is any doubt, it is best for the ground crew to maintain contact with the climber and wait for a high-angle rescue team to arrive at the scene.

For SRS, it is also preferred to bring the victim down on their own system, although the use of ascenders can affect that decision. Any non-life-support ascenders will need to be removed, such as foot and knee ascenders. If the life-support component cannot be used for descent, a separate system will need to be used. The climber can either be transferred onto that separate system, or the rescuer can attach them to their own system. Attaching a victim to the rescuer's system can add a great deal of weight, which might exceed the friction control of the hitch or device, requiring additional friction to be added. This technique requires proficiency in climbing and equipment use, an understanding of forces, and knowledge about victim care.

The ability to react swiftly and safely to save a life depends on keeping a cool head, using common sense, and being prepared. Saving a victim from a tree is not about a race to the climber and a swift descent. It is about systematically executing the rescue plan, keeping the safety of both the victim and the rescuer at the forefront. Proper training and practice can save crucial minutes that could mean the difference between life and death.

KEY CONCEPTS

1. All climbers must be trained to inspect every tree and the vicinity before climbing. Hazards, and procedures to minimize them, must be discussed as part of the job briefing.
2. Arborists have developed a number of techniques for throwing, launching, and manipulating throwlines to put them in the specific branch union desired. The climbing line is then attached to the throwline and pulled into the tree.
3. Using climbing spikes to climb trees for pruning is generally unacceptable and strongly discouraged because it can cause irreparable damage to a tree (including palms). Using spurs for tree removal, however, is common and considered a standard technique.
4. Every worker on the crew should be trained in first aid, cardiopulmonary resuscitation (CPR), and emergency response. Practicing emergency response will reduce the likelihood of panic and ensure that all workers will know what steps to take.
5. No aerial rescue should ever be attempted unless it is safe for the rescuer and absolutely necessary.

WORKBOOK

MATCHING

_____ conk	A. tool used to "sound" for decay
_____ access line	B. thin, slick cordage for installing a climbing line
_____ throwline	C. tree without branches
_____ mallet	D. second climbing line pre-installed for emergency
_____ gaffing out	E. bringing an injured climber to the ground
_____ trunk flare	F. root crown
_____ spar	G. fruiting body of a decay fungus
_____ aerial rescue	H. climbing spikes dislodging from a tree

TRUE/FALSE

1. T F If there are electrical conductors nearby, workers must know and abide by minimum approach distances (MAD).
2. T F The pre-climb inspection is limited to checking for electrical hazards and tree defects.
3. T F Signs of decay in the root crown (trunk flare) could indicate a defect that can lead to whole-tree failure.
4. T F Snow, vines, debris, soil, and landscaping could hide conks or fruiting bodies of decay organisms, which indicate decay in the tree.
5. T F Dieback in the top of the tree could indicate root damage but is never a serious concern.
6. T F Along the trunk, included bark, cankers, and other structural defects could result in trunk failure.
7. T F A throwing knot can be used in an open or closed form; the closed version will not come undone when the rope is thrown.
8. T F If friction from tree bark makes it challenging to get a throw weight down to the ground, the only option is to pull the line out and begin again.
9. T F A poorly managed throwline can easily become a rat's nest of tangled string when some loose twigs and leaves get involved.
10. T F Sloughing of fronds is a leading cause for fatalities among climbers in fan palms, as they can pose an asphyxiation risk, which is why climbing and pruning from under the skirt must be avoided.

11. T F Ladders are never an acceptable means of entering a tree.
12. T F Using climbing spikes to climb trees for pruning is generally unacceptable and strongly discouraged because it can do irreparable damage to a tree.
13. T F When using climbing spikes, the correct placement of the feet should be at a comfortable, natural-feeling distance apart on the tree, approximately shoulder-distance apart.
14. T F Lanyards that have a wire core should not be assumed to provide protection from cutting with a chain saw.
15. T F The tie-in method for working on a spar must allow the climber to be secured while working, but should also allow for quick and easy descent, if necessary.
16. T F When calling for emergency assistance, it is best to give the location information as quickly as possible, then hang up and return to the victim.
17. T F The rescue kit should be kept on the truck at all times so that every worker knows where to look for it in an emergency.
18. T F Emergency personnel will generally defer to crew members to perform an aerial rescue.
19. T F A victim should not be moved unless necessary, such as to perform CPR or control serious bleeding.
20. T F In an aerial rescue, both the victim and the rescuer must remain secured at all times.

SAMPLE TEST QUESTIONS

1. When performing a pre-climb inspection, in addition to looking for hazards, the climber should

   a. perform a thorough root crown excavation to look for decay
   b. always use both a mallet and a probe on each tree climbed
   c. plan the climb, look for a tie-in point, and consider loads
   d. determine each branch to prune or remove in the tree

2. The main limitation to using a throwline to install a climbing line in a tree is

   a. that the line cannot be installed higher than 30 ft (10 m)
   b. the inability to inspect the tie-in point from the ground
   c. that it is not possible to install a line over a branch and around the main stem
   d. that the line must always pass over only one branch

3. When considering whether to attempt an aerial rescue, it is essential to consider

   a. electrical and other potential hazards to the rescuer
   b. the safety of the rescuer and other workers
   c. whether the victim can self-rescue
   d. all of the above

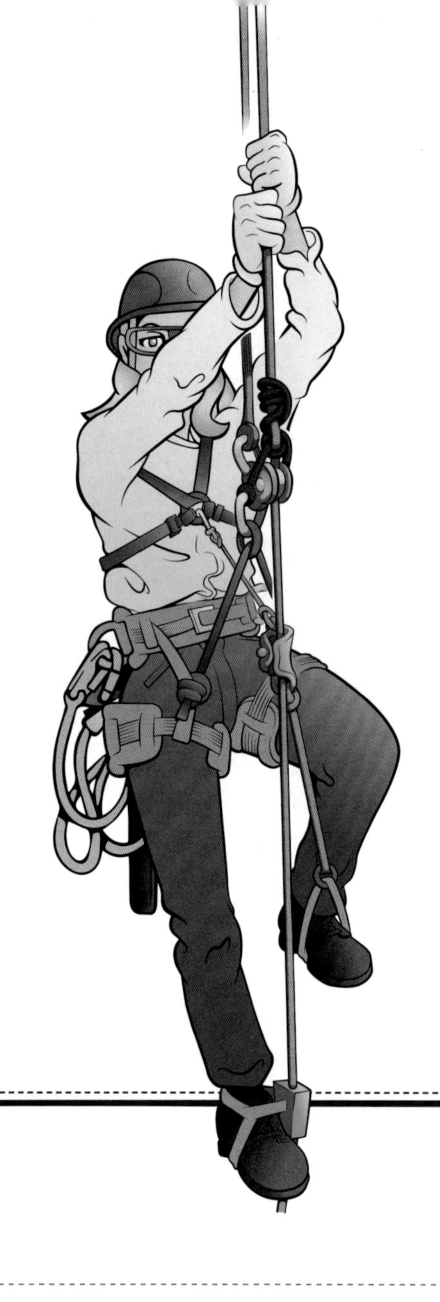

CHAPTER

6 MOVING ROPE SYSTEMS

LEARNING OBJECTIVES

The tree worker will be able to:

- Explain the meaning of the term "moving rope systems" and how it differs from stationary rope systems.
- Describe how to select an appropriate tie-in point and methods for installing a climbing line into the branch union.
- List the knots and hitches used in a moving rope system and explain how they are applied.
- Describe the techniques used to ascend into a tree using moving rope systems, including their advantages and limitations.
- Explain techniques for managing friction and optimizing rope angles in a moving rope system.

IMPORTANT TERMS

Blake's hitch
body-thrust
bridge
closed hitch
clove hitch
Distel hitch
double-tying
ergonomic
figure-8 knot
footlocking
friction-saving device
hitch cord
hitch-tending pulley
isolate
lanyard crawl
limb walking
Michoacán
micropulley
moving rope system (MRS)
open hitch
redirect
rope angle
rope walking
scabbard
Schwabisch
secured footlock
split-tail
standing part
stationary rope system (SRS)
stopper knot
tautline hitch
tie-in point
triple-action carabiner
***Valdôtain tresse* (Vt)**
working end

INTRODUCTION

There are many systems for ascending into and working within a tree; each offers its own set of advantages and limitations. The systems can be divided into two main types: **moving rope systems (MRS)** and **stationary rope systems (SRS)**. The equipment and techniques vary somewhat, but the basic principles remain the same: keeping safety first and managing friction to move efficiently in a tree. Both types of system are viable options for any climber, but not necessarily for any tree. Many employers and trainers require that beginners learn the fundamental skills of MRS before learning SRS. Knowing these skills can be essential for self-rescue or descent if a key piece of equipment is dropped during work.

The next two chapters will explain the main differences between MRS and SRS and their applications. This chapter will cover the fundamentals of building an MRS, including the mechanics and the advantages and limitations. The minimal gear required for MRS can be a nice incentive to start, but with time, climbers will generally incorporate additional gear into the system to make it more efficient and ergonomic. Many employers require learning MRS first because there are MRS techniques that allow descent with no gear other than a rope. This is a key safety tool for any climber to have.

FIGURE 6.1 The basic setup for a moving rope system (MRS) includes the working end that is fixed to the harness, attached by a piece of hardware, and the standing part that is adjusted by use of a climbing hitch. As the climber moves in the tree, the rope moves over the branch, which is why these are called moving rope systems.

This chapter will continue with different ascent techniques that can be used with an MRS. Climbers may select a favorite ascent technique, but most will adapt their techniques with each climb. As a climber gains experience, they will learn new techniques and adapt them to pick the best climbing technique for any given tree.

WHAT IS A MOVING ROPE SYSTEM?

Moving rope systems are so named because the climbing line moves through the tie-in point when the climber moves up and down in the tree. One end of the line is fixed to the climber's harness—either directly or by using a connecting link such as a carabiner or rope snap. This part of the line is called the **working end**. The working end of the line runs up and over a branch and around the trunk, and then back down to the climber, more or less parallel with itself. The part of the line that continues from the tie-in branch to the ground is known as the **standing part**. After securing the working end to their harness, the climber can leave a sufficient length of the working end to tie into the standing part using a friction hitch (climbing hitch). The length of line used to tie a friction hitch is sometimes referred to as the tail. Instead of leaving a tail to tie a friction hitch, climbers often use a separate (and shorter) piece of rope, known as a **split-tail**, to tie the friction hitch. A variation of the split-tail is called a **hitch cord**, which is a short length of rope with an eye on each end. Split-tails can be the same diameter or smaller than the climbing line itself. The friction hitch is tied around the standing part of the climbing line and can be pushed up or down as the climber ascends, descends, or moves throughout the tree. As the climber moves in the tree, the rope moves over the branch, which is why these are called *moving* rope systems. The friction hitch releases when pulled, allowing movement, but it grips the rope firmly when loaded to hold the climber in place. This allows the climber to have two free hands to work.

Many years ago, arborists ascended into and worked in trees using only a 3-strand rope. Using their knot-tying skills, arborists could fashion a makeshift harness and a friction hitch out of a single line to work in a tree. The systems arborists were climbing on in those days were moving rope systems. Tree climbing has since undergone many generations of innovation, making climbing more comfortable, ergonomic, and efficient.

MRS climbing has undergone many iterations over the years, and gear has been added, although MRS tends to be less gear intensive than SRS. This means it's less expensive. It also leaves less of a chance for error for a new climber: when there are fewer components in the climbing system, it's easier for a new climber to understand how the system works and to make sure the system is working correctly. The equipment needed ranges from, at the minimum, a suitable climbing harness and climbing line, plus a work-positioning lanyard, to a more complex setup, with carabiners, a **hitch-tending pulley**, a split-tail, and multiple slings for redirecting a line. The simpler setup is often taught as an introductory climbing technique. Often, new climbers master this technique and subsequently either stick with this system or evolve, maintaining this foundational skill set as part of their toolbox.

The main limitation with MRS is the ascent, which is slower than ascending on SRS. Because the rope moves as the climber moves in MRS, the climber advances only 1 ft (30 cm) for every 2 ft (60 cm) of rope pulled. Even though it's slower to ascend, the climber's weight is split between the two parts of the line, creating a mechanical advantage. Certain ascent techniques, such as **body-thrusting**, can only be used on an MRS; body-thrusting, in particular, relies heavily on core and upper body strength, so long ascents can be exhausting. Another limitation of MRS is associated with setting a climbing line in the tree. For MRS to work, the two parts of the climbing line must be **isolated** over a single branch, meaning both ends follow the same path from the branch to the ground.

SELECTING A TIE-IN POINT

The **tie-in point** is the branch union around which the climber has installed the climbing line to work in the tree. The climber may ascend into the tree in stages, using progressively higher branches to reach the final tie-in point. The position of the tie-in point affects the climber's ability to access various parts of the tree. It is also the point from which the climbing line and climber are

FIGURE 6.2 **Generally, it is desirable to pick a high, central location in the tree for the tie-in point. It is very important not to tie into a union that would allow a swing toward power lines in the event of a slip or fall.**

FIGURE 6.3 The branch union selected for tying in should be wide enough for the climbing line to pass through easily. The line should pass over the lateral branch and around the leader.

suspended, so a strong branch union is needed. For these reasons, the selection of a suitable tie-in point is essential for a good climb.

Generally, it is desirable to pick a high, central location in the tree. This allows freedom of movement and easy access to most points in the tree. The higher the tie-in point, the farther the climber can move out on the limbs. However, the tie-in point cannot be too high or the branches may be too small to support the climber. It is easiest to work when tied in directly above the working area. The more vertical the climbing line, the more secure the climber. It is very important not to tie into a union that would allow a swing toward power lines in the event of a slip or fall.

The branch union selected for tying in should be wide enough for the climbing line to pass through easily. The size of the limbs varies with species and wood strength, but generally the main branch should be at least 4 in (10 cm) in diameter. The branch needs to be alive and healthy, with signs of life, such as leaves or buds. If there are signs of sapwood decay or possible internal decay, that branch union must not be used. The climbing line is installed by passing it through a union, around the larger branch or trunk, and over the smaller or lateral branch. This way, if the smaller branch breaks clean, the line will simply drop to the next branch down, rather than out of the tree.

FRICTION-SAVING DEVICES

Climbers may also choose to use a **friction-saving device** when tying in. A friction-saving device is a device used at the tie-in point to reduce friction, or wrapped on a stem to create a tie-in point where there is no branch union. Friction-saving devices can reduce wear on the climbing line and damage to the tree, and, in some cases, can facilitate climbing. It is important to remember, however, that if there is less friction between the climbing line and the bark in the tie-in point, as happens when using a friction-saving device, the friction hitch will experience greater friction because it needs to carry more of the climber's weight.

Friction-saving devices come in many different styles, including a sheath-type and a ring-type (double ring), with the additional option to be adjustable. The sheath-style friction-saving device (cambium saver) is the simplest. It rests on top of a branch union, protecting it from abrasion resulting from friction with the climbing line. The line runs through the friction-saving device, running freely back and forth. The friction-saving device can be moved with the climbing line as the tie-in point is changed. The advantage to this style of friction-saving device is the ease of use and minimal training required. It is relatively inexpensive and can be installed and retrieved from the ground. The limitations come with the branch size. A larger branch means that the two

FIGURE 6.4 **A friction-saving device is a device used at the tie-in point to reduce friction, or wrapped on a stem to create a tie-in point where there is no branch union. This illustration depicts the use of a ring-style friction-saving device.**

parts of the line are spread farther apart, which can sometimes be a limiting factor for some systems, such as when **footlocking**. A ring-style friction-saving device can remedy this problem, as it brings both parts of the line together.

The ring-style friction-saving device typically consists of a short length of webbing or rope with a small ring attached to one end and a larger ring attached to the other. Variations include thimbles, pulleys, carabiners, and other hardware in place of the rings. The friction-saving device is installed in a branch union and the climbing line is then run through the two pieces of hardware (rings) instead of over the branch. This style can be purchased in different lengths. To make it even more versatile, these friction-saving devices can also be purchased in an adjustable style, which allows it to be used over many different-sized branches.

There is usually much less friction with ring-style friction-saving devices compared to natural branch unions, and even compared to sheath-style friction-saving devices. This makes it easier for the climber to ascend because there is less friction force that opposes the motion of the climbing line. But as the climber works in the tree or descends, less friction means that the friction hitch will need to exert more friction on the rope, possibly wearing the hitch cord or tail of the climbing line faster than if a friction-saving device was not used. Ring-style friction-saving devices also provide greater freedom of movement because the rings swing around the trunk as the climber moves. One limitation of ring-style friction-saving devices is that installation is less intuitive. Though they can be installed from the ground, they take more time to learn how to install, adjust, retrieve, and inspect.

A ring-style friction-saving device can also be wrapped around a stem to create a tie-in point where there is no branch union (this is sometimes known as a "false crotch"). Because it supports the climber, the ring-style friction-saving device must meet the same safety standards as other fall protection, as the climber would fall if it failed.

If the tie-in point used for the ascent is not the final tie-in point, the climber must remove and replace the friction-saving device during ascent. This can be challenging, as the line cannot simply be tossed over the next limb, as with the sheath type. For this reason, often, if the final tie-in point is not achieved with a throwline, climbers may choose not to install the friction-saving device until they have climbed to their desired tie-in point.

RING-STYLE FRICTION SAVER RETRIEVAL TOOLS

Some ring-style friction-saving devices come with a retrieval tool. These can usually be girthed to the end of the climbing line instead of using a connecting link or overhand knot. If a retrieval tool did not come with the device, a simple washer with a short loop girthed can be used. The washer must be small enough to fit through the big ring and large enough to not pass through the small ring.

Installing a Ring-Style Friction-Saving Device

First, the throwline is installed over the desired branch. The line must be isolated over that branch and no others. The friction-saving device is installed on the throwline, with the standing part of the throwline through the larger of the two rings and the working end through the smaller ring. To do this, the weight will need to be removed and retied on the opposite side of the small ring from which it was passed. The throw weight ring must not be able to pass through the smaller ring of the friction-saving device.

With the friction-saving device installed on the throwline, the standing end of the line (below the larger ring) is pulled until the friction-saving device is just below the target branch. Then, with a quick tug and release, the friction-saving device is pulled over the branch along with the throw weight. The throw weight can then be lowered to the ground with the friction-saving device remaining installed at the tie-in point. Then the climbing line is attached to the throwline and pulled through the friction-saving device rings.

The friction-saving device can later be retrieved from the ground. First, any snaps or carabiners must be removed from the climbing line. An overhand knot is tied (or a connecting link attached) in the end of the climbing line below the larger ring, and a throwline is attached to the climbing line at that point. Pulling on the other end of the climbing line, the knot is pulled up and through the larger ring. It will catch on the smaller ring. Pulling more will dislodge the friction-saving device. The throwline is simply used to control the lowering to avoid any damage to the rings, which could later damage a climbing line.

FIGURE 6.5 A ring-style friction-saving device can be both installed and retrieved from the ground.

TYING THE MOVING ROPE SYSTEM

MRS offers several options for building a climbing system. When a climbing line is set for MRS, both parts of the line are isolated over one branch, meaning both ends follow the same path through the branches from the tie-in point to the ground. The basic principle of MRS is to create a loop of line, where the climber is at one end, the tie-in point is at the other end, and there are no obstructions in between. The simplest assembly is created using only the climbing line to form a "closed" loop that cannot be opened without untying. The friction hitch is tied with the tail of the working end of the line, coming from the point of attachment to the climbing harness. This is the least gear-intensive option, as no additional hardware is required. An alternative is to use a separate hitch cord and some attachment hardware to create a split-tail. The split-tail allows the loop to be "opened" and reset without the need to untie and retie knots, making it more efficient. The type of system used will determine the tie-in procedure.

FIGURE 6.6 A closed-loop climbing system cannot be opened without untying. The friction hitch is tied with the tail of the working end of the line, coming from the point of attachment to the climbing harness.

FIGURE 6.7 A separate split-tail allows the loop to be "opened" and reset without the need to untie and retie knots. A hitch-tending pulley below the climbing hitch will help to move the hitch up while the climber ascends.

To tie into the traditional, closed-loop climbing system, the climber leaves a long tail in the working end of the climbing line beyond where it attaches to the carabiner or hardware on the D-rings or the **bridge** of the harness. An endline knot, such as an anchor bend, a double fisherman's knot, or a buntline hitch, is tied about 3 ft (1 m) from the working end of the line to attach to a connecting link (a carabiner or rope snap), which is then attached to the harness.

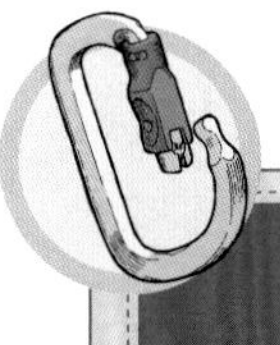

A NOTE ABOUT THE BRIDGE OF A HARNESS

The bridge of the harness is the key attachment point from a climber's harness to their climbing system. Bridges can vary, from stitched webbing with fixed loops, to a short piece of rope, spliced, stitched, or knotted on both ends. The different bridges offer variability in their function and versatility.

Because bridges are exposed to repeated loads, friction, and overall wear and tear, this portion of a harness should be inspected with every use and replaced regularly. A bridge will wear out much more quickly than the rest of the harness.

The tail of the climbing line is then used to tie a friction hitch to the standing part of the climbing line. A friction hitch is formed using an **open hitch**, which is a knot where only one end of the hitch is secured. When tying in with a **tautline hitch** or a **Blake's hitch**, a **stopper knot**, such as a **figure-8**, must be tied in the tail of the line to prevent the end from going through the friction hitch.

When tying the climbing system using a split-tail that can be "opened," the working end of the climbing line is attached to hardware on the bridge, typically using a **triple-action carabiner** or a double-action snap and an approved termination knot, such as an anchor bend, a double (or triple) fisherman's knot, or a buntline hitch, leaving enough tail to tie a stopper knot. More often, climbers use a climbing line with a spliced eye in place of a termination knot, and attach to bridge hardware using an approved carabiner.

Using a separate piece of cordage for the split-tail, a friction hitch is tied to the standing part of the climbing line. The split-tail typically has at least one spliced eye to attach a carabiner for connecting to the harness bridge. If the split-tail is a section of rope similar to the climbing line, traditional open-ended knots, such as the tautline hitch or Blake's hitch, are typically used to tie in and require a stopper knot in the end of the line. Hitch cords can be used to tie a **closed hitch**, which is when both ends of the hitch are secured. When using a closed hitch, such as a **Schwabisch**, **Distel**, **Michoacán**, or ***Valdôtain tresse* (Vt)**, a stopper knot does not need to be tied, as both sides of the hitch cord will be captured. Using an additional carabiner and **micropulley** (for tending the hitch), the full system can be attached to the bridge of the harness on a single carabiner.

FIGURE 6.8 Hitch cords can be used to tie a closed hitch, which is when both ends of the hitch are secured.

TIP!

WARNING

A bowline must not be used as a termination knot. When repeatedly loaded and unloaded, a bowline can easily loosen and become untied.

ASCENT

When climbing MRS, the climber will need a climbing line that is at least twice as long as their final tie-in point is high. Because of the possibility of lateral movements and redirects (described later), it is best to use a line that far exceeds that measurement. The best practice is to use a climbing line that is long enough to allow the climber to reach the ground while tied to the highest attachment point. Even with a long-enough line, it is a good practice to tie a stopper knot in the tail end of the climbing line. This practice is intended to prevent the end from

FIGURE 6.9 Using a hitch-tending pulley, slack can be removed from the system with one hand while working.

passing through the friction hitch or mechanical device if the climber reaches the end of the line prior to reaching the ground when descending. This could happen even on a shorter climb when redirects are used. The stopper knot should be placed 3 to 5 ft (1 to 1.5 m) from the end of the line, allowing the climber to use the remaining tail of the line to ascend back up should the need arise.

After the tree, site, and climbing gear have been inspected and deemed safe, the climber can plan a climbing strategy. Usually a tie-in point is selected (at least preliminarily) from the ground and an ascent route is planned. There are many ways of getting into and ascending a tree. As mentioned in Chapter 5, the climber can use the climbing line, a ladder, or climbing spurs (if the tree is to be removed). An additional technique is to use two lanyards (or a two-in-one lanyard) so that the second can be secured when the first must be moved around a limb during ascent. Each technique has advantages and limitations. A climber must always be secured while entering or working in a tree.

Body-Thrusting

A tree can also be climbed without the aid of ladders or spurs. Once a climbing line has been set in the tree, there are several techniques for ascending. When the climbing line is set close to the trunk of the tree or when on a tree with many horizontal branches along the trunk, body-thrusting is an effective way to ascend. Using the inner edges of the boot, the climber straddles the trunk of the tree, orienting their body in a horizontal position. Using leg, hip, and core muscles, the hips are thrust upward, creating slack in the line; simultaneously, the climber pulls down on the standing part of the line to take up the slack and keep the line taut. Technique is important when body-thrusting; the climber who relies solely on upper body strength to body-thrust can be exhausted after reaching the top. The addition of a micropulley below the friction hitch allows a ground worker to advance the knot and pull slack out of the climber's line while the climber ascends.

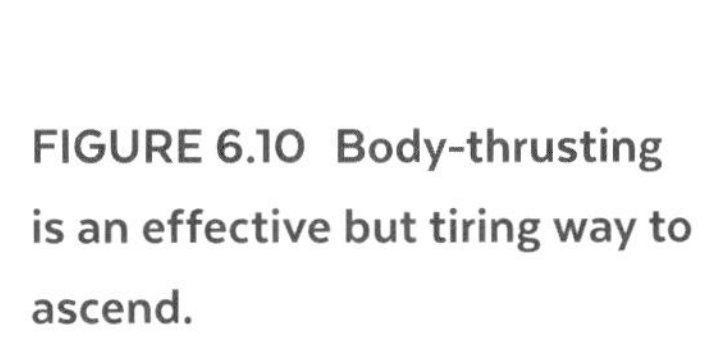

FIGURE 6.10 Body-thrusting is an effective but tiring way to ascend.

Lanyard Crawl

The **lanyard crawl** is another technique for ascending when close to the trunk. After passing the lanyard around the trunk, the climber attaches the lanyard to side D-rings on their harness. The lanyard should be adjusted so the climber's legs can barely reach full extension when the soles of their boots are pressed against the trunk. Flicking the lanyard up to around shoulder height or above, the climber can step up the trunk, pressing against the lanyard, all while advancing their hitch. Once the lanyard reaches between knee and waist height, the climber will drop their legs, causing their body to move back into the trunk, flick the lanyard up, and repeat the process. This technique more effectively utilizes leg and hip muscles, reducing fatigue on longer ascents. It is important for the climber to remember to take up the slack in their climbing line regularly. Another option is to have a ground worker tend the slack by installing a hitch-tending micropulley below the friction hitch. The technique can only be used until the climber reaches the branches. Although the technique is slow, it is an effective approach for a climber with limited upper body strength.

FIGURE 6.11 In MRS, the climber can "lock" on the standing part of the climbing line to facilitate ascending. Alternatively, a cammed foot ascender can be used.

Footlocking the Standing Part of the Line

Another ascent technique is the **secured footlock**, in which the climber ascends the line itself. This technique is discussed in further detail in Chapter 7 because it is not a moving rope technique. A variation of this technique, however, can be applied with MRS ascent. If the climbing line is installed far from the trunk, the climber can execute a single-line footlock, which is performed by "footlocking" on the fall of the line below the friction hitch. The climber pulls their legs up into a squatting position, wraps the fall of the line around one boot, then locks it in place with the other boot. Then the climber "stands" on the lock, advancing the friction hitch and taking up the slack. A slightly more sophisticated variation is to simply add a foot ascender to grip the climbing line below the friction hitch.

Rope Walking

Another option is to incorporate cammed ascending devices. The simple addition of a foot and knee ascender can shift a climber from the horizontal body-thrust to the more efficient, vertical "**rope walk**." The ascenders grip the line and take out slack as the climber advances the friction hitch. Though more gear intensive, this technique will save time and energy. The addition of a chest harness can further assist with keeping the climber in an upright position and help pull the system upward with the climber. Rope walking and footlocking can be a bit awkward if the climbing line is set close to the trunk, however.

FIGURE 6.12 Rope walking incorporates cammed ascending devices. Cammed devices grip the line and take out slack as the climber advances the friction hitch.

Endurance and Ergonomics

Tree climbing is a strenuous physical activity that can wear down a climber's body. To avoid career-ending injuries, it is good to minimize wear and tear on the body. The ascent into a tree presents the most significant limitations to MRS climbing. Each technique has its advantages and limitations. The technique selected may vary based on the location of the tie-in point, the climber's gear selection, the height of the ascent, and personal preference. It is best for a climber to master several techniques available to be able to adapt as needed. Using techniques and equipment that minimize exertion and stress on the body—those that are more **ergonomic**—will save energy and reduce long-term injuries.

Even small modifications in how techniques are employed can make a difference. For example, although people are naturally inclined to use their left or right hand, or left or right foot, dominantly, climbers should try to switch dominance to balance muscle groups. For example, always using a left foot ascender could be damaging over time. The climber should switch sides between climbs to balance physical exertion. Otherwise, it would be like going to the gym for "leg day" and only exercising one leg. Normally, climbers will footlock only on one side, but this can cause hip problems over time.

RESETTING THE TIE-IN POINT

When ascending large trees, it may be necessary to reset the climbing line several times. While this is being done, the climber must be secured with a work-positioning lanyard or a second climbing line. Another technique is to alternate the ends of the climbing line when repositioning the tie-in point. Any of these alternatives is appropriate; the key is for the climber to remain tied in at all times. In large trees, the climber should use two separate lines so that one line is in contact with the ground for access or emergency descent.

Often, the climbing line must be set in a branch union well above the climber's head. One technique is to throw the line over a higher limb. This can be achieved by tying a throwing knot at the end of the line, or tying the line to a spare throw weight (if a single throw weight is not heavy enough, a carabiner can be tied to the line and connected to the throw weight). If the end of the climbing line is terminated in an eye splice, a carabiner is the best way to connect it to the throw weight. Another technique is to use a pole saw to advance the line, though it is essential to keep the rope away from the cutting portion.

FIGURE 6.13 While resetting the climbing line, the climber must be secured with a work-positioning lanyard or a second climbing line. In this illustration, the climber is using a pole saw to advance the line, though it is essential to keep the rope away from the cutting portion.

Some climbers use a pole saw with no blade—just a hook—for setting ropes.

While resetting the tie-in point, the climber must remain tied in at all times. If the lanyard is used to secure, the climber should make sure to keep one part of the climbing line attached to their harness. This way, even if the new tie-in point is not successfully installed, the line does not fall to the ground. Once the system is reset and tied but prior to removing the lanyard, the climber should load test their system to ensure that it will hold their weight.

NAVIGATING A TREE

During the pre-climb inspection, the climber will have planned a route based on the work to be done. Once the climber has reached their tie-in point, they will have a better sense of how to navigate the canopy. For MRS, because ascending tends to be physically demanding and inefficient, the climber may select a work plan based on height levels of the canopy, starting near the top of the tree and working their way down. Alternatively, for a wide-spreading tree, a climber may instead work on one side, reset the tie-in point, and then work another side.

Another consideration is maintaining clear pathways from the tie-in point to the target destination. If the climber has to cross multiple branches or through branch unions, their climbing system will be affected by increased friction. Added friction can change a simple movement into a back-breaking task. Ideally, the climbing line will follow a clear path from the tie-in point to the work area, minimizing added friction and exertion. Sometimes the easiest remedy is to cross over a branch instead of under. A carefully designed work plan will minimize friction in the system, the number of ascents, and repeat visits to areas of the tree.

One major factor in the work plan is how the location of the tie-in point affects the climber's ability to access different parts of the tree. The

FIGURE 6.14 Ascending can be time consuming in MRS. One way to minimize the ups and downs is to use this retrieval trick: simply lanyard in, tie a slip knot above the friction hitch, and detach the system from the harness. Carefully pull the system over the branch. Reattach the system and pull out the slip knot. Remember to weight the system before removing your lanyard. This trick only works if the tail of the line is still hanging in the direction you intend on moving.

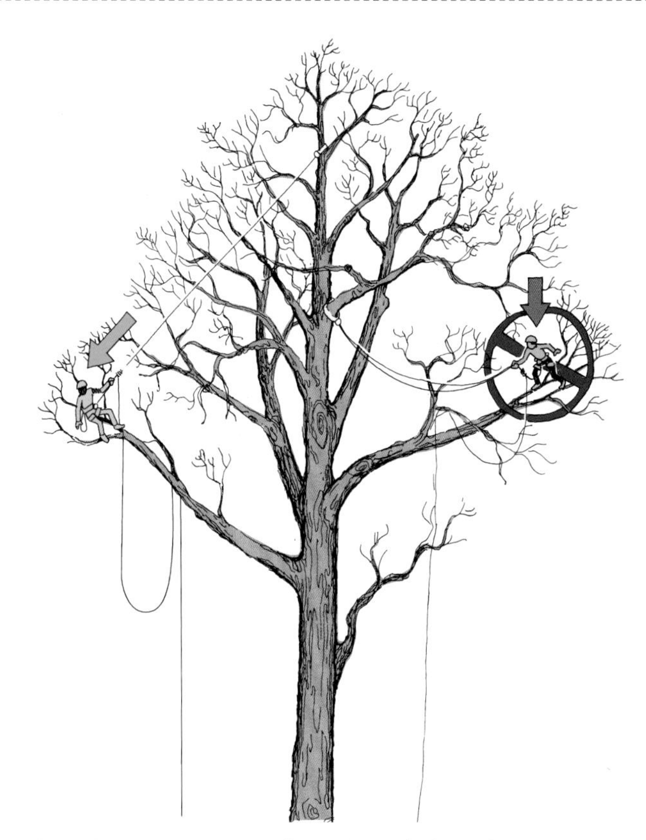

FIGURE 6.15 The location of the tie-in point affects the climber's ability to keep the line taut and at a good angle for working.

climbing line is more than a safety device to secure the climber against falling. A good climber uses the climbing line to ascend the tree, access branch tips, maintain balance, and move freely within the tree. If the climber is able to keep their weight on the climbing line, both hands can be used for working. The location of the tie-in point affects the climber's ability to keep the line taut and at a good angle for working.

To be stable, a climber should maintain three points of contact with the tree. Each of the climber's hands and feet can be considered a point of contact. The climbing line, when taut, can also be considered one point of contact. The lanyard, if used, is also a contact point and must be as secure as the primary tie-in point. Whenever the climber's weight is not on the climbing line, three alternate points of contact should be maintained with the tree.

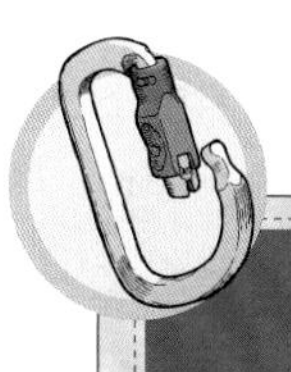

KEEPING THE CLIMBING LINE TAUT

The climbing line is not intended to catch a climber in a fall. Some harnesses are designed to support fall-arrest; however, safe tree climbing requires keeping the rope taut. Though climbers may swing from branch to branch, they are not falling into their climbing line to be caught. Rather, they use their climbing line to support their movements throughout the tree.

Controlled Swings

Another technique that the climber relies on the climbing line for is controlled swinging. When suspended on their climbing line, the climber can sometimes swing to reach the other parts of the tree. Climbers should never attempt a fast, uncontrolled swing. Control is crucial when swinging to avoid crashing back into the trunk of the tree. In large, open canopies, a long, purposeful swing may be necessary to navigate large gaps in the canopy. A failed attempt could result in the climber landing in a "dead zone" in the canopy, forcing them to ascend or descend back to the branches. Swinging in the canopy is a learned skill that should be practiced where there are minimal consequences to a failed attempt.

Limb Walking

Limb walking is an important skill to learn to be able to reach all parts of a tree. A climber can walk out on limbs to reach the tips of branches. Generally, the preferred method is to walk backward or sideways on the limb, with the climber's rear end opposing the direction of the tie-in point, keeping the climbing line taut at all times. When climbing out toward the tip of a horizontal limb, it

FIGURE 6.16 When limb walking, the preferred method is to walk backward or sideways on the limb, with the climber's rear end opposing the direction of the tie-in point, keeping the climbing line taut at all times.

is important for the climber to keep their weight on the climbing line. If the climber allows their weight to be on the limb, the limb may break. The angle of tie-in is very important here. As a rule, the higher above the work area the tie-in point is, the greater the distance the climber can move horizontally away from the trunk. Ideally, the angle formed by the trunk and the climbing line should not exceed 45°. One way to maintain a favorable rope angle is to incorporate a redirect.

WARNING

When performing a low limb walk, it is important to estimate the length of the walk in proportion to the height of the tie-in point. A slip off a low, long limb walk could land a climber on the ground.

Using Redirects

Rope angles are an essential consideration for route planning. The rope is parallel to the trunk (0°) during an ascent. If a climber walked on a horizontal branch at the same height as the tie-in point, the rope would be perpendicular to the trunk (90°). If the climber climbed above the tie-in point, the rope angle would be greater than 90° to the trunk, but climbing above the tie-in point must always be avoided. Ideally, climbers should work with rope angles between 0° and 45° to the trunk. If working at a particular location in the canopy requires a rope angle greater than 45° to the trunk, the climber should consider using a redirect.

A **redirect** is a change in the direction of the climbing line to create a safer or more efficient rope angle and reduce the chances of an uncontrolled swing. Redirects can be achieved two ways. The simplest is to descend through a branch union above the work. This type of redirect, a natural redirect, can be challenging to undo because it requires the climber to ascend back through the union—a tricky maneuver—and is usually only performed before the climber descends out of the tree. When using a natural redirect prior to descent, the climber must first check that their climbing line will be long enough to allow them to reach the ground.

Another type of redirect can be established by girth-hitching a webbing loop around a branch. A carabiner or pulley can be attached to the loop and one or both sides of the climbing line can be run through the hardware. This method is preferable because the climber can set the webbing loop to optimize the rope angle relative to

FIGURE 6.17 A redirect is a change in the direction of the climbing line to create a safer or more efficient rope angle and reduce the chances of an uncontrolled swing.

the work location. It is also preferable to a natural branch union redirect because there is less friction, and it is relatively easy to return to the redirect and remove it from the tree once the climber has finished working that area of the tree, rather than having to ascend back through a natural branch union redirect.

This technique can be easily applied during a long lateral movement when there's a large branch above the climber. A tight 70° angle can immediately be turned into a 0° angle when a redirect is installed above the work zone. Because the climber can descend to the lower branch from the redirect, they will have greater range of motion than when installing a work-positioning lanyard. This redirect now serves as a new tie-in point. This also means that the equipment used for the redirect must meet the same safety standards as other climbing equipment, and the attachment point must be able to support the climber should they slip.

Redirects are widely used in MRS, as well as SRS (explained in Chapter 7). Using a redirect not only helps improve rope angles, it also helps achieve safe and efficient work positioning. When the tie-in point does not place the climber in the optimal position, a redirect can help. Effective redirects minimally impact friction. When trying out any new techniques, though, it is important to practice in a controlled setting where mistakes will not cause serious injuries or damage property.

Double Tie-In Points

Sometimes it is helpful for a climber to use double tie-in points (sometimes referred to as **double-tying** or double-crotching). This technique involves tying in at a second branch union in a large tree, using the other end of the climbing line, a second climbing line, or an extra-long lanyard. The double-tying technique might be used if the climber is ascending a second leader in a tree with a wide-spreading canopy. The climbing line can be used to help the climber ascend the upright limb without sacrificing the original tie-in point. Another use of the double-tying technique is to allow the climber to be suspended between limbs. This can be useful for installing cables, working on hazardous lower limbs, working on storm-damaged trees, or transferring from one tree to another.

There are, however, limitations with the double-tying technique. When using the opposite end of the climbing line for the second tie-in, a loop of line is created between the two friction hitches. If this loop does not reach the ground, ground workers will be unable to use the line to send anything up to the climber. Also, unless the

FIGURE 6.18 Using double tie-in points involves tying in at a second branch union in a large tree or a second tree. One reason to use this method is to help the climber to access another part of the tree without sacrificing the original tie-in point. The climber must either ensure there is enough rope to descend or untie one of the tie-in points.

climbing line is long enough, the climber may not be able to descend to the ground without untying one of the tie-in points. This could present an extra difficulty in an emergency situation.

FIGURE 6.19 Most climbers climb with their hand saw and scabbard (sheath for the hand saw). Carrying a hand saw is always recommended and may be required in safety regulations.

WORKING IN A TREE

While in a tree, the climber may require various tools and equipment, including a chain saw, a pole pruner, a pole saw, cabling hardware, and/or other tools. Most climbers climb with their hand saw and **scabbard** (sheath for the hand saw), which is always recommended and may be required in safety regulations. Ground workers send up other tools as needed. Workers may tie equipment onto the climber's line using a **clove hitch** or a similar hitch.

If pole pruners or pole saws are used in the tree, they should be hung vertically in the tree when not in use. They should be hung in such a way that the sharp edge is away from the climber and such that they will not accidentally dislodge. If a tool lanyard is used to hang the pole, it should be long enough to keep the cutting edge of the saw below the climber's feet.

Chain saws can be equipped with a chain saw lanyard for use in a tree. Chain saws weighing

FIGURE 6.20 If pole pruners or pole saws are used in the tree, they should be hung vertically in such a way that the sharp edge is away from the climber.

more than 15 lb (7 kg) should be supported by a separate line when used in a tree. The climber must be stable and secure when using a chain saw and other equipment in the tree. Chain saws should be shut off, with the chain brake engaged, when the climber moves to another position. Because it is extremely hazardous to use a chain saw in a tree, safety precautions are important. A climber must be secured with a work-positioning lanyard or a second climbing line in addition to the main climbing line when using a chain saw in a tree. These precautions are taken for added stability and safety in case either line is severed accidentally.

FIGURE 6.21 Before descending, the climber must pull up the tail of the line and check that the loop formed touches the ground. If it does not, as shown here, the climber will not reach the ground during their descent.

DESCENT

When the work is complete, it can be tempting to descend quickly to the ground, but a poorly executed descent could result in injury or fatality, or at a minimum a tangled mess. Line management is an important component of the descent. While navigating the tree, the climber has likely ascended through multiple branch unions, switched sides of the tree, walked out on limbs, and swung through the canopy. Through all this, the climbing line is not far behind, mirroring all these movements. If line management is not employed, the climber could spend several minutes untangling their line from the tree, or worse, the line could get stuck, forcing the climber to re-climb the tree to free it. Throughout the climb, the climber should be pulling the end of their line through branch unions and keeping it free from branches as they go. Generally, the line should hang in a direct path down to the ground.

Before descending, there are a few things to check. First, because MRS requires a doubled line, simply looking to see if the line is touching the ground is not enough. The climber must pull up the tail of the line and check that the loop formed touches the ground. While holding onto the tail, the climber should double-check that there is still a stopper knot several feet from the end. Additionally, during the course of their work, debris has likely accumulated at the base of the tree. The climber should communicate with the ground crew to clear a path and check that the line is not tangled in the debris. Finally, the climber should perform one last spot check of the canopy for hanging branches (hangers), deadwood, stubs, and remaining equipment, such as a redirect or pole saw. Once the tree is clear, the climber can descend in a slow, controlled manner. A fast descent could cause the ropes to overheat, causing the fibers to glaze. An uncontrolled descent could also result in injury to the climber or to an unsuspecting ground worker.

KEY CONCEPTS

1. Moving rope systems are so named because the climbing line moves through the tie-in point when the climber moves up and down in the tree. One end of the line is fixed to the climber, then runs up and over a branch and back down to the climber. A friction hitch is tied around the standing part of the climbing line and slides along the line, allowing movement, but gripping when stopped to hold the climber in place.
2. The main drawback with MRS is in the ascent. The climber advances only 1 ft (30 cm) for every 2 ft (60 cm) of line pulled. In addition, much of the work is done by the upper body, which can be exhausting for the climber. Another limitation is that when installing the climbing line, the two ends of the climbing line must be isolated over a single branch.
3. The position of the tie-in point affects the climber's ability to access various parts of the tree. It is also the point from which the line and climber are suspended, so a strong branch union is needed. Generally, it is desirable to pick a high, central location in the tree to allow freedom of movement and easy access to most points in the tree.
4. Each ascent technique has its advantages and limitations. The technique selected may vary based on the location of the tie-in point, the climber's gear selection, the height of the ascent, and personal preference.
5. The climbing line is more than a safety device to secure the climber against falling. A good climber uses the climbing line to ascend the tree, access branch tips, maintain balance, and move freely within the tree. It is important to keep the line taut, to maintain a safe work angle, and to maintain a clear climbing line path between the tie-in point and the climber.
6. Using a redirect can improve rope angles and help achieve safe and efficient work positioning.

WORKBOOK

MATCHING

_____ split-tail	A. change in the path of the climbing line
_____ open hitch	B. inefficient ascent technique used with MRS
_____ body-thrust	C. tied in a tail to prevent it from slipping through
_____ closed hitch	D. device to reduce friction at the tie-in point
_____ stopper knot	E. separate cord used to tie the friction hitch
_____ redirect	F. tied with both ends of the hitch cord connected
_____ friction-saving device	G. rope ascent technique that utilizes ascenders
_____ rope walking	H. friction hitch with a “loose” unconnected tail

TRUE/FALSE

1. T F Climbing systems can be divided into two main types: moving rope systems (MRS) and stationary rope systems (SRS).
2. T F Moving rope systems are so named because the climbing line moves through the friction hitch.
3. T F Because the climbing line is doubled in MRS, the climber’s weight is split between the two parts of the line, creating a mechanical advantage for the climber.
4. T F With MRS ascent, though only half of the climber’s body weight must be pulled when ascending, the climber advances only 1 ft (30 cm) for every 2 ft (60 cm) of line pulled.
5. T F The position of the tie-in point affects the climber’s ability to access various parts of the tree.
6. T F Because the tie-in point is not part of life support, a strong branch union is not needed.
7. T F Generally, when selecting a tie-in point, it is desirable to pick a high, central location in the tree.
8. T F The more vertical the climbing line, the more secure the climber.
9. T F Friction-saving devices can reduce wear on the climbing line and damage to the tree, and, in some cases, can facilitate climbing.
10. T F A sheath-type friction-saving device cannot be installed or removed from the ground.

11. T F Ring-style friction-saving devices can be installed from the ground, but they take some time to learn how to install, adjust, and retrieve, as well as inspect.
12. T F When tying in with a tautline hitch or a Blake's hitch, a stopper knot such as a figure-8 must be tied in the tail of the friction hitch to prevent the end from going through the friction hitch.
13. T F Even if a climber uses a climbing line with a spliced eye and attaches to bridge hardware using an approved carabiner, a termination knot is still required.
14. T F When climbing MRS, the climber will need a climbing line at least twice as long as their final tie-in point is high.
15. T F A climber must always be tied in or otherwise secured while entering or working in a tree.
16. T F The body-thrust technique for ascending can be used most effectively when the climbing line is set well away from the trunk of the tree.
17. T F The rope walking technique for ascent is best applied if the climbing line is set directly adjacent to the tree trunk.
18. T F When ascending large trees, it may be necessary to reset the climbing line several times.
19. T F If an MRS climber has to cross around multiple branches or through branch unions, the added friction can make a simple movement much more difficult.
20. T F A climber uses the climbing line to ascend the tree, access branch tips, maintain balance, and move freely within the tree.
21. T F The location of the tie-in point affects the climber's ability to keep the line taut and at a good angle for working.
22. T F The preferred method of limb walking is to walk forward along the limb to prevent tension in the climbing line.
23. T F Ideally, the angle formed by the trunk below the tie-in point and the climbing line should not exceed 45°.
24. T F The simplest redirect is achieved by descending down through a branch union above the work.
25. T F The equipment used for the redirect must meet the same safety standards as other climbing equipment, and the attachment point must be able to support the climber.
26. T F Using a redirect not only helps improve rope angles, it also can help to achieve safe and efficient work positioning.
27. T F Double-tying involves installing the climbing line through two branch unions at the tie-in point.
28. T F Equipment, other than the hand saw, is usually sent up to the climber on the climbing line after the climber is set in the tree.
29. T F Chain saws should be shut off, with the chain brake engaged, when the climber moves to another position.
30. T F Throughout the climb, the climber should be pulling the tail of their climbing line through branch unions and untangling it as they go.

SAMPLE TEST QUESTIONS

1. Which of the following is a limitation of MRS climbing?
   a. The climber advances only 1 ft (30 cm) for every 2 ft (60 cm) of line pulled.
   b. Much of the work is done by the upper body, which can be exhausting for the climber.
   c. Both ends of the climbing line must be isolated over a single branch.
   d. All of the above.

2. Most of the time, the best way to install the climbing line at the tie-in point is to pass it
   a. over a lateral branch at least 3 ft (1 m) out from the trunk of the tree
   b. wrapped around a lateral branch, then passed around the trunk of the tree
   c. through a union, around the larger limb or trunk, and over the smaller or lateral branch
   d. wrapped around the trunk a full wrap and over a lateral branch

3. Which of the following is NOT an MRS ascent technique?
   a. body-thrusting
   b. lanyard crawl
   c. secured footlocking
   d. rope walking

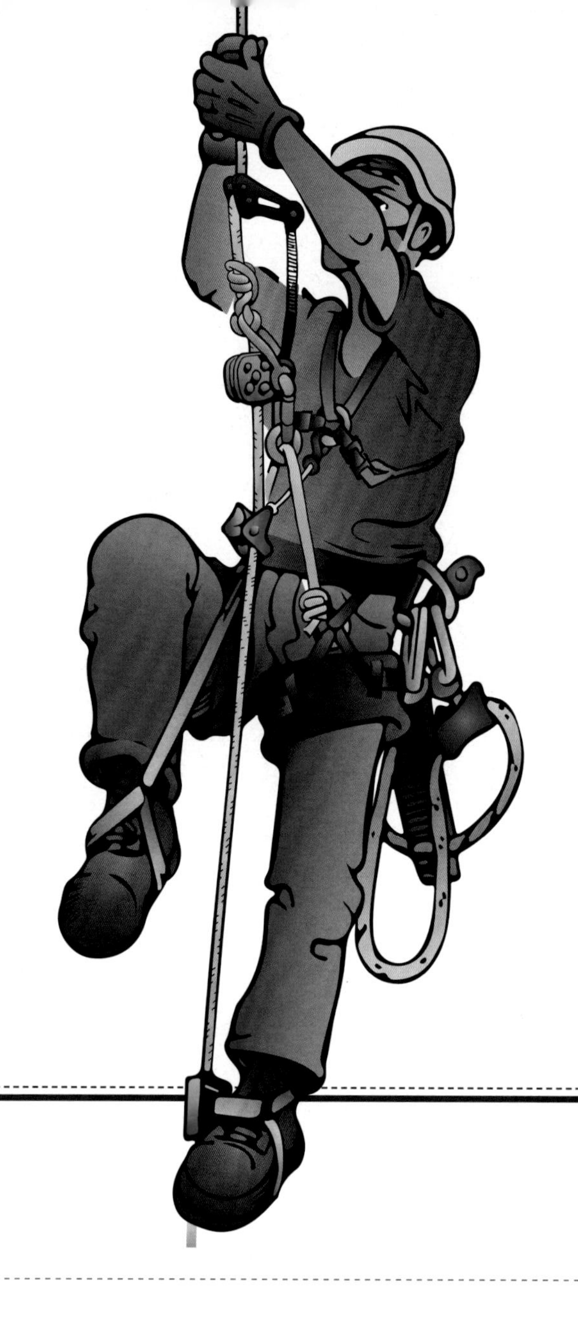

CHAPTER

7 STATIONARY ROPE SYSTEMS

LEARNING OBJECTIVES

The tree worker will be able to:

- Describe the main differences between MRS and SRS.
- Explain the principles of establishing an anchor.
- Discuss the advantages and limitations of using a basal anchor.
- Discuss the advantages and limitations of using a canopy anchor.
- Describe how working with a stationary rope system differs from working with a moving rope system, including the use of redirects, friction management, and tie-in point selection.

IMPORTANT TERMS

access line
anchor
ascender
basal anchor
body-thrust
canopy anchor
compatible
configuration
ergonomic
footlocking
hitch-tending pulley
isolate
limb walking
lowerable
mechanical friction device
moving rope system (MRS)
primary suspension point (PSP)
Prusik loop
redirect
retrievable
rope walking
secured footlock
stationary rope system (SRS)
triple-action carabiner

INTRODUCTION

Climbing techniques have evolved rapidly in recent years, starting with doubled rope technique (DdRT), which is now called **moving rope systems (MRS)**. In more recent decades, the industry has seen a rise in the use of single-rope technique (SRT), which itself has already seen an evolution and is now referred to as **stationary rope systems (SRS)**. With this evolution of techniques has come an equally complicated array of new equipment, some of which is approved for only one type of system, and some of which can be used for either.

When trying new equipment, techniques, and systems, it is essential to read the user manuals and to understand the equipment's intended use, application, and working-load limits. It is also important to make sure the equipment has been tested to meet industry safety standards and is approved for use in tree care. Finally, and perhaps most importantly, all the equipment configured together must be compatible, as explained later in this chapter.

When a climber is trying new equipment or techniques, they must work low and slow, where fall exposure is minimized. Before introducing a new piece of equipment to the gear kit, climbers must read through the manufacturer's user information and instruction manual. Often these manuals are available online. Manufacturer information usually includes how the equipment has been tested for use. The information also includes appropriate **configurations** and compatible equipment. Failure to comply with manufacturer specifications may result in serious injury or death. It is also essential to be aware of the possibility of manufacturers sending out technical notices, recalls, or updated user manuals. Climbers should stay informed of possible equipment updates by regularly visiting manufacturer websites, or by joining e-mail distribution lists or managed industry forums, for the latest information.

TIP!

PROPER USE OF NEW EQUIPMENT

New climbing equipment will come with manufacturer information regarding proper use of that equipment. That documentation will include working-load limits, appropriate configurations, and compatible equipment requirements. If the documentation is not completely clear, contact the manufacturer or ask a trained professional before using that equipment.

This chapter contrasts moving and stationary rope systems while explaining many of the advantages and limitations associated with stationary rope system climbing. Though many aspects of the two climbing systems are similar, including much of the equipment, there are different considerations for tie-in points, gear selection, rope constructions, and other factors. Even strategies for navigating a tree may differ depending on the climbing system chosen.

Equipment used in SRS climbing is extremely variable, depending on the specific system assembly chosen. Because of this variability, specific equipment and techniques will not be discussed. This chapter will focus on fundamental concepts and on basic methods and climbing strategies.

The best plan for learning SRS climbing techniques is to obtain formal training through reputable trainers. If that is not practical, working with an experienced mentor is a good way to try new equipment and systems. No climber should ever climb alone, and, as previously mentioned, new equipment and techniques should always be practiced low and slow.

MRS VS. SRS

When climbing using moving rope systems, the rope runs over a branch union or through a friction-saving device, constantly moving as the climber navigates the tree. Comparatively, in stationary rope systems, one end of the rope is anchored in place while the climber navigates up and down the single leg of rope. This difference is how the two systems earned their names. SRS climbing lines can run through one or more branch unions and are held taut at an anchor point, either at the base of the tree or within the canopy.

FIGURE 7.1 **When climbing a moving rope system (left), the rope runs over a branch union or through a friction saver, constantly moving as the climber navigates the tree. In stationary rope systems (right), one end of the rope is anchored in place while the climber navigates up and down the single leg of rope.**

Climbing only one leg of the rope changes the dynamics of the system. As the climber ascends using SRS climbing, advancing the gear 12 in (30 cm) up the rope translates into 12 in (30 cm) of upward movement for the climber. In MRS, there is a 2:1 mechanical advantage; however, that corresponds to only 50 percent gain in upward movement. For every 12 in (30 cm) of rope the climber pulls through the climbing hitch, only 6 in (15 cm) of advancement in height is achieved.

SRS ascent is not only more efficient, it is also easier on the body. Climbers ascend in a more comfortable, vertical position and use the larger muscles in their legs to ascend. MRS ascent, by contrast, can rely much more heavily on arm, core, and upper body strength.

Also, because the rope is not moving through a branch union or friction-saving device in SRS, the reduced friction conserves energy and reduces wear on the climbing rope. Because of these advantages, many climbers have adopted SRS ascent techniques even when they work the tree using the MRS climbing method.

Choosing between working with MRS or SRS depends on personal preference. Climbers may choose to work with MRS on one tree and SRS on another. Or, they may choose to ascend a tree using SRS and transfer to MRS once in the canopy. Which system a climber uses will depend on numerous factors, including, but not limited to, climber preference, the height and spread of the canopy, the location of viable tie-in points, and the work objective. Each system has advantages and limitations.

BASIC SRS TECHNIQUE

With traditional MRS climbing, the ascent method is often determined by climber preference, the height of the ascent, and the location of where the rope is hanging relative to the tree trunk. If the rope is hanging close to the trunk, a climber will likely body-thrust or use a ladder to reach the canopy. Then the climber might ascend by using the branches, either while tied in above, by using a two-in-one lanyard, or by alternating systems to remain secured. If the rope is not hanging close to the trunk, foot and knee ascenders can be used to climb the rope (**rope walking**) instead of the tree. Footlocking is also an option, but that requires a significant expenditure of energy and a safe method of transfer once reaching the top. Footlocking is sometimes preferred when the rope is set too far from the trunk for body-thrusting with MRS.

With SRS, ascending is so efficient, there is no need to set the rope near the trunk. As the climber ascends, the rope remains stationary at the tie-in point. With some system configurations, a climber can ascend part way, switch to a work-positioning mode to move laterally, prune a branch, and then easily switch back to ascending.

Stationary rope systems are extremely varied. A fundamental principle is that, because the climber's entire body weight is on the single leg of the climbing line, more friction is required than is provided by a friction hitch. In contrast, with MRS, the friction from the hitch is sufficient because the load is shared by the two legs of

FIGURE 7.2 In some SRS configurations, a climber can ascend part way, switch to a work-positioning mode to move laterally, prune a branch, and then easily switch back to ascending.

rope attached to the climber. With SRS, a climber may use a traditional climbing hitch in combination with other devices that introduce a bend in the rope (added friction). Alternatively, a climber could use a mechanical device in the place of a climbing hitch. Both of these system options are often combined with additional rope-climbing aids, such as foot, knee, and/or handled ascenders.

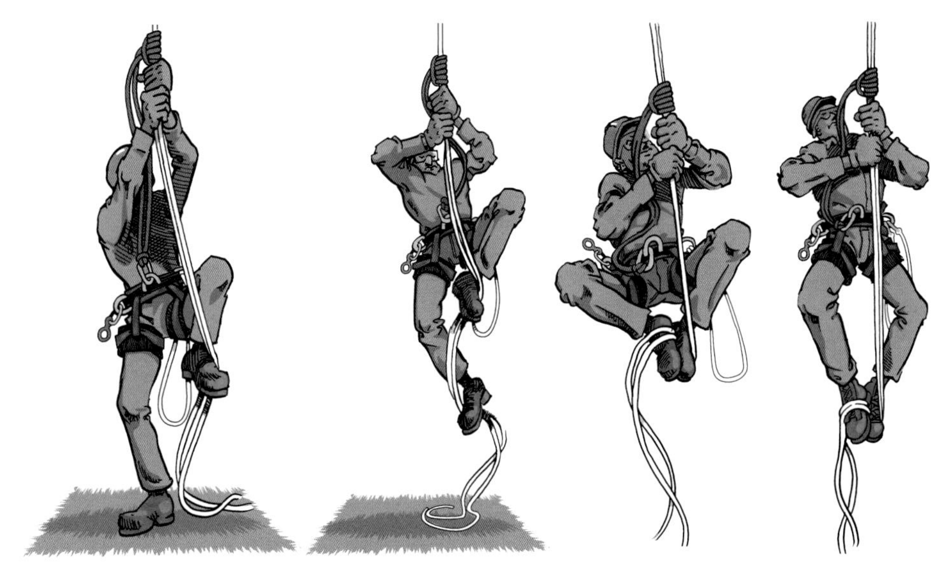

FIGURE 7.3 The secured footlock technique.

Engaging the full body, instead of just the core, keeps the climber upright. Using SRS, the climber will often "walk" up the rope, taking small steps, allowing the knee ascender to grip first, followed by the foot ascender. This method uses the leg muscles, freeing the arms, hands, and core body muscles from major physical exertion. Most climbers will also add a chest harness that can be connected to the climbing system. The chest harness keeps the climber in a more comfortable, upright position and can help tend slack in the line.

FOOTLOCKING

Footlocking is one SRS method for ascending a tree, although it has been taught to tree climbers much longer than other SRS methods. When footlocking, the climber actually climbs the rope and might not contact the tree until reaching the tie-in point. Both ends of the climbing line are isolated over a single branch union. The rope can either be installed directly over a moderately large branch, fed through a ring-to-ring friction-saving device over a large branch, or girth-hitched around a branch using an alpine butterfly or running bowline with a Yosemite finish.

If the footlocking method is used, the climber must use the **secured footlock** technique. In the secured footlock technique, the use of a **Prusik loop** makes footlocking much safer. A Prusik loop is tied to the climber's line using a Prusik hitch, Klemheist, or a mechanical device, and is attached to the bridge of the harness using an approved **triple-action carabiner**. The Prusik loop serves as a means of securing the climber.

Standing with hands high on the climbing line and with the Prusik hitch above the hands, the climber grabs the rope, raises one foot, and aligns the rope on the inside of the knee and across the top of the instep. Then, with knees apart, the feet are raised high and the second foot pulls the rope from below and over the first foot. The rope is locked off by standing on top of the section of rope that is wrapped around the foot. The climber then stands up, pushing the hitch up with their hands, and the process is repeated, much like

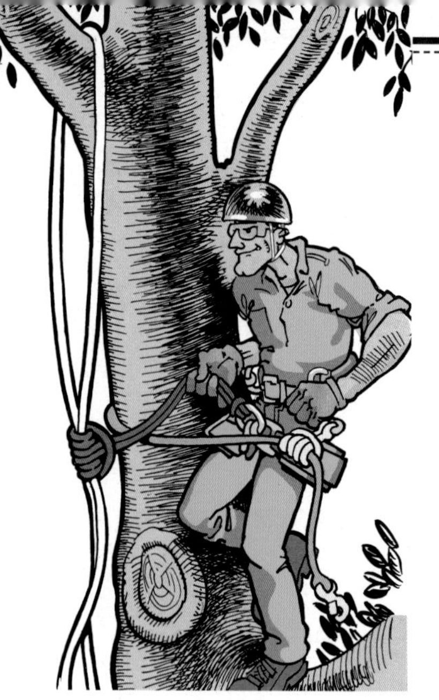

FIGURE 7.4 **After ascending, the climber must transfer into the tree. This is a potentially dangerous transfer, so the climber must either tie in or use a work-positioning lanyard before removing the hitch.**

an inchworm moves. The climber's hands must always stay below the hitch. Putting the hands on or above the hitch could cause it to slide down the climbing line, leading to a fall. It is also important not to ascend close to the limb on which the line is installed because the spread in the line will cause the Prusik to loosen.

After ascending, the climber must transfer into the tree. This is a potentially dangerous transfer, so the climber must either tie in or use a work-positioning lanyard before removing the hitch. If the footlocking rope has been set above a nearby branch that is lower, the climber will be able to enter the tree onto the lower limb and transfer will be facilitated.

Although footlocking is more efficient than body-thrusting on a moving rope system, footlocking can be fatiguing, and the transfer at the top can be tricky. Additionally, during each lock, slack is generated in the Prusik loop. This slack exposes the climber to a potential short fall during each lock, which could cause injury to the body and damage to the climbing equipment. Because of these limitations, footlocking has largely been replaced with other SRS methods.

ANCHORS

In stationary rope system climbing, the climbing line must be anchored. The **anchor** serves as a stable attachment point for the climbing line that allows the climber to navigate the tree using only one side of the line. Two different kinds of anchors are used: canopy and basal. A **canopy anchor** is isolated over a single branch union in the canopy. As its name suggests, a **basal anchor** is set at the base of the tree.

A basal anchor can be configured in ways that make it **lowerable**, which could potentially aid in a rescue. Basal anchors can be equipped with a descent or friction device that allows a ground worker to lower the climbing line to bring down an injured climber. Anchors can also be set to be **retrievable**, which allows the climber to remove the full system without being physically near the anchor point. Not having to return to an anchor point to remove it is extremely time- and energy-saving, so this is a valuable feature.

The selection of the type of anchor used is based on several factors. One factor is the tree itself and the work to be done. The branch configuration or the amount and location of the work to be performed may dictate the type of anchor used. Personal preference and experience are always factors as well.

Features of a Stable Anchor

Because stationary rope systems are relatively new to arboriculture and the equipment market is vast, configurations for both basal and canopy anchors are seemingly infinite. However, basic principles can be applied to ensure a stable anchor. Anchors may consist of just the rope, or may include multiple pieces of gear, such as slings, carabiners, hitch cords, pulleys, traditional rigging equipment, and mechanical devices. All components should be compatible with one another, as well as appropriately applied in their intended use. For instance, some devices are approved as a mechanical device on a harness, but cannot be used as a fixed point to an anchor.

Anchors should also be backed up, so that if one component were to fail, another one would hold the anchor in place until the climber can safely reach the ground.

Once the anchor is assembled, there should be minimal slack in the configuration. Minimizing slack helps prevent shock loading or incorrectly loading the system during regular climbing operations. The climber should load the working end of the line to look for movement at the primary suspension point and check for slippage or excess movement in the anchor. A good anchor should experience little movement once the climber is ascending the line.

Whatever anchor configuration is employed, it is essential that the ground workers be trained in emergency response in case the climber is injured. The more complex the anchor system, or the more variations in systems used, the more likely a mistake could be made.

BASAL ANCHORS

Basal anchors are set up at the base of the tree, generally at knee or waist height. A climbing line is run from the base of the trunk up through one or more branch unions, and then run back down to the ground. This climbing line may be used for ascent, work positioning, or both. This line can also be left in the tree as an **access line** for another climber or for use in case of a rescue.

FIGURE 7.5 Basal anchors are set up at the base of the tree, generally at knee or waist height. A climbing line is run from the base of the trunk up through one or more branch unions, and then run back down to the ground.

Advantages

Basal anchor climbing lines can be installed and uninstalled from the ground. Some configurations can allow the climber to be lowered should the climber need to be rescued. The two legs of the climbing line do not need to be **isolated** (passing through just one branch union with the two legs hanging parallel), unlike with MRS tie-in points or with canopy anchors. Not having to isolate makes the throwline and rope installation step easier and much more efficient. Additionally, and possibly most importantly, the anchor setup can be inspected from the ground by both the climber and the ground crew. The climber can inspect the anchor and can load test the **primary suspension point (PSP)** from the ground to ensure there is no slippage or other movement. The primary suspension point is the branch or branch union that carries the majority of the load on the climbing line. While aloft, the climber can easily work through numerous redirects, creating new rope angles and access points. It is important, however, to make sure the PSP is able to carry the load when redirects are removed.

Limitations

Basal anchors have their limitations, however. Once the climber is aloft, they will no longer have physical access to the anchor and may not be able to properly inspect it. The climber cannot inspect the anchor from the canopy and will rely on the ground workers to communicate any movement, or if the anchor has otherwise been compromised.

The basal anchor is also situated in close proximity to ground work. In this high-tension state, the rope could be mistakenly cut by a hand saw, chain saw, or pole saw. The climbing line could also be compromised by rigging. Friction from a running rigging line could melt the anchored climbing line, or a log or piece of rigging equipment could damage the line. For these reasons, some companies do not allow the use of basal anchors for climbing during rigging operations. Even the climber could accidentally cut their own line should they lose track of its location. This is particularly worrisome when working in palms where the dead frond skirt could easily hide the climbing line. For these reasons, developing and adhering to policies and procedures to protect the tensioned side of a basal-anchored line should be considered, including possibly transferring to a different system or anchor after ascending.

Additionally, slippage must be considered when building a basal anchor. Preloading the anchor will allow the climber to cinch it tightly at the base of the tree, ensuring that all components are loaded appropriately. If bark easily sloughs off or is smooth, however, the rope or sling may slide up the trunk. If movement cannot be minimized, a basal anchor may not be appropriate.

A very important consideration is that the load exerted at the PSP is greater when using a basal anchor than when using a canopy anchor or MRS. Also, loads exerted on canopy **redirects** in a basal anchor configuration will be different from those used in a canopy anchor. This will be described in greater detail later in this chapter.

DIRECTIONAL KNOTS

Remember, some knots are "directional," meaning they perform one way when weighted in one direction, and another when weighted in the opposing direction. A slip knot is an example of a directional knot. When pulled in one direction, the knot cinches. In the other direction, the knot "slips" out.

FIGURE 7.6 A canopy anchor is a tie-in point set up in the canopy, usually at a branch union.

Installation

Depending on the diameter of the tree and friction from the bark, either the rope can be cinched around the trunk or a separate basal anchoring sling or loop can be installed. When setting up the initial cinching around the trunk, it is important to ensure that the system will not loosen as it's loaded and unloaded repeatedly. A girth hitch, a running bowline with a Yosemite finish, or a cow hitch with a half hitch can all be used for this application. These hitches are all directional and need to be tied and loaded correctly.

Using the standing part of the rope to cinch a running bowline with a Yosemite finish around the trunk is the simplest form of basal anchor. Some climbers will add an alpine butterfly above the cinching system to provide the ground crew an attachment point to install a rescue system. Another option is to use a separate piece of cordage, such as a dead-eye sling. In this kind of setup, an additional device must be added to connect the sling to the climbing line. Descent or friction-management devices used in this application must be approved by the manufacturer and must be compatible with the diameter and construction of the rope used.

Whichever setup is selected, it is important to build in backups.

CANOPY ANCHORS

A canopy anchor is a tie-in point set up in the canopy, usually at a branch union, much like with a moving rope system. When using a canopy anchor, the branch union must be wide enough for the rope to pass through and the branches need to be sturdy enough to support the climber and their activities. Canopy anchors can be used for ascent, for work positioning, or for both. As with most things, canopy anchors have their advantages and limitations.

Advantages

Canopy anchors are usually not gear intensive, requiring little more than just the rope. The anchor can be set from the ground and loaded. The load exerted by a climber on the anchor point is comparable to the typical load using MRS. This means selection of a tie-in point can be based on the same

FIGURE 7.7 This canopy anchor is set with a running bowline with a Yosemite finish. It is made retrievable by installing a throwline on the end, or by leaving enough tail of the climbing line to be reached from the ground.

principles as those used in MRS setups. Once the climber is aloft, they have full access to the anchor, allowing them to reset, move, or adjust it. They also have access to move both ends of the rope once they are aloft.

Limitations

Canopy anchors have their drawbacks, too. As with the traditional MRS and footlock, the climbing line must be isolated—installed over a single branch. If not, the bowline or butterfly used to establish the anchor will not be properly cinched at the branch union. Another limitation is that the branch union cannot be inspected from the ground. This is the same challenge as with MRS.

FIGURE 7.8 Retrievable canopy anchor set with an alpine butterfly.

In both of these setups, it is absolutely essential to inspect the tree during the ascent and inspect the branch union used for the canopy anchor once aloft. Canopy anchors are not lowerable, meaning the climber cannot be rescued from the ground. Should there be an emergency, a second person will need to ascend on a different climbing line. At times, the canopy anchor setup might only be used for a quick ascent and then maintained as an access line, once the climber has transferred to a new line and system.

Installation

To install a canopy anchor, the climbing line must be isolated over a single branch for the anchor to be properly cinched. The line is cinched most often using one of two knots: a running bowline with a Yosemite finish, or an alpine butterfly.

With the running bowline and Yosemite finish, the tail of the line is used to tie around the working end. Then, the working end is pulled through until the bowline sits tight on the branch union. This type of system is not retrievable, but it only requires the rope length to be at least twice the height of the anchor point when installed from the ground. To make it retrievable, a throwline or second climbing line can be attached to the tail of the bowline.

When using an alpine butterfly, the location of the knot can help with retrievability and can reduce the amount of rope needed. First, the line is installed over an isolated branch. Then, once both ends of the line are on the ground, an alpine butterfly is tied on the longer leg of rope. The shorter leg is fed through the loop of the butterfly and pulled until the knot cinches on the branch. This setup requires a length of rope three times the height of the branch union to be fully retrievable. An alternative method is to pull the climbing line up to the branch union using a throwline. While holding the throwline in place, an alpine butterfly is tied in the climbing line and the throw weight and throwline are passed through the loop. The line is pulled, ensuring the tail of the climbing line passes through the loop of the butterfly and cinches properly at the union. This setup requires a length of rope only twice the height of the branch union and is retrievable from the ground. Additional pulleys or thimbles can be incorporated into the canopy anchor to aid in retrieval. A limitation of this technique is that it is very cumbersome to untie and advance from the initial anchor point, so it is not often used if moving the anchor is anticipated.

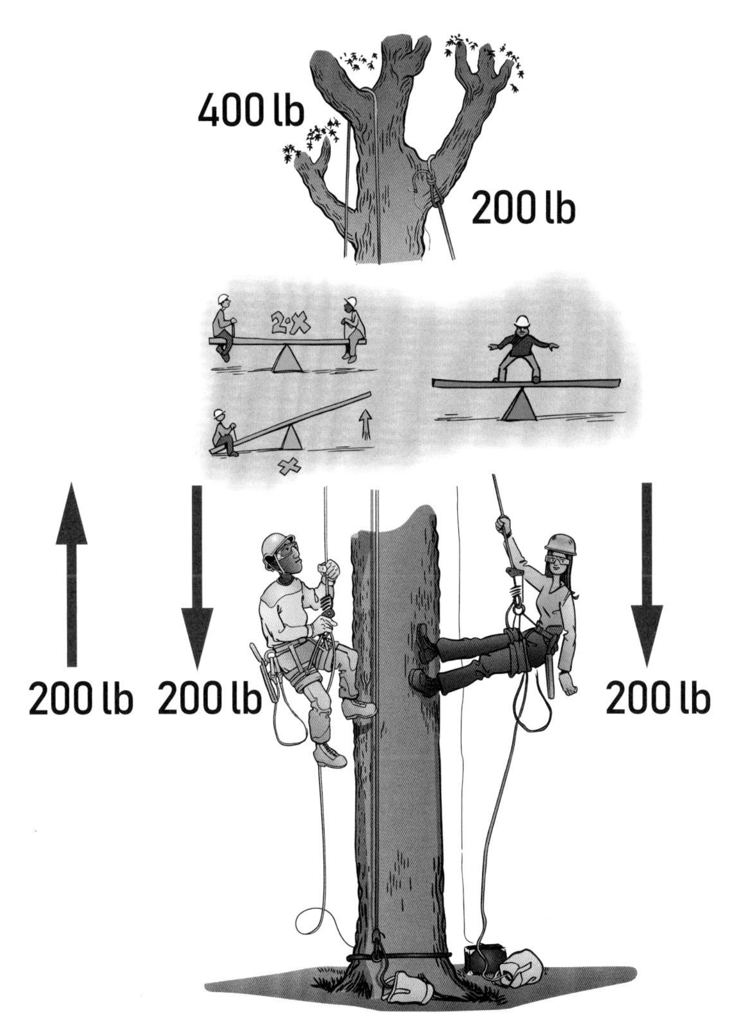

FIGURE 7.9 If using a basal anchor (left), 200 lb (90 kg) of force will be needed to balance out a 200 lb climber, translating to 400 lb (180 kg) at the primary suspension point (PSP). If using a canopy anchor, only 200 lb of force will be exerted at the PSP.

UNDERSTANDING FORCES

SRS introduces loads that are different from those experienced with MRS. Most of the differences are focused on loads at the anchor and suspension points, as well as increased loads by movement of the climber.

When using MRS, the load from the climber is shared between the two legs of rope in the system. Excluding friction at the tie-in point, if a climber weighs 200 lb (90 kg), each leg of the climbing line will experience, roughly, 100 lb (45 kg) of force. That shared load of 100 lb each equals 200 lb at the tie-in point.

When using SRS with a basal anchor, however, the 200 lb climber will be balanced out by 200 lb of force holding the load at the base of the tree. That shared load of 200 lb each will translate to 400 lb (180 kg) in the canopy. For this reason, climbers need to be mindful of the added load, selecting larger branch unions for the primary suspension point (PSP). Often, especially on ascent, the PSP is the only branch or union that the climbing line passes over. In these cases, all of the load is on that branch. If the climber's line passes through multiple canopy redirects between the basal anchor and the climber, the total load will be distributed. Another consideration is the loading of the branches involved with suspension points and redirects. Care should be taken to avoid loading branches in unnatural ways, which can lead to breakage. Most importantly, the climber should always select a PSP that is strong enough to support the full load, which can be much greater than the climber's weight.

Unlike equipment used in climbing, branch unions are not rated for breaking strength. There are many variables, such as tree species, health, and structure, and compounding the problem,

FIGURE 7.10 Climbers can incorporate climbing aids, such as handled, foot, knee, and chest ascenders, to make ascending easier.

the PSP cannot be thoroughly inspected from the ground. Climbers often employ various methods to "test" the PSP. Some will footlock on the rope just off the ground and bounce. Others may try bouncing on the rope with a coworker. There are some concerns with load testing, though. First, the bouncing can cause debris to fall on the climber and other workers below. Second, it might cause the PSP to be weakened, unknown to the climber.

Another critique is that these load testing methods have not proven to suitably replicate the loads generated at the anchor point by a climber. These methods load with only vertical movement and lack lateral movement, as will happen in the canopy. Also, bouncy, jostling movements that occur with climbing can create significant increases in loads. Although these drawbacks are real, it is considered better to discover potential problems while still on or near the ground than after ascending.

Load testing an anchor or PSP is generally considered to be an important safety check. Many companies require PSP testing before ascent. Climbers must be aware of the cautions and limitations of the testing procedure. When using a basal anchor, climbers should let the tension out of the climbing line after testing the PSP to reduce the load in the line when ascending. Additionally, to minimize excessive loads, the climber should aim for a smooth ascent, with minimal loading and unloading of the anchor. Even a short drop can generate a much larger load than the weight of the climber. Once at the top, the climber has the opportunity to inspect the PSP before continuing with the work.

EQUIPMENT

Much of the equipment used in MRS can also be used in SRS, although certain harnesses are much better suited for SRS than others. Often, a few extra pieces of equipment can help convert a moving rope system into a stationary rope system. Additionally, SRS can be as gear intensive or simplified as the climber desires. Climbers can incorporate climbing aids, such as handled, foot, knee, and chest ascenders, to make ascending easier. They may choose to use additional slings, pulleys, or other devices to incorporate desirable features. These are all optional.

Climbers should check with the manufacturer of each piece of equipment involved in their SRS configuration to ensure that it is approved for use in the manner desired. For example, a descent device used on a climber's harness may not be suitable for use on a fixed, stationary anchor point, such as at the base of a tree. Additionally, equipment used in recreational rock climbing as

WORK POSITIONING VS. SUSPENSION

Did you know that your climbing system is a suspension system, while your lanyard is typically a work-positioning system? Suspension raises and lowers you into position, while work positioning holds you in a hands-free position. In some cases, your lanyard can be moved into a suspension system. Neither suspension nor work positioning are intended to sustain a fall.

well as other high-angle occupations may not be approved for use in tree care.

Climbing Lines

Rope selection is already complicated with climbing and rigging, but SRS adds an additional layer of complexity. The use of basal anchors, mechanical devices, and ascenders with toothed cams changes the functionality requirements of climbing lines. With basal anchors, there is so much added rope in the system that stretch can make the system bouncy and challenging. A lower-stretch rope can help with efficiency. Also, toothed cams can be damaging to ropes that are not compatible. Use of 3-strand, 12-strand, or 16-strand ropes are not advised for use with toothed ascenders.

When using mechanical descent devices, as well as when using many other devices, ropes must be within certain diameter ranges, be of appropriate construction, and meet specific standards. Ropes and mechanical devices must be compatible. Also, when selecting a rope, climbers must ensure the length meets the needs of the tree and the type of system. A canopy anchor will require a rope length comparable to MRS, depending on how the anchor is set. A basal anchor, however, will require extra length to be lowerable and to accommodate multiple redirects. A rope with a length three or more times the height of the canopy may be needed to ensure clear descent.

FIGURE 7.11 Simple basal anchor setup with running bowline with Yosemite finish, secured with a carabiner. This system is not lowerable.

Lanyards

SRS climbing has influenced climbers' lanyard preferences. It is common for climbers to use extra-long, work-positioning lanyards to briefly and safely access remote areas of the tree while remaining secured. These extra-long lanyards, ranging roughly 12 to 33 ft (3.5 to 10 m), can function as a second, compact climbing system, allowing for better rope angles and work positioning.

FIGURE 7.12 More complex basal anchor set with a mechanical friction device, backed with a slip knot and hardware into a basal sling. This system is lowerable, but considerably more gear intensive than in Figure 7.11. It is important to ensure all equipment is compatible and appropriate for use in its configuration.

Lanyard configurations have also evolved, with additions such as small Prusik loops, pulleys, mechanical devices, and other friction-management tools. Though lanyards are typically attached to the harness on the two side D-rings, if a lanyard is used above the shoulders or in a single-leg configuration, the lanyard attachment should be moved to the bridge. Depending on the harness in use, an above-the-shoulders application could also be attached using the lower Ds.

Mechanical Friction Devices

Mechanical friction devices are relatively new to tree climbing, but there are already many variations on the market. A mechanical friction device serves to provide friction on the climbing line, allowing a climber to ascend and, in some cases, work the tree and descend. Most have been designed specifically for SRS climbing, where more friction is needed than what is achieved with a common friction hitch. Some are designed to work in conjunction with a friction hitch, but others replace the hitch entirely.

Each device is unique, so it is essential to read and follow all manufacturer instructions. Because of the variations in how different configurations operate, it can be difficult to determine what standards the equipment should meet. It is up to the climber to ensure that their device has been tested and meets standards for tree climbing. Manufacturers typically advise what other components can be used with their device to ensure compatibility.

Configurations and Compatibility

Much like with MRS, SRS offers endless possibilities for equipment configurations. Incorporation of new equipment should be done systematically and carefully. One of the most important concerns is the compatibility of the various components and how they are configured.

Equipment is **compatible** when the various components work properly together, function as a system, and do not cause damage to any component. For example, cordage used as hitch cord on a climbing line must be of a diameter (generally equal to or smaller than the climbing line) and construction that will allow the hitch to slide and hold when desired.

Several guidelines for equipment compatibility should be considered. As already mentioned, rope construction is important when using ascenders. Equipment diameters of pulleys and mechanical friction devices, and the rope or other cordage used with them, should match. As a general principle, it is a good idea to avoid rope-on-rope connections (except for friction hitches) and, in some cases, metal-on-metal. Most configurations consist primarily of metal-on-cordage connections.

It is important to ensure that all pieces of gear are compatible with the climbing line and with each other. In some cases, components are sold as a kit to help ensure that the equipment is all compatible. The climber must read user manuals thoroughly, checking for compatibility and applicability. As always, new equipment and configurations should be tried low and slow.

DEVELOPING A CLIMBING PLAN

Following proper tree, site, and equipment inspections, the climber can plan a climbing strategy. The climber must evaluate each tree and determine what work needs to be done. The location in the tree and the nature of the work will determine what parts of the tree need to be accessed, and in what order. Experienced SRS climbers learn to look for viable anchor points, locations for redirects, and possible obstacles to achieving safe rope angles. A thoughtful plan will result in a more efficient climb.

In MRS, the work plan often involves establishing a high, central tie-in point, making the long ascent, and working down the tree. This plan is largely due to the labor-intensive nature of MRS ascents. A central tie-in point, when available, allows the climber to access all or most parts of the tree. If a climber chooses to ascend with SRS and work the tree using MRS, the work plan will be based on the MRS, as the work-positioning system affects the strategy for working the tree.

In SRS, ascending is more efficient, resulting in minimal physical exertion. With an easier ascent, climbers are less deterred by repeated ascents and can plan their work differently. This efficiency allows climbers to plan their work in vertical space, instead of horizontal planes. Climbers can utilize one tie-in point from top to bottom, using redirects, if necessary, to access various sections of the tree. Because the friction in the system doesn't increase with additional redirects, as it does with MRS, SRS climbers can employ multiple redirects to access parts of a tree.

Depending on the type of anchor system used, moving the PSP can be a challenge. Strategic placement of the PSP and the type of anchor used are important for SRS climbing. Clear communication with the ground workers and planning the work ahead are essential.

ASCENDERS

Ascenders are mechanical devices that slide easily up a rope but grip the rope when loaded.

Simple cammed ascenders use a grooved cam to grip the host rope. They are commonly used as lanyard adjusters and belay devices, and they should not be shock loaded.

Toothed cammed ascenders rely on small, spike-like teeth on the cam to grip the rope. Toothed cam ascenders can destroy a climbing rope if exposed to a dynamic load. Only kernmantle ropes should be used with toothed ascenders.

All cammed ascenders are intended for a straight-line pull, without side loading.

It is important to follow manufacturer's recommendations for proper use.

SETTING A LINE

Much like with the tie-in point of MRS, the PSP must be sturdy with a branch union wide enough for the rope to comfortably move through for setting. Unlike with MRS, it can be difficult to advance the PSP in the tree, so it is usually best to get the preferred PSP before setting the anchor. When setting a basal anchor, one end of the line will usually hang close to the trunk, while the other end will pass through one or many branch unions, including the PSP. Because of the added load described earlier, choosing a single lateral branch far from the trunk could exceed the load limit of the branch. Passing the rope through a second branch union elsewhere in the canopy can distribute the load. Small twigs, stubs, or other obstructions that could cause undue slippage of the system should be avoided in the setup. A basal anchor can be set from the ground without the need to isolate the PSP.

When setting a canopy anchor, branch unions comparable to those used in MRS can be selected, but isolation of the branch union is required. Usually, anchor installation from the ground involves tying an inline loop (a running bowline or an alpine butterfly) in the line. The size of the tie-in point can be used to help guide the size of the loop needed in the bowline and alpine. The loop should comfortably allow the tail of the line to feed through, but not be so large as to wrap around the branch. Ideally, the full loop can be seen and inspected from the underside of the branch. The line should pass over the branch and around the main part of the stem (same as with an MRS tie-in point) before cinching.

ASCENT

Ascending a tree using the **body-thrust** technique has traditionally been the most fatiguing part of tree climbing using MRS. Often, a climber will ascend to the top without working along the way, using core, hand, and arm muscles, arriving at the top exhausted. Additionally, the inefficiency of only ascending half the distance pulled makes for a slow ascent.

FIGURE 7.13 Many SRS configurations keep the climber's body upright, which is more ergonomic.

SRS largely uses leg muscles, the strongest muscle group in the human body. Footlocking, rope walking, and other SRS techniques require coordination of the legs to do most of the work. This frees the hands to help guide the system up. The use of a chest harness can also help, not only with tending the system (advancing the friction device and/or climbing aids), but also with helping to keep the body upright. The overall upright body positioning is more **ergonomic**.

Sometimes, climbers will use SRS techniques for ascent only. When using this strategy, it is necessary to switch to MRS climbing, which might involve a different climbing line and equipment. It is essential to remain secured while establishing the tie-in point and transitioning. Sometimes the ascent line is left in place as an access line.

When selecting an ascent system, a climber should consider the nature of the work being done, the height of the ascent, the potential for an emergency descent, climbing skill, and the tree itself. If the tree is to be worked using SRS climbing, an ascent system that can be easily converted to a work-positioning system may be more desirable. Ascenders are designed to be used vertically for ascent only and cannot be used for work positioning or lateral movement. Also, a climber should not work while suspended on cammed ascenders because of the inability to self-rescue. Climbers should transfer to a work-positioning system before commencing work. Often, a mechanical friction device is used for work positioning.

Similar to anchor selection, there are many possibilities for building an ascent system, and many of the same principles apply. The equipment employed must be approved for tree work and used only as intended and recommended by the manufacturer. Excess slack in the system must be avoided. The system selected should be timely and efficient to set up and transfer. If a system is too complicated to assemble or disassemble, it could become a hazard in the tree should the climber become fatigued.

WORKING WITH STATIONARY ROPE SYSTEMS

Friction

As mentioned previously, SRS can be used quite similarly to MRS with some key differences. Because only one leg of the rope is used, and the rope at the PSP is stationary, friction is consistent throughout the tree. Friction is controlled with the friction hitch/device, and the climber moves along the stationary rope. If a climber redirects around a branch or through a union, the friction at the climbing system remains unchanged. This allows for greater freedom of movement and consistent action from the climbing system.

FIGURE 7.14 In MRS (right), redirects greatly affect the friction in the climbing system, creating considerable drag. The additional friction makes both climbing and rope retrieval difficult. In SRS (left), redirects do not affect how the climbing system functions, but retrieval may be difficult.

Using Redirects

Because the friction remains unchanged, redirects are often used with SRS climbing. A redirect changes the path of the climbing line and modifies the forces on or the direction of the climbing line. With MRS, multiple redirects can add too much friction. With SRS, no matter how many redirects in the line, the friction remains the same for the climber. Branches and branch unions can be used to the climber's advantage for accessing parts of the tree distant from the tie-in point. This difference is significant because it creates many possibilities for working the tree. An SRS climber learns to strategize differently when planning the route and order of work in the tree.

One common example of a good use of a redirect is when a climber must walk a long way out on a limb. The farther the climber moves horizontally away from the last suspension point, the flatter the rope angle becomes, making the climber less stable. If, however, the climber establishes a redirect more directly over the end of the limb, the rope angle will be more vertical and safer.

This also allows the climber to exert less force on the limb, which can be important, especially for distant limb walks or weak limbs.

Redirects are created either by climbing over or through a natural branch union or using hardware with some cordage to establish the redirect. Though the redirect cordage and hardware are not attached to the climber, it must still meet the same requirements as other equipment used for climbing. A girth hitch or basket hitch can be wrapped over a branch using a webbing loop and carabiner. This redirect is simple to install, but the climber will need to return to that point to collect the equipment. For this reason, manufacturers have created a variety of styles of retrievable redirects to allow climbers to continue their work without returning to that point. A retrievable redirect is highly desirable in many situations.

One important consideration with using redirects is that the rope angles created can affect not only the ease of climbing but also the forces on the tree and the primary suspension point. The forces in the climbing line can bend, and potentially break, branches. The rope angles can also significantly increase or decrease forces at the PSP. Climbers must always be aware of how their climbing line is affecting the tree, their PSP, and any other redirects they are using.

Limb Walking

Another difference with working in SRS is the mechanics of **limb walking**. In MRS, when returning from a limb walk, the climber can leverage the friction in the system by taking up slack in the line while advancing, pulling it through a **hitch-tending pulley** or the hitch alone. The friction makes it easy for the climber to hold their own weight. Conversely, with SRS, when returning from a long limb walk, the climber is now pulling a large portion of their body weight while advancing along the line using a pushing motion.

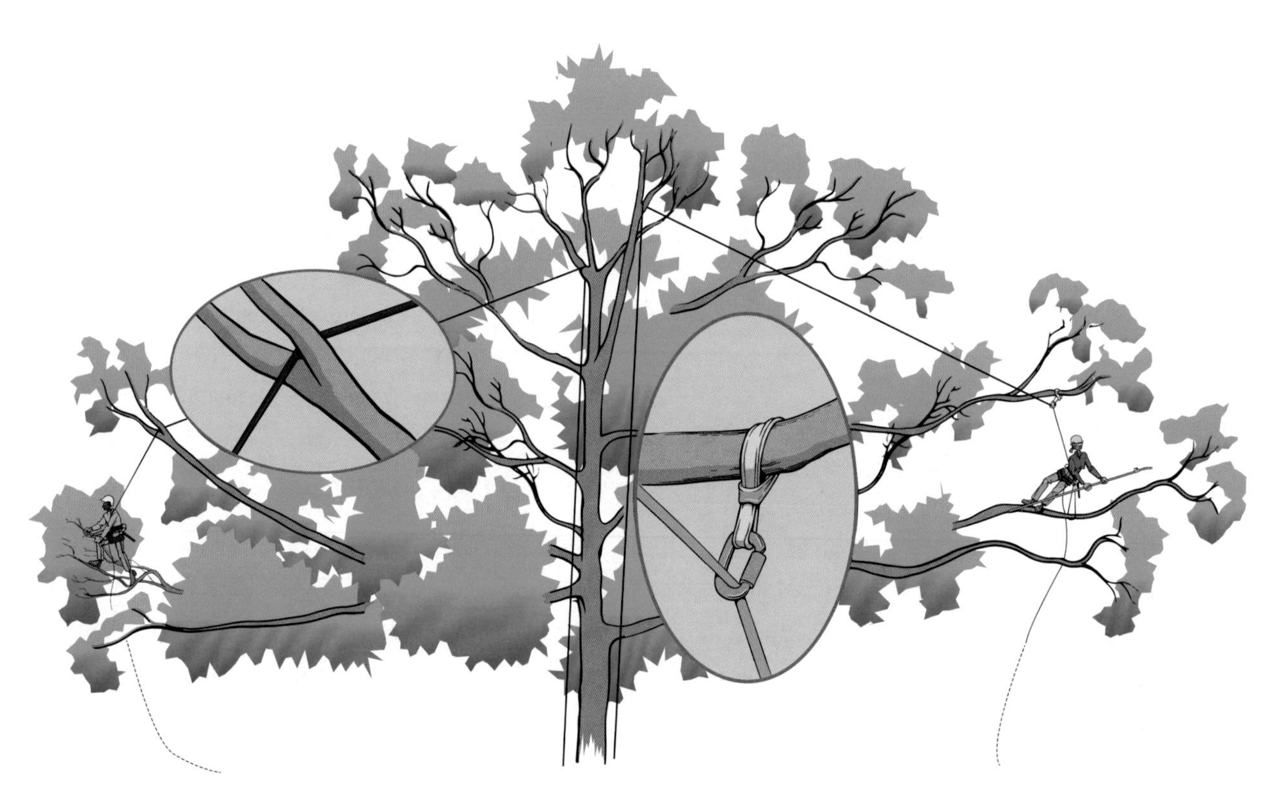

FIGURE 7.15 In SRS, a climber can use redirects without changing the friction in the system. Examples of redirects include natural branch unions, webbing loops, or retrievable redirects.

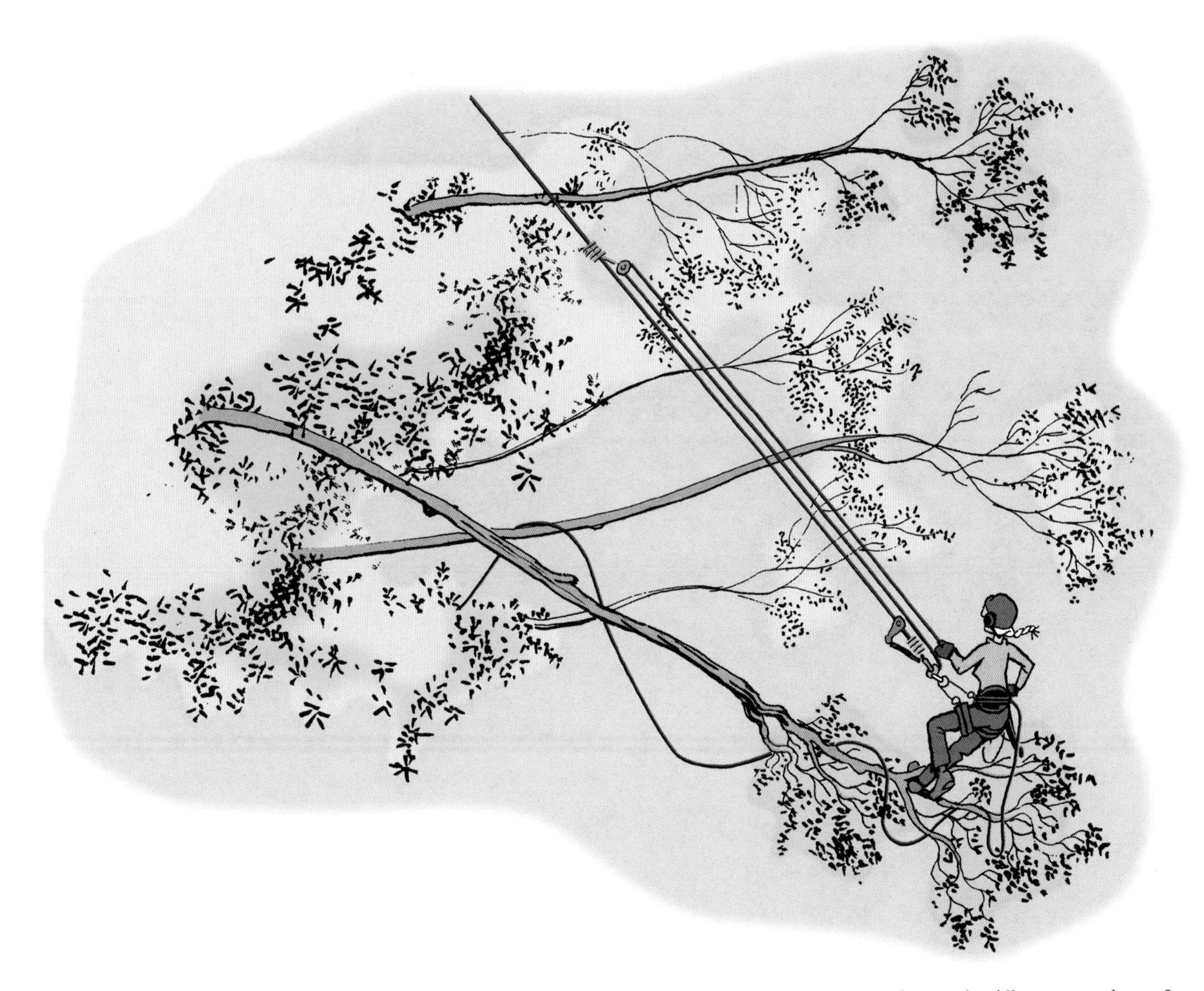

FIGURE 7.16 In SRS, when returning from a long limb walk, the climber is now pulling a significant portion of their body weight while advancing along the line. One way to combat this is to attach a fixed attachment point in the climbing line between the climber and the last suspension point and pull the climbing line through prior to beginning the limb walk.

One way to combat this is to attach a fixed attachment point in the climbing line between the climber and the last suspension point prior to beginning the limb walk. This attachment point can be an **ascender** or Prusik loop with a carabiner, or an alpine butterfly with a carabiner. The tail of the climbing line is fed through the carabiner and the climber maintains control of the tail, possibly on a non-locking component of the harness. When ready to return from the limb walk, the climber can pull on the tail, similarly to MRS, to facilitate coming back in. This system will not inhibit the limb walk out and will create a mechanical advantage on the walk back in. Adding a micropulley to the carabiner makes this technique even easier.

Safe Work Practices

While working the tree, an SRS climber maintains the same safe work principles as with MRS. This includes lanyarding in when making cuts and maintaining three points of contact on the tree. For added stability, a climber might attach a webbing loop to the stem for a foot placement. Climbers must remain secure at all times and minimize rope angles that exceed 45° (with 0° being directly below the suspension point).

Maintaining regular communication with the ground crew is important, including informing them when making cuts or when dropping or lowering anything from the tree. Finally, before any descent, it is always important to ensure there is enough rope to reach the ground. Whereas with MRS a climber would need to pull up the tail of the line to test this, for SRS it is relatively easy to check that the rope touches the ground prior to starting the final descent.

KEY CONCEPTS

1. SRS climbing involves climbing one leg of a stationary rope. Ascent techniques are generally more efficient than MRS ascent techniques and are easier on the body. Climbers ascend in a more comfortable, vertical position and use the larger muscles in their legs to ascend.
2. SRS climbing lines run through one or more branch unions and are held taut at an anchor point, either at the base of the tree or within the canopy.
3. Basal anchors do not require isolation of a branch union for the climbing line installation and can be set up to lower a climber from the ground. Limitations include significantly higher forces at the primary suspension point (PSP) and risks associated with potential damage to the line from the PSP to the anchor.
4. Canopy anchors can be simple and retrievable, and their loads are similar to MRS tie-in points. However, the branch union must be isolated, and they are not lowerable from the ground.
5. SRS can become gear intensive as climbers incorporate climbing aids, mechanical friction devices, additional slings, pulleys, or other devices. Climbers must ensure that all gear is compatible and should check with the manufacturer of each piece of equipment in their SRS configuration to ensure that it is approved for use in the manner desired.
6. Because the friction in the climbing system remains unchanged, redirects are often used with SRS climbing. Branches and branch unions can be used to the climber's advantage for accessing parts of the tree distant from the tie-in point, making the rope angle more vertical and safer.

WORKBOOK

MATCHING

_____ basal anchor	A. changes the path of the climbing line
_____ canopy anchor	B. does not require returning to dismantle
_____ ergonomic	C. functioning together in a system without damage
_____ isolated	D. climbing line tied off at a branch union
_____ PSP	E. passing over only one branch
_____ redirect	F. primary suspension point
_____ retrievable	G. climbing line tied off at the base of a tree
_____ compatible	H. efficient, comfortable, and minimizing bodily damage

TRUE/FALSE

1. T F While trying new equipment, techniques, and systems, it is essential to read the user manuals and to understand the equipment's intended use, application, and working-load limits.
2. T F When climbing using stationary rope systems, the rope runs over a branch union or through a friction-saving device, constantly moving as the climber navigates the tree.
3. T F SRS climbing lines can run through one or more branch unions and are held taut at an anchor point, either at the base of the tree or within the canopy.
4. T F Climbers may choose to ascend the tree using SRS and transfer to MRS once in the canopy.
5. T F With stationary rope systems, because the climber's entire body weight is on the single leg of the climbing line, the friction from a friction hitch is insufficient.
6. T F Using SRS, the climber will often "walk" up the rope, taking small steps, allowing the knee ascender to grip first, followed by the foot ascender.
7. T F Because it can be fatiguing and transferring to another system for working the tree can be tricky, footlocking has largely been replaced with other SRS methods.
8. T F An advantage of using a canopy anchor is that it can be configured in ways that make the climbing system lowerable.
9. T F The line for a basal anchor must be isolated over a single branch union.
10. T F To install a basal anchor, either the rope can be cinched around the trunk or a separate basal anchoring sling or loop can be installed.

11. T F The line for a canopy anchor is cinched most often using one of two knots: a running bowline with a Yosemite finish, or an alpine butterfly.

12. T F When using a basal anchor, a 200 lb (90 kg) climber will be balanced out by about 200 lb of force holding the load at the base of the tree, which will translate to nearly 400 lb (180 kg) in the canopy.

13. T F The type and size of ropes used with toothed ascenders are not important.

14. T F With basal anchors, there is so much added rope in the system, the additional stretch can make the system bouncy and challenging.

15. T F A mechanical friction device serves to provide friction on the climbing line, allowing a climber to ascend and, in some cases, to work the tree and descend.

16. T F Equipment is compatible when the various components work properly together, function as a system, and do not cause damage to any component.

17. T F Toothed ascenders are designed for ascent only and cannot be used for work positioning or lateral movement.

18. T F With SRS, the rope at the PSP is stationary; friction is consistent and is controlled with the friction hitch/device as the climber moves along the stationary rope.

19. T F Because the friction remains unchanged, redirects are rarely used with SRS climbing.

20. T F With SRS, when returning from a long limb walk, the climber is now pulling a large portion of their body weight while advancing along the line using a pushing motion.

SAMPLE TEST QUESTIONS

1. An advantage associated with SRS ascent is that

   a. the line pull equals the upward advancement
   b. it is more ergonomic and less fatiguing
   c. the body is in a more upright, comfortable position
   d. all of the above

2. The load at the primary suspension point, with no redirects, would be highest using a/an

   a. basal anchor
   b. canopy anchor
   c. MRS tie-in point
   d. friction-saving device

3. In SRS, a technique that can be employed to make returning from a limb walk much easier is

   a. installing a carabiner in the climbing line and passing the tail of the line through it to create mechanical advantage
   b. installing a redirect above the work area and passing the tail of the climbing line through it and back to the harness
   c. adding a hitch-tending pulley above a mechanical friction device as a mechanical advantage mechanism
   d. reversing the position of the hitch-tending pulley to add friction back into the climbing system

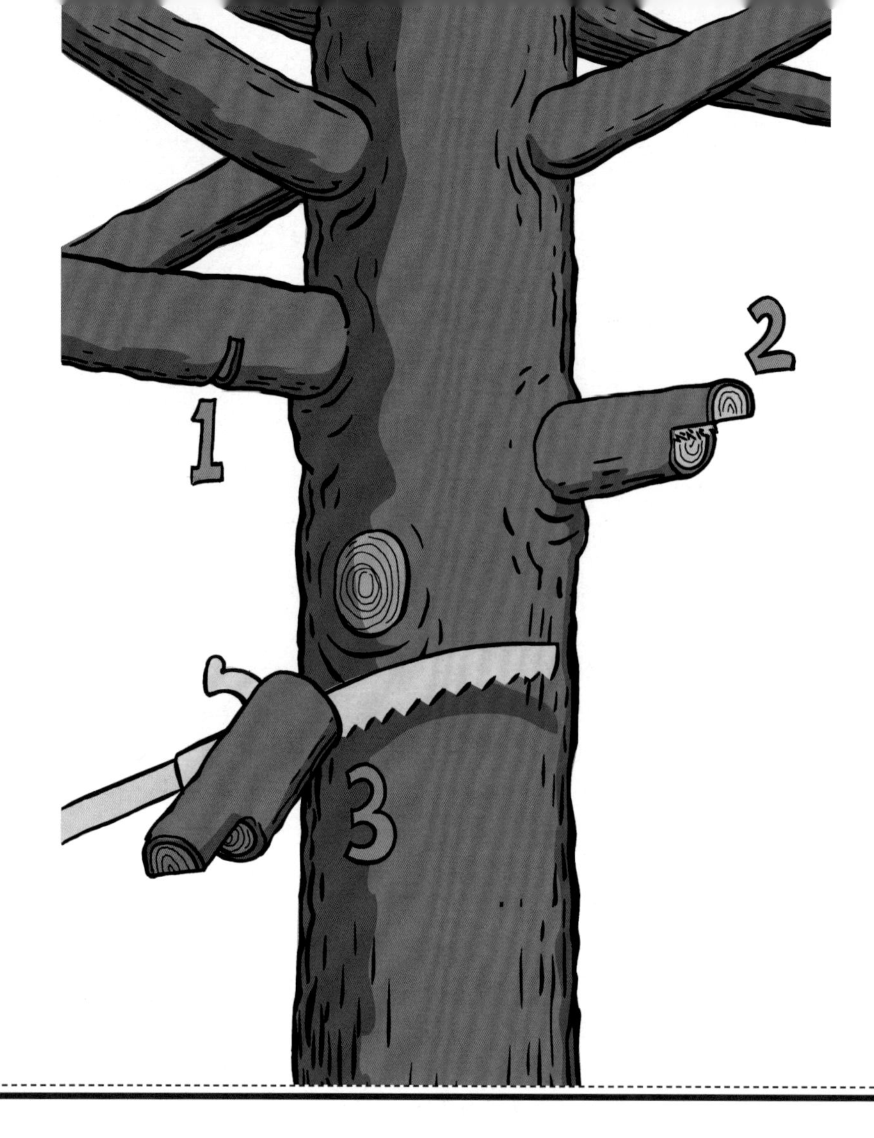

CHAPTER

PRUNING

LEARNING OBJECTIVES

The tree worker will be able to:

- Summarize the objectives of pruning.
- Select tools that are appropriate for the pruning to be done.
- Describe the types of pruning cuts and how they are used.
- Explain the proper placement of various types of pruning cuts.
- Discuss strategies for pruning to accomplish objectives.
- Recognize the fundamental responses of trees to pruning.

IMPORTANT TERMS

arborist
branch bark ridge
branch collar
branch protection zone
branch removal cut
branch union
caliper
codominant stems
compartmentalization
espalier
hand pruners
heading cut
hedge shears
included bark
kerf
lateral branch
leader
lion tailing
loppers
lopping shears
natural pruning
pleaching
pole pruner
pole saw
pollarding
pruning saw
raising
reduction
reduction cut
restoration
scabbard
scaffold branches
secateurs
skinning
taper
topiary
topping
watersprout
wound dressing

INTRODUCTION

Pruning is the most common tree maintenance procedure for urban and landscape trees. Forest trees grow quite well with little or no pruning. Dead or weak branches simply die and are shed as they decay. Landscape trees, however, often require pruning to remove dead branches, improve tree structure, and maintain public safety. Pruning cuts must be made with an understanding of how the tree will respond to the cut. Improper pruning can cause damage that will affect the future health and structure of the tree. Knowledge of pruning standards and proper techniques is essential to the tree climber.

This chapter begins with the reasons for pruning. Pruning can take a toll on tree health, so it is important to have a good reason for every pruning operation. The chapter goes on to introduce pruning tools and types of pruning cuts. Pruning objectives are usually accomplished using a variety of cut types. Understanding the pruning objectives is important to achieving the goals without damaging health or structure. This chapter also includes information on pruning techniques, when to prune, and wound dressings.

REASONS FOR PRUNING

Because each cut changes the growth of the tree, no branch should be removed without a reason. Common reasons for pruning are to remove dead, diseased, and damaged branches; to establish good structure; to provide clearance; and to decrease likelihood of tree failure. In most cases, tree pruning is a corrective or preventive procedure.

COMMON REASONS FOR PRUNING TREES

- Establish good structure
- Provide clearance
- Reduce the risk of tree or tree part failure
- Improve the appearance

PRUNING TOOLS

When pruning trees, it is important to have the right tool for the job. When doing fine pruning, with cuts less than 1/2 in (1 to 2 cm) in diameter, **hand pruners (secateurs)** can be used. The scissor-type hand pruners, with a bypass blade configuration, are preferred over the anvil type because they make cleaner, more accurate cuts. The bypass blade configuration is also preferred when choosing **lopping shears (loppers)**. Lopping shears have long handles and can cut branches 1/2 to 2 in (1 to 5 cm) in diameter.

FIGURE 8.1 Fine pruning is best performed using hand pruners (secateurs) with a bypass blade configuration.

Hedge shears are used for shearing hedges or formal-shaped plants and are generally not recommended for pruning trees.

Pruning saws are specially designed hand saws for pruning trees. Most have an arched blade and cut primarily on the back (pull) stroke. Pruning saws are available in various sizes and with different tooth configurations. New technology has helped to develop some pruning saws that are

FIGURE 8.2 Lopping shears are used to prune small to medium stems.

FIGURE 8.3 Hedge shears have a very specific purpose. They are generally NOT recommended for pruning trees.

extremely sharp and efficient. Climbers should carry at least one pruning saw when pruning trees aloft. For safety and convenience, the saw is carried in a sheath called a **scabbard**. Some scabbards have pouches that carry hand pruners as well.

It is often difficult to reach certain branches when pruning trees. Two additional tools can make these cuts possible. A **pole pruner** can be compared to lopping shears on the end of a pole. Pole pruners, if used correctly, can make a clean cut up to about 2 in (5 cm) in diameter. A **pole saw** can make larger cuts from a distance. Both pole tools should be used with care, as clean, accurate cuts are made only when the climber is in a good position and can place the tool at the correct angle.

Climbers can use a chain saw when pruning, but its use should be limited to large cuts. The chain must be sharp in order to make clean, straight cuts. Using a chain saw in a tree is potentially dangerous and should not be attempted without proper training. Climbers should use two means of securing in the tree when using a chain saw and should always carry a hand saw.

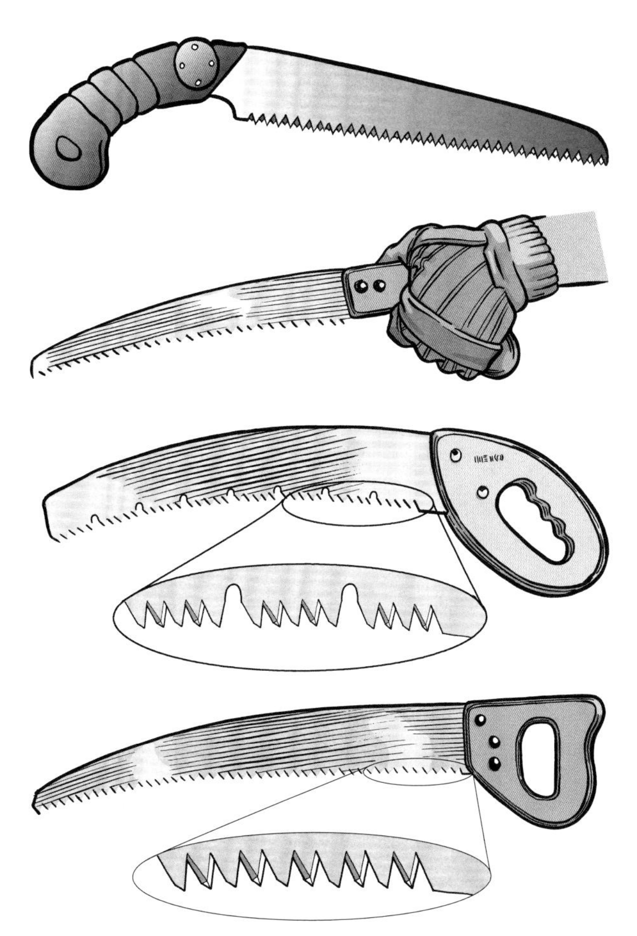

FIGURE 8.4 There are many types and sizes of pruning saws available, with a variety of blade shapes and tooth configurations.

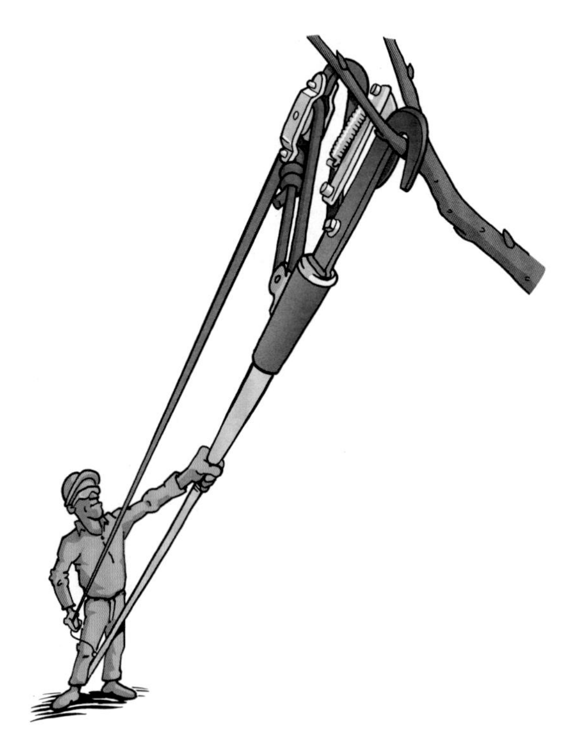

FIGURE 8.5 Pole pruners cut like lopping shears but can reach much farther.

WHEN TO PRUNE

Most routine pruning to remove weak, diseased, undesirable, or dead limbs can be accomplished at any time of the year with minimal effect on the tree. As a general rule, growth is maximized and wound closure is fastest if pruning takes place just before the initial growth flush in the spring. Some trees, such as maples and birches, tend to "bleed" if pruned in the early spring. This may be unsightly but has little negative effect on the tree. Flowering trees should be pruned after flowering to avoid removing flower buds. Some tree diseases, such as oak wilt, can be spread when pruning wounds allow access into the tree. Susceptible trees should not be pruned when diseases can be spread.

PRUNING CUTS

Each pruning cut should be made carefully at the correct location, leaving a smooth surface with no jagged edges or torn bark. When a tree sheds a branch naturally, it is typically shed back to its point of origin (a larger branch or the trunk). The point where a branch joins its parent branch or the trunk is called the **branch union**. At the branch union there is often a swollen area called the **branch collar**. The branch collar is stem tissue that wraps around the branch attachment. A ridge of bark tissue is sometimes pushed up into the union. This is called the **branch bark ridge**. Inside the branch union is a **branch protection zone**. Cells in the branch protection zone help protect the remaining stem from decay if the branch dies, breaks off, or is pruned.

FIGURE 8.6 Pole saws can be used to make relatively large cuts from a distance.

The correct location for a cut that removes a branch back to its point of origin (sometimes called a **branch removal cut**) is just outside the branch collar. It is important not to cut into the collar or the branch bark ridge because doing so will damage the branch protection zone, making it easier for decay to spread from the branch cut into the trunk or parent branch—this process is known as **compartmentalization**. A well-made cut will close evenly from all sides.

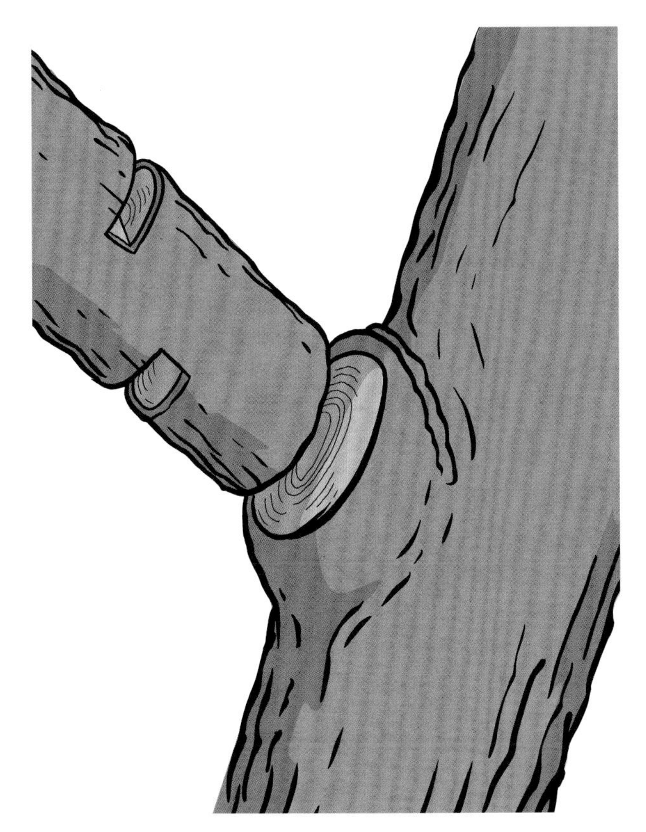

FIGURE 8.7 Cuts should be made just beyond the branch collar. Leaving a stub inhibits effective closure of the wound.

FIGURE 8.8 If the tree has started closing over a stub, cut just the dead stub and not the live tissue.

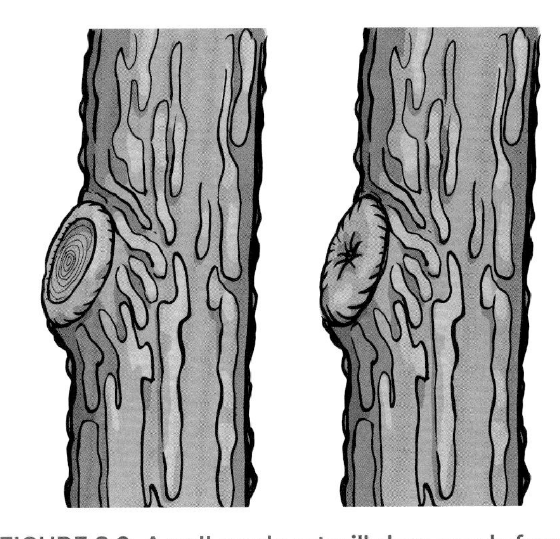

FIGURE 8.9 A well-made cut will close evenly from all sides.

Another type of cut, which prunes a **leader** back to a **lateral branch**, is called a **reduction cut**. The lateral chosen for the remaining branch should be large enough to sustain growth and assume the terminal role. Ideally, the lateral should be at least one-third the diameter of the leader being removed, although this is not always possible. Figure 8.10 illustrates the placement of a reduction cut. A reduction cut cannot take advantage of a tree's natural defense system for closing and compartmentalizing wounds because there is not a collar or branch protection zone at the point of the cut. Therefore, it is best to limit reduction cuts to smaller cuts that are more likely to close quickly and outgrow decay.

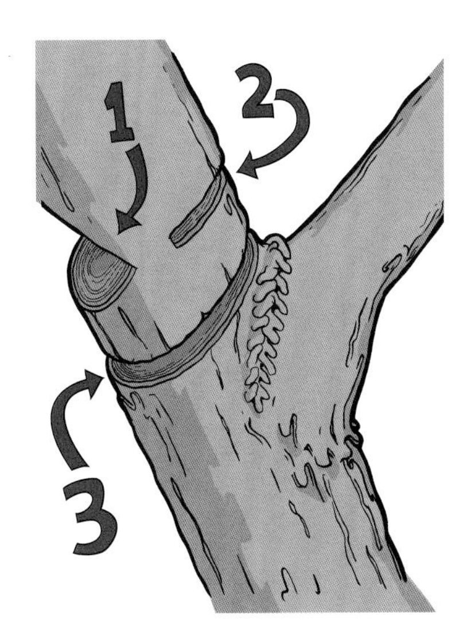

FIGURE 8.10 A reduction cut prunes a leader back to a lateral branch.

A **heading cut** prunes a branch back to a bud, stub, or lateral branch not large enough to assume the terminal role. Heading cuts are

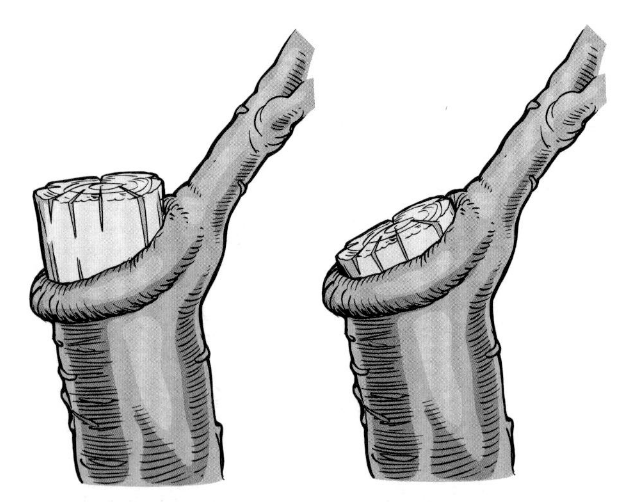

FIGURE 8.11 **It is best to limit reduction cuts to smaller cuts that are more likely to close quickly and outgrow decay. A reduction cut made in the wrong place will close slowly, if at all.**

FIGURE 8.12 **Often multiple watersprouts develop following a heading cut.**

usually not the first choice for arborists, and their use is more common in nursery production and shrub pruning. Sometimes, however, using heading cuts makes sense when restoring trees from damage due to storms or other factors. Making a cut back to the point of origin of a branch or cutting a branch back to a large lateral can sometimes remove much more than is desirable.

Large or heavy limbs should be removed using three cuts. The first cut is on the underside of the limb 1 or 2 ft (30 to 60 cm) out from the parent branch or trunk. A properly made undercut will eliminate the chance of the branch "peeling," or tearing bark as it is removed. The second cut is the top cut, which is made slightly farther out on the limb than the undercut. This allows the limb to drop smoothly. The third cut, often called the collar cut, removes the remaining stub. If large limbs are being removed with a chain saw, care must be exercised in using this three-cut method. The **kerf** that is created as the saw makes the second (top) cut can pinch the saw bar as the branch

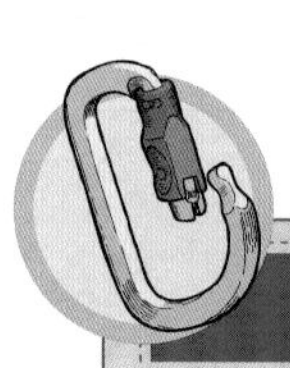

TYPES OF PRUNING CUTS

- Removal cut
- Reduction cut
- Heading cut

FIGURE 8.13 **A properly made undercut will eliminate the chance of the branch "peeling," or tearing bark as it is removed.**

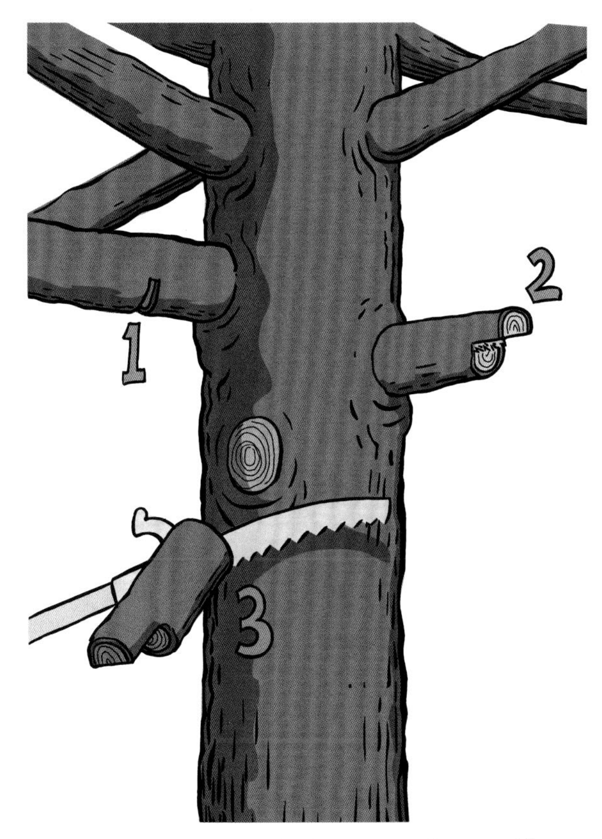

FIGURE 8.14 Pruning principles. The first cut (1) undercuts the limb. The second cut (2) removes the limb. The final cut (3) should be just outside the branch collar to remove the stub.

is cut and can pull the saw out of the climber's hands as the limb falls away. This can be avoided if the top cut is made directly above the undercut and the chain speed is kept high.

PRUNING TO ESTABLISH GOOD STRUCTURE

A good structure of **scaffold branches** should be established while the tree is young. Scaffold branches provide the primary framework of a mature tree. Properly trained young trees will develop into trees with a strong structure and will require less corrective pruning as they mature. In addition, young trees can more effectively close and compartmentalize relatively small pruning wounds.

FIGURE 8.15 Trees should be pruned when young to establish a strong scaffold system like the tree on the left. The tree on the right will become more prone to failure as it matures.

The goal in pruning for structure is to establish a good framework with sturdy branches, strong branch unions, and, usually, a dominant leader. The strength of the branch structure is dependent upon the sizes, spacing, and attachment of the branches. Naturally, this will vary with the growth habit of the tree species. Some tree species naturally grow with a strong central leader and well-spaced scaffold branches. Others tend toward a dense crown of weakly attached branches. Good pruning techniques can remove or reduce structurally weak branches while maintaining the natural form of the tree.

Branches that are to be part of the permanent branch scaffold should be selected for good

TRAINING YOUNG TREES

Establishing good structure when a tree is young reduces the need to prune when it matures. Young trees also respond quickly to pruning and the smaller wounds close faster.

FIGURE 8.16 If two branches develop from terminal buds at the tip of the same stem, they will form codominant stems.

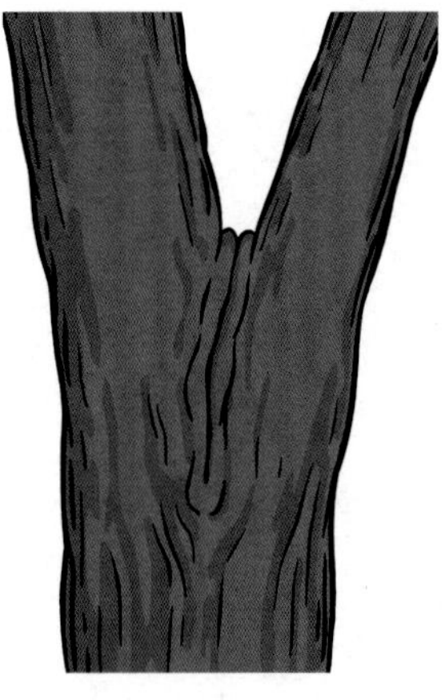

FIGURE 8.17 Included bark can be a problem in a tight branch union. This condition weakens the branch attachment.

structural integrity. Generally, it is best if they are no more than half the diameter of the parent branch or trunk. It is best to choose branches that do not have flaws or defects, especially at the point of attachment. If two branches develop from terminal buds at the tip of the same stem, they will form **codominant stems** (codominant branches). Each codominant stem is a direct extension of the trunk, so there is no normal branch-to-trunk attachment, no branch collar or branch bark ridge, and no protection zone formed in these unions. Because codominant stems can sometimes be weaker than branch-to-trunk unions, it may be a good idea to remove or reduce one of the codominant stems while the tree is young.

Branches that have narrow angles of attachment and codominant branches are more prone to breaking at the branch union, especially if there is **included bark**. Included bark is bark that gets enclosed inside the branch union as the branch and trunk increase in diameter. This weakens the branch attachment, increasing the likelihood of failure.

The spacing of branches, both vertically and around the trunk, is very important for a strong framework. Scaffold branches should be well spaced on the trunk. Balance must be maintained around the trunk (radially) with branches growing outward in each direction. If two scaffold branches arise, one directly above another, on the same side of the tree, it is best to remove one while they are small.

Generally, the leader in a tree is not pruned back unless a multiple-stemmed tree is desired or unless the leader has become too dominant. If a young tree has more than one leader, one leader should be selected and the others reduced or removed.

There is often a tendency to remove too many lower branches and inside branches. Maintaining inner branches and lower branches promotes optimal development of **caliper** (diameter) and branch or trunk **taper**. Each smaller branch contributes to the growth and development of larger, parent branches. Leaving lower and inside branches along a limb helps the limb to grow thicker and stronger.

PRUNING OBJECTIVES AND TECHNIQUES

Before beginning any tree pruning operation, the objectives should be clearly understood. Pruning objectives typically include one or more of the following:

- Managing risk
- Managing tree health

- Developing good structure
- Providing clearance
- Improving aesthetics
- Managing size or shape
- Managing production of fruit or flowers

Most of the time, these objectives are met while striving to maintain a tree's natural form, sometimes called **natural pruning**. The characteristic form includes the tree's natural size, growth habit, and branching structure. Natural pruning can allow for changes in a tree's appearance while still accomplishing objectives such as **raising** the crown, enhancing views, improving structure, providing clearance, or reducing risk.

Other, less frequent approaches are the specialty pruning systems such as **pollarding**, **topiary**, **espalier**, and **pleaching**, illustrated in Figures 8.18 through 8.21. Specialty pruning is often found in formal gardens and arboretums.

Arborists will often remove the dead, broken, and diseased branches from trees to manage tree health or the risk of tree failure. It is usually preferable to limit the removal of live, healthy branches, though, because these branches are needed to maintain health and strong structure.

Sometimes trees' inner branches are removed to promote light, air, or water penetration. This often triggers new growth (sometimes weakly attached sprouts) where branches have been removed to capture more sunlight. The goal of

FIGURE 8.18 Pollarding.

FIGURE 8.19 Topiary.

FIGURE 8.20 Espalier.

FIGURE 8.21 Pleaching.

FIGURE 8.22 When natural pruning, the arborist is trying to maintain a tree's natural form. An effort should be made to maintain well-spaced inner branches and achieve an even distribution of foliage along each branch.

FIGURE 8.23 Workers must be careful not to remove all of the inner laterals and foliage, an effect known as lion tailing. Lion tailing makes branches tip-heavy and may result in sunburned bark tissue, watersprout development, and weakened branches.

increasing light is achieved only temporarily, and excessive removal of inner branches can lead to branch failure. When pruning a tree, an effort should be made to maintain well-spaced inner branches. It is important to achieve an even distribution of foliage along the branch and avoid hollowing out the center of the crown. Workers must be careful not to create an effect known as **lion tailing**, which is caused by removing all or most of the inner laterals and foliage. Lion tailing makes branches tip-heavy and may result in sunburned bark tissue, **watersprout** development, and weakened branches. Lion-tailed branches tend to whip and break in the wind because they are slender and end-weighted.

FIGURE 8.24 Raising, also known as lifting or elevating, removes lower branches of a tree to provide clearance for buildings, vehicles, pedestrians, and views.

Trees in urban and landscape settings may need to have lower limbs removed. Raising, also known as lifting or elevating, removes lower branches of a tree to provide clearance for buildings, vehicles, pedestrians, and views. Excessive removal of lower limbs should be avoided so that the development of trunk taper is not affected and structural stability is maintained.

Sometimes the height or spread of a tree's crown must be reduced, as is the case with utility pruning (line clearance). **Reduction** is used to reduce the height or width of a tree. This is usually accomplished with a combination of branch removal cuts and reduction cuts. When using reduction cuts, it is best to cut back limbs back to laterals that are large enough to sustain growth. One rule of thumb is to cut back to a lateral that is at least one-third the diameter of the branch

FIGURE 8.25 Side pruning to provide clearance, before and after.

being reduced. When reducing the length of a branch by making a reduction cut, the final cut should not cut through any part of the branch bark ridge and it should not leave a stub. Small reduction cuts are more likely to close and compartmentalize than large cuts. Some species of trees are more tolerant of reduction than others, but technique is important for all trees. At times it may be appropriate to use heading cuts, especially if the alternative is to make a much larger cut and if the species can readily produce new shoots. Proper reduction maintains the structural integrity and natural form of the tree, and it requires less follow-up work.

FIGURE 8.26 Proper reduction maintains the structural integrity and natural form of the tree and requires less follow-up work.

Topping involves the cutting of limbs back to stubs, buds, or small lateral branches, often to a predetermined crown size, without regard to long-term health or structural integrity. Topping often leads to decay and sprout production from the cut ends of the branches. These sprouts are weakly attached and have a greater likelihood of failure; this can lead to greater risk when they become larger. Many of the stubs that are left are likely to decay, and decay may progress down the stem. Topping, like lion tailing, is an unacceptable pruning practice.

FIGURE 8.27 If a tree has been topped, it is unlikely to completely regain its natural shape and structural strength. Topping, like lion tailing, is an unacceptable pruning practice.

FIGURE 8.28 Topping often leads to decay and sprout production from the cut ends of the branches. These sprouts are weakly attached and have a greater likelihood of failure.

If a tree has been topped, it is unlikely to completely regain its natural shape and structural strength. However, **restoration** pruning can help improve the tree's safety and appearance. Decayed stubs and branches should be pruned back to structurally sound branches. One or two sprouts on main branches are selected to become permanent branches, and the rest are removed. It is best to select sprouts with the strongest attachment to the branch. These sprouts may have to be pruned to control and direct their growth. Restoration usually requires repeated pruning over a number of years. Restoration pruning can also be employed following storm damage.

PRUNING MATURE TREES

Whether pruning a young nursery tree or a large, mature shade tree, many of the principles remain the same. There are, however, some very significant differences. Mature trees have developed large scaffold branches. If one is removed, the large wound will not close readily, and compartmentalization may be slow and less effective. Although young trees can often tolerate aggressive pruning, with mature trees, removal of even 10 percent can have negative effects. And, if the tree is very old or not healthy, it may not have the energy reserves to recover from the removal of a single large limb. Proper training of a tree when it is young will minimize the amount of pruning required when it is mature. It is best to minimize the removal of live branches on mature trees.

FIGURE 8.29 Severe reduction of a mature tree can be stressful to the tree, even when proper cuts are made. It is best to minimize the removal of live branches on mature trees.

PRUNING PALMS

Pruning of palms is mostly limited to removal of dead and

FIGURE 8.30 **When working with palms, removal of live, healthy fronds should be minimized. They should only be removed as necessary to provide clearance. If clearance is required, it is best to avoid removing fronds that originate above a horizontal line at the base of the crown.**

diseased fronds, fruits, and inflorescences. Palms that require management of fruit fall should be pruned on a regular cycle. Some species of palms can be pruned annually to remove all unwanted material in one visit. Depending on the species, the leaf bases may be persistent, which to some people is unattractive. Arborists may be hired to **skin** the palm, meaning to remove the leaf bases. This practice is not required for the health of the palm, and may cause damage if not conducted carefully. Care should be taken to avoid damage to the living tissue.

Removal of live, healthy fronds should be minimized unless necessary to accomplish the objectives. A guide is to only remove fronds where the tip of the frond hangs below an imaginary, horizontal line drawn from the base of the palm crown. A three-point cut should be used for large fronds to avoid tearing into live tissue.

Some diseases of palms spread readily, making the sterilization of pruning tools necessary. Hand tools, such as machetes and hand saws, that are commonly used to prune palm parts should be sterilized after pruning a palm suspected of disease. Especially susceptible species such as *Phoenix* spp. should not be pruned with a chain saw, which cannot easily be sterilized.

Fronds and debris cut from the crown can be quite heavy. Drop zone management will require awareness of the weight of fruits, as well as the unpredictable nature of falling fronds. An expanded drop zone is recommended.

WOUND DRESSINGS

Wound dressings were once thought to accelerate wound closure, protect against insects and diseases, and reduce decay. However, research has shown that conventional, asphalt-based dressings do not reduce decay. With few exceptions, dressings usually are not effective in preventing insect or disease penetration or accelerating wound closure. Although some studies have shown beneficial effects in specific cases, wound dressings are primarily used for cosmetic purposes. If they are used, only a light coating of a material that is not toxic to the tree should be applied.

KEY CONCEPTS

1. Pruning is the most common maintenance practice for urban and landscape trees. Some of the primary objectives are removing dead, damaged, and diseased branches; developing good branch structure; providing clearance; and reducing the risk of branch or tree failure.
2. Selecting appropriate pruning tools for the application is important. Common pruning tools include hand pruners, lopping shears, pruning saws, pole saws, pole pruners, and chain saws.
3. Pruning cuts should be made cleanly and in the right place. The three types of pruning cuts are branch removal cuts, reduction cuts, and heading cuts.
4. Each pruning cut should be made with a purpose, as excessive pruning will stress a tree.
5. It is best to develop good branch structure in young trees when the cuts will be small and will close quickly. Codominant leaders should be removed or reduced to develop single, strong leaders.
6. The interior portion of the crown should not be over-pruned because doing so will inhibit the growth of branch taper and could increase the likelihood of branch failure.
7. Lion tailing and topping are considered unacceptable practices.

WORKBOOK

MATCHING

_____ topping	A. removes a branch back to its point of origin
_____ scabbard	B. hand pruning shears
_____ raising	C. removal of lower branches
_____ included bark	D. excessive removal of inner branches
_____ branch collar	E. sheath for pruning saw
_____ secateurs	F. “swollen” zone at base of branch
_____ lion tailing	G. poor crown reduction technique
_____ branch removal cut	H. sometimes found in codominant branch unions

TRUE/FALSE

1. T F Improper pruning can cause permanent damage to a tree.
2. T F Anvil-type hand pruners are preferred over the bypass blade type.
3. T F Hedge shears are the best tool for pruning most small trees.
4. T F Most pruning saws are designed to cut on the forward or push stroke.
5. T F “Bleeding” that results when certain trees are pruned in the spring has little negative effect on the tree.
6. T F The final pruning cut in branch removal should be made just outside the branch collar.
7. T F Large or heavy branches should be removed using the three-cut technique.
8. T F It is preferable to develop a sturdy scaffold branch structure while the tree is young.
9. T F The branch bark ridge is located under the branch.
10. T F A tree’s growth habit and rate are irrelevant in pruning.
11. T F Removing a large limb from a very mature tree can cause significant stress.
12. T F Young trees are generally more tolerant of severe pruning than older, mature trees.
13. T F Included bark in a branch union can weaken branch attachment.
14. T F If a young tree has more than one leader, usually one leader should be selected and the others reduced or removed.
15. T F Topping is the recommended technique for crown reduction.
16. T F Lion-tailed branches tend to whip and break in the wind because they are slender and end-weighted.

17. T F Restoration pruning may improve the structure and appearance of a tree that has been topped or storm damaged previously.

18. T F Pollarding, topiary, espalier, and pleaching are specialty systems of pruning, which are not appropriate for trees.

19. T F Large, mature trees are generally very tolerant of severe pruning.

20. T F Tree wound dressings are widely recommended to accelerate healing and prevent insect and disease penetration in wounds.

SAMPLE TEST QUESTIONS

1. The goal in pruning for structure is to

   a. establish a good framework with sturdy branches
   b. encourage development of strong branch unions
   c. reduce future risk of branch failure
   d. all of the above

2. The final cut in removing a branch should be made just outside the

   a. branch collar
   b. cambium layer
   c. trunk taper
   d. internode

3. One result of topping or lion tailing is often the production of

   a. excessive taper
   b. scaffold branches
   c. bark inclusions
   d. watersprouts

CHAPTER

9

RIGGING

LEARNING OBJECTIVES

The tree worker will be able to:

- Summarize how ropes are used to safely lower tree parts.
- Explain how rigging forces are affected by the methods used.
- Describe the uses of common rigging equipment.
- Discuss the applications and limitations of common rigging techniques.
- Describe the options for tying off limbs and making cuts.
- Summarize the role of the ground worker in rigging operations.

IMPORTANT TERMS

arborist block
balance
bend ratio
block
block and tackle
bollard
butt-tied
carabiner
clevis
clove hitch
command-and-response system
connecting link
cow hitch
cut-and-chuck method
cycles to failure
damping
dead-eye sling
design factor
double-locking gate
drop cut
drop zone
dynamic load
eye-and-eye sling
eye-spliced rope
force
friction
friction device
girth hitch
half hitch
hinge cut
kerf
landing zone
load line
locking gate
mechanical advantage
notch
pull line
pulley
rescue pulley
rigging
rigging point
running bowline
screw link
shackle
shock-loading
sling
snap cut
static load
tagline
tensile strength
tip-tie
whoopie sling
working-load limit (WLL)

FIGURE 9.1 Rigging involves the use of ropes and various pieces of hardware to remove large sections of trees safely and efficiently.

FIGURE 9.2 It is always best to practice new techniques in open areas so that techniques can be learned in a low-consequence environment. Remember, low and slow.

INTRODUCTION

In arboriculture, **rigging** is the use of ropes and other equipment to take down trees or remove limbs. Rigging is usually associated with removals, but the procedures can be very important in pruning operations. Rigging is necessary when it is not possible to "free fall" or drop tree sections due to potential hazards, obstacles below, or power lines. When removing limbs from a tree that is being pruned, care must be taken not to damage the remaining branches, trunk, and root system. Rigging techniques can allow the climber or lift operator to remove large limbs in less time and with more control than if the sections had to be "pieced out" (cut into small sections that can be dropped).

This chapter will describe and illustrate common rigging equipment and techniques. The procedures discussed will be limited to the more basic practices. The terminology will be explained, and the more commonly accepted terms will be used.

Rigging involves the use of ropes and hardware to remove sections of trees safely and efficiently. All ropes and equipment have strength ratings and limitations. It is vitally important to know these limitations and not to exceed them. There are techniques that can limit the load placed on rigging equipment. Because the weight of any tree section or limb to be cut can only be estimated, experience with rigging equipment and the use of proper techniques are essential.

The rigging of large sections of trees to be removed can involve significant risks that must be managed. Even for experienced workers, it is always best to practice new techniques in open areas so that safety and control will not be in question on more difficult trees. And, of course, new techniques should always be practiced low and slow.

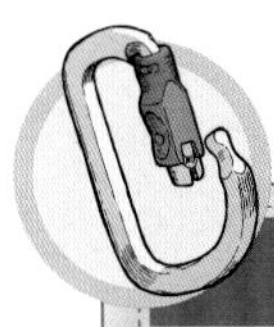

"LOW AND SLOW"

Tree climbers often use the expression "low and slow." This refers to the principle that new equipment, knots, and techniques should always be introduced in a low-risk environment—low to the ground and tried out slowly.

The same concept is especially important in rigging. It is best to avoid combining multiple new processes in a work environment in which the consequences of a mistake are severe.

This text is an educational tool for introductory arboriculture. It may be used as part of, but not as a replacement for, a comprehensive training program. While some equipment and techniques are explained and illustrated, actual use requires knowledge of and experience with them prior to use in an actual work environment. The equipment and techniques described or depicted in this book must be analyzed, and at times modified, to meet the specific needs of the situation.

Workers must understand the proper use of all equipment required and use safe work practices at all times. It is essential to become familiar with local, state, provincial, national, or federal government standards as applicable to the job assignment and requirements. Also, it is a good idea to take advantage of other sources of information and training available from the International Society of Arboriculture, the Tree Care Industry Association, and other arborist associations.

FORCES IN RIGGING

Removing large, heavy sections of trees using ropes and other equipment generates large **forces**. These forces are affected significantly by the equipment and techniques employed. The size and weight of the piece removed is the base factor in determining the force involved, but forces are also affected by the distance of fall, the type and amount of rope in the system, and the angles involved. A very significant factor in rigging forces is whether the rigging point is above the load (sometimes called positive rigging) or below the load (negative rigging). By selecting appropriate equipment and employing rigging techniques that minimize forces, arborists can mitigate the potential risks of rigging. While rigging equipment and ropes have become stronger over the years, trees have not, and anchor points can sometimes be the weakest point in the rigging system.

Friction is essential in rigging systems. Without it, ground workers could not lower pieces that

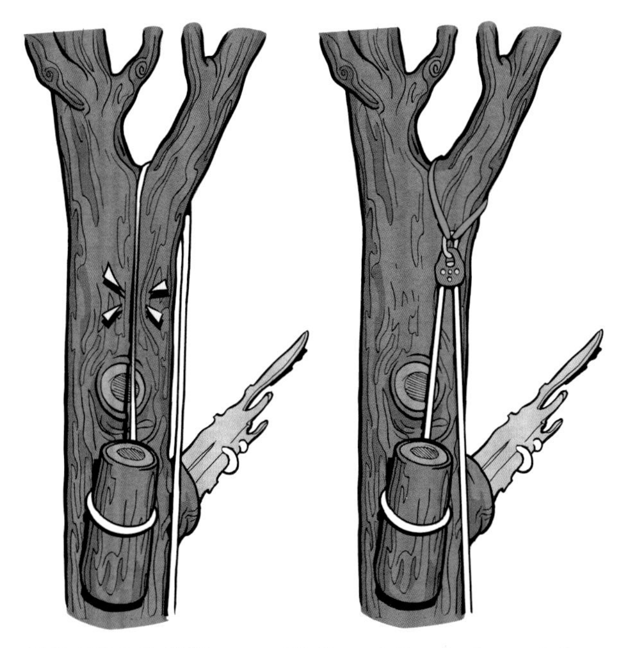

FIGURE 9.3 With more friction at the rigging point, as with rigging using a natural branch union, the lead (the part of the line from the rigging point to the piece being cut) experiences significantly more of the force in this relatively short length of line than does the rest of the line. Using an arborist block helps distribute the force along a greater length of line.

weigh more than the workers. Friction is a force acting opposite the relative motion between two objects. Equipment experiences friction and heats up. A rope absorbs some of the energy of a falling piece of wood by stretching. With more friction at the **rigging point**, as with rigging using a natural branch union, the lead (the part of the line from the rigging point to the piece being cut) experiences significantly more of the force in this relatively short length of rope than does the rest of the rope. Over time, these forces shorten the life of the rigging line. While friction is always a concern, it is most important for large pieces and in cases where there will be significant shock-loading (sudden, heavy loading).

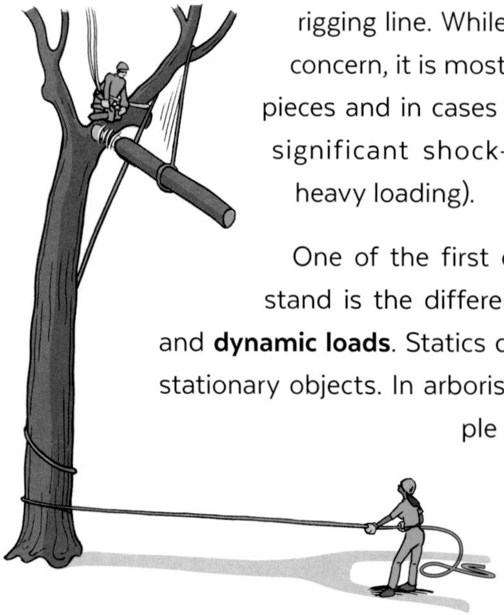

FIGURE 9.4 Shock-loading occurs when a dynamic, sudden force is placed on a rope or rigging apparatus when a moving load/piece is stopped.

One of the first concepts to understand is the difference between **static** and **dynamic loads**. Statics deals with forces on stationary objects. In arborist rigging, an example of a static load is the weight of a tree section or piece of wood. Dynamics is the study of the action of forces on bodies and the changes in motion they produce. An example of a dynamic load in arborist rigging is the load experienced by stopping a piece of wood that is falling with rigging. The dynamic load can be many times the static load (the weight of the piece of wood).

FIGURE 9.5
A dynamic load is created by moving forces acting upon an object and the changes in motion they produce.

Dynamic loads damage ropes, other equipment, and tree parts more quickly than equivalent static loads. That is, dropping 200 lb (90 kg) to produce a 1,000 lb (450 kg) dynamic load is worse for the rope than slowly lifting a 1,000 lb load. Failure to account for dynamic loads can lead to premature or sudden equipment failure or tree failure.

The **tensile strength** reported by the manufacturer is the breaking strength (force at which the tested item fails) of a rope or piece of hardware. As a rope is used, its strength is reduced due to wear caused by dirt and friction, knots, and, of course, loading. The concept of **cycles to failure** must also be considered. One cycle means one lift or drop for a rigging line. Each cycle creates some degree of permanent damage in the rope, and eventually the rope will fail. Cycles to failure are directly correlated to the loads the equipment is subjected to. The larger the load, the higher the amount of permanent damage done. This results in fewer cycles to failure. If the load on a rope

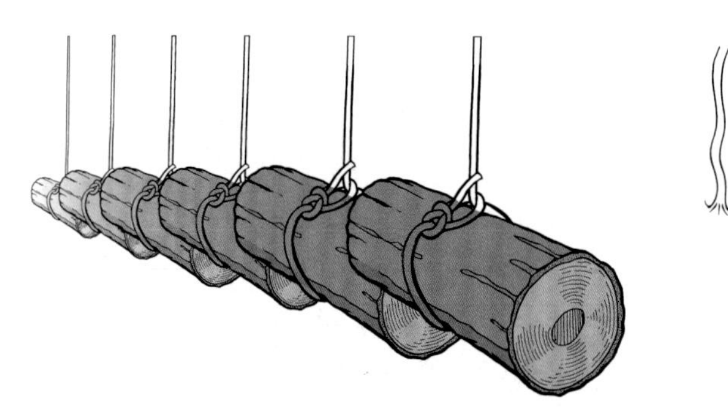

FIGURE 9.6 Each time a rope or piece of rigging equipment is used, it is considered one cycle. Every piece of equipment has a finite number of cycles to failure. That number decreases with increases in loads.

is equal to its tensile strength, the rope may fail when used only once (one cycle to failure).

A **design factor** (sometimes called safety factor) must be established based on the application and conditions of use. For arborist rigging, with dynamic loading, high wear, and dirty conditions, design factors of 5 to 7 for hardware and 10 or greater for textiles are often chosen. Dividing the published tensile strength of a rope or piece of equipment by the design factor yields the **working-load limit (WLL)**, which should not be exceeded. The working-load limit is significantly lower than the tensile strength. For example, if the published tensile strength of a piece of equipment is 20,000 lb (9,000 kg) and a design factor of 5 has been established, then the working-load limit will be 4,000 lb (1,800 kg) for that piece of equipment. It is important to keep in mind that the load on the equipment is often many times greater than the actual weight of the log!

Various components of any rigging system have different working-load limits, and it is important to consider each component. Arborists generally design rigging systems so that the rigging line (load line) is the weakest link in the system, then they avoid loading the rigging line beyond its WLL. Understanding the design and limitations of each piece of equipment employed, as well as the tree itself, is an important part of setting up a safe and efficient rigging system. Too often, arborists fail to think through the forces, loads, and direction of movement that might be involved in rigging out large limbs. The failure of any link in the system can have disastrous effects, including property damage, injuries, or even a fatality. Few practices in arboriculture are as involved or have as many potential risks as rigging; professional knowledge and experience are essential.

FIGURE 9.7 Arborists generally design rigging systems so that the rigging line (load line) is the weakest link in the system.

LEARNING THE ROPES

The "Ropes and Knots" chapter of this study guide contains a comparison of several rope types. Materials and construction methods are described briefly. Ropes used in rigging must have certain characteristics. They must be strong enough to support heavy loads; they must be durable enough to withstand the friction of being run over coarse bark while under load; and they must have limited stretch, because the dropping distance of the loads must be controlled. Arborists should limit their rope selections to those ropes that are recommended by manufacturers for tree care operations and, more specifically, rigging. The rigging line must be long enough to allow the ground worker to manage the line while standing outside the drop zone.

For rigging, the ropes selected must be large enough and strong enough for the job required. The working-load limit for new, unused ropes used in tree care procedures is often considered to be 10 percent of the tensile strength. This may need to be lowered for ropes that have seen a lot of use (many cycles). The working-load limit is an estimate of the limit at which a rope can be loaded safely and cycled repeatedly. Obviously, as a rope is worn by repeated use or subjected to shock-loading, its working-load limit will

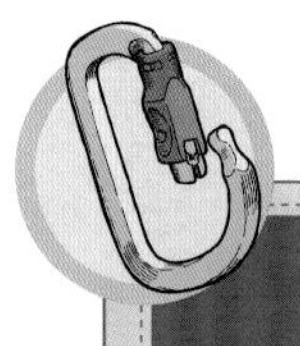

FACTORS THAT REDUCE THE STRENGTH OF A ROPE

- Use (cycles) and heavy loads, especially shock-loading
- Dirt, grit, chemicals, and foreign substances
- Abrasion, heat (friction), deformation, and torn fibers
- Knots and tight bends

decrease. Another important consideration is the use of knots. Knots tied in arborists' climbing or rigging lines can reduce the working-load limit by as much as 50 percent, depending on the knot used and the type of rope.

Remember that the tensile strength of a rope is determined by using a steady (static) load. In tree work, loading is rarely static. Ropes are often used to "catch" a moving (dropping) cut section of a tree. The farther the load drops, the greater the force on the rigging system (rope, hardware, and tree). Stopping a falling load puts a shock load (sudden dynamic load) on the rope that is much greater than the weight of the object itself. It is easy to exceed the working-load limit of the rope in this manner.

Ropes should always be inspected before use to look for cuts, deformation, shredding, or glazing (melted rope fiber), as well as inconsistencies in the rope diameter. Shock-loading or stretching can ruin a rope's construction. This may show up as lumps or as an hourglass-shaped narrowing in the rope.

FIGURE 9.8 Ropes should always be inspected before use to look for cuts, deformation, shredding, or glazing (melted rope fiber), as well as inconsistencies in the rope diameter.

Proper care of ropes is essential if they are to be relied upon. Ropes must never be stored near fuels, oils, salt, batteries, or chemicals. They must be kept away from sharp edges or pointed objects, such as pruning equipment and chain saws. Ropes are best kept clean and dry. The extended use of a dirty rope can accelerate wear of the fibers. When using wet ropes, the WLL should be reduced.

EQUIPMENT

Choosing appropriate equipment for a given rigging situation can make a job safer and much more productive, provided the science behind each device is understood. New equipment seems to come on the market every day. Some of this equipment has been adapted from other industries, and some has been designed for arborist uses. Arborists demand a great deal from equipment used in rigging, so using appropriate

FIGURE 9.9 Arborists need to understand the advantages and limitations of each piece of equipment, as well as how the components interface with each other, in order to select equipment appropriate to the job.

equipment within its design limitations and in the correct configuration is imperative. Arborists need to understand the advantages and limitations of each piece of equipment, as well as how the components interface with each other, in order to select equipment appropriate to the job.

Blocks and Pulleys

The terms **block** and **pulley** are sometimes used interchangeably. A pulley is a small wheel with a grooved rim (sheave) where a rope can run. Most pulleys require a separate connecting link to attach them to a rope or other equipment. The term "block" refers to heavy-duty pulleys that have an integrated connection point for attaching a rope sling. Many blocks are designed to be opened from the side to insert the bight of a rope. This is a nice feature because the worker can install the rope on the pulley midline and not have to run the rope through from the end.

Tree workers sometimes use blocks in rigging. A **block and tackle** can be used as part of a **mechanical advantage** system to increase the pulling power on a rope. More commonly, blocks are hung in trees to form a rigging point. This technique will be described later.

Using a block can provide many benefits over natural branch union rigging. It can reduce wear on the rigging lines. Friction created by running the ropes through branch unions can be virtually eliminated when the rope is run through a block instead. Blocks also offer a rigging point in places where a branch union was not available where needed. The use of blocks, when rigged correctly, can decrease the force needed to pull or lift an object. Compared to running lines through branch unions, blocks can decrease wear on ropes, give predictable friction, reduce dynamic loading, allow ropes to be loaded more evenly, and limit damage to the tree.

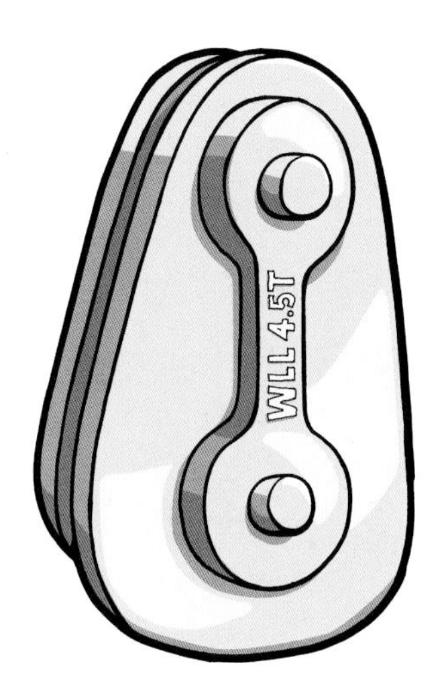

FIGURE 9.10 Arborist block with the manufacturer's recommended working-load limit (WLL).

Blocks and pulleys are constructed of steel, aluminum, or some combination of the two. Because these devices can be subjected to dynamic loading, strength and fatigue properties are a concern. **Arborist blocks** are heavy-duty pulleys with a large, rotating sheave for the lowering line and a smaller fixed sheave to accept a rope sling. Most significantly, the side plates of an arborist block extend beyond the sheaves to protect the line from abrasion.

Another type of pulley commonly used in arboriculture is the **rescue pulley**. Rescue pulleys are designed for static rigging, such as redirection of a line, mechanical advantage systems, and overhead rigging, where the loads are known and very low friction is required. They are not designed for heavy or dynamic loading, such as with a rigging point below the load.

It is important to consider rope type and size when using blocks in rigging. Workers should never try to squeeze an oversized rope or sling into a block; it will not function properly and could damage both the block and the rope.

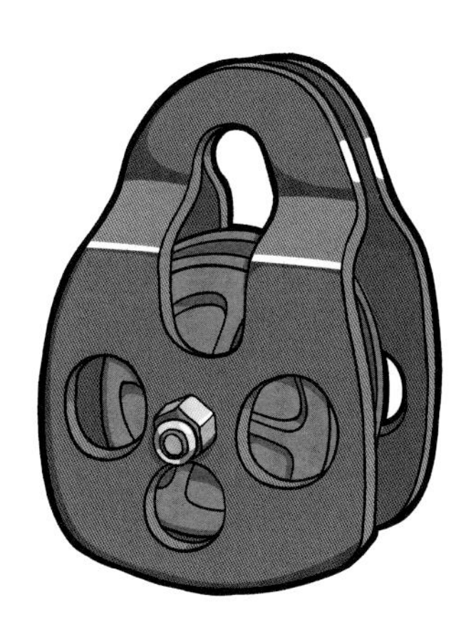

FIGURE 9.11 Rescue pulley.

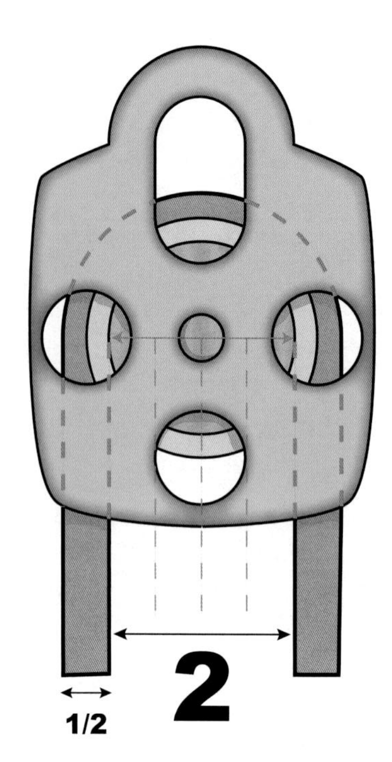

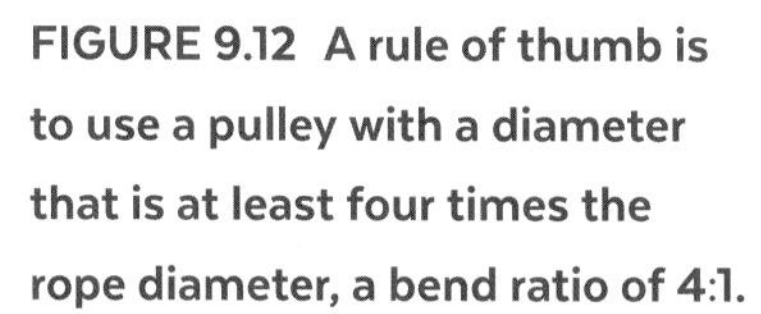
FIGURE 9.12 A rule of thumb is to use a pulley with a diameter that is at least four times the rope diameter, a bend ratio of 4:1.

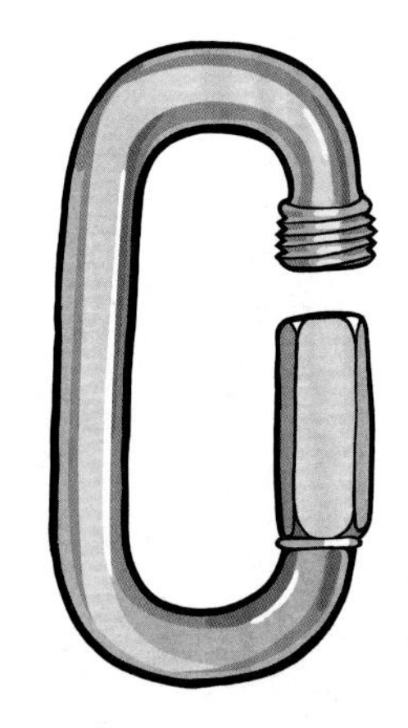
FIGURE 9.13 Screw link.

FIGURE 9.14 Clevis.

Another rule of thumb is to use a pulley with a sheave diameter that is at least four times the rope diameter, that is, a **bend ratio** of 4:1. This ratio will minimize the unequal tension in the rope fibers caused by forming tight bends. Braided ropes generally work better with blocks than 3-strand ropes do. Workers must be sure to inspect and maintain the blocks. A spur of metal can destroy a rigging line.

Connecting Links

Connecting links are used to make a faster or more convenient connection between a rope and another piece of equipment. Most connecting links are not designed for dynamic loading, which eliminates their use in most trunk- and top-removal operations.

While aluminum is preferred for climbing because of its light weight, steel has far better strength and fatigue properties. With heavy loads, many loading cycles, and the potential for dynamic loading, steel connecting links are an appropriate choice in rigging.

Screw links (also known as quick links) can be a useful tool for a connector that does not need to be opened frequently. They are strong for their compact size, but, as with other screw-locking connectors, there is the potential to open accidentally. Any configuration in which a rope may run over the screw gate should be avoided. Unlike screw-lock carabiners, the screw link can be secured with a wrench. As with all equipment, it is important to ensure that all connecting links are rated for the work to be done.

Clevises or **shackles** are common in industrial rigging. They are easily found in large sizes and are a good substitute when large screw links are not available. The constraints on their use are also similar to those of screw links.

Carabiners are used to attach or connect rigging equipment and ropes. They may be used to hang pulleys, secure ropes, or connect rigging devices together. Carabiners are available in a variety of sizes and strengths. Only heavy-duty steel carabiners should be used in rigging operations, and carabiners with **locking** or **double-locking gates** should be selected. Carabiners must always be loaded along their major axes. This reduces the stress on the gate, which is the weakest point of the carabiner. Note that the rated tensile strength of a carabiner is based on loading along the major axis. When loaded in any other manner, the carabiner will not be as strong. Carabiners should be inspected regularly, including a check to see that the gate is functioning properly.

Slings

A **sling** is a loop of rope, sewn nylon tubing or webbing, or a section of **eye-spliced rope** designed

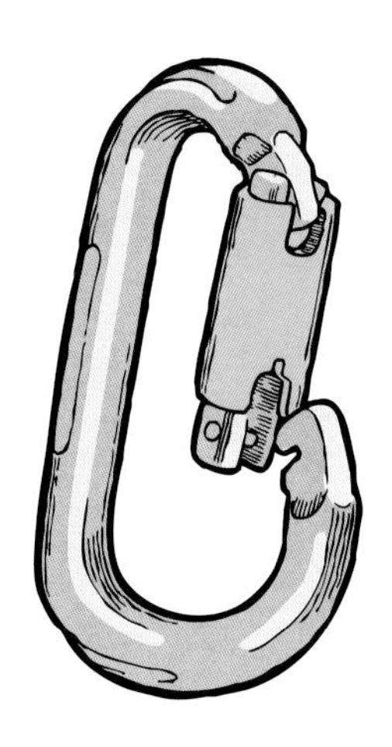

FIGURE 9.15 Carabiners are available in a variety of sizes and strengths. Only heavy-duty steel carabiners should be used in rigging operations, and carabiners with locking or double-locking gates should be selected.

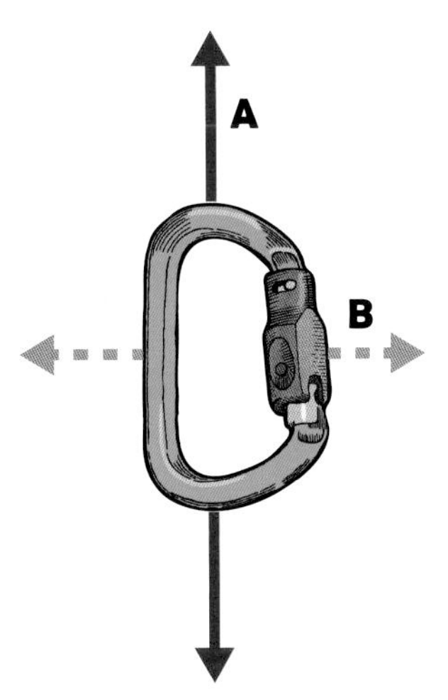

FIGURE 9.16 Major axis (A) and minor axis (B). Carabiners must always be loaded along the major axis.

as a quick, convenient way to attach ropes, tools, and equipment together or to tree parts. Slings come in a variety of sizes and lengths. Most arborist slings are capable of withstanding heavy loads. Usually a webbing sling is placed in a tree by wrapping it around the limb and looping it upon itself in a choker fashion (**girth hitch**), although there are other ways to configure a webbing loop sling.

An alternative to using a webbing sling is the use of an eye-spliced rope (**dead-eye sling**) to secure rigging in a tree. It may be attached to the tree using a cow hitch, a timber hitch, or various other knots. The "eye" of the sling is used to hang the block or other rigging equipment, and can usually be girth-hitched to hardware. The load line should never be passed through the eye of a sling, creating an unwanted rope-on-rope configuration. Slings also can be spliced with an eye at both ends. In larger diameters, these slings are useful in balancing limbs; in smaller diameters, they are useful to tie a midline attachment to

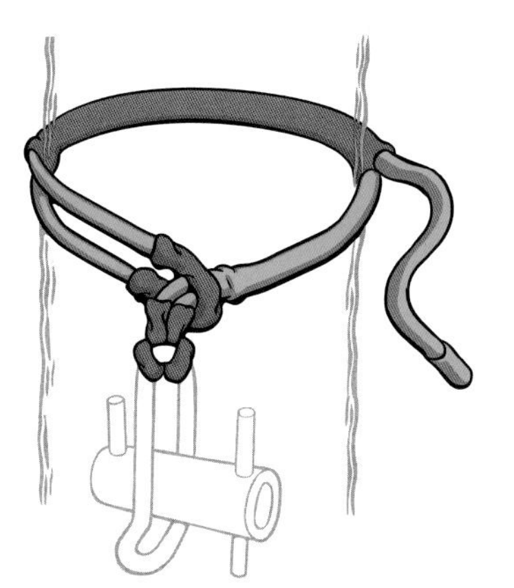

FIGURE 9.17 Rigging hardware can be secured to the base of a tree or a branch by using a sling, including a whoopie sling (pictured here).

another line. Another variation is the adjustable **eye-and-eye sling**, sometimes called a "**whoopie sling**." This type of sling has a fixed eye and an adjustable eye, which allows for great versatility in length adjustment.

Friction Devices

Arborists rely on friction to help control loads when lowering branches out of a tree. Historically, rigging lines were wrapped around the trunk of the tree to add some friction. It takes experience to get this right, because not all trees are alike and carrying armfuls of rope around the tree has never been much fun. **Friction devices** have been designed for tree work, and they have some obvious control advantages over taking wraps around the tree. The wear on the rope is much less and damage to the tree can be avoided. Also, taking up the slack is easier. With a friction device, wraps can be taken in the middle of the rope.

Designed specifically for tree work, the Port-a-Wrap III™ is a portable friction device for use in lowering limbs. It is available in steel or aluminum. It is attached to the tree with a sling, and the rigging line is wrapped around it to add friction for controlling the tree section to be lowered.

In tree work, a **bollard** is a heavy-duty cylinder that straps to the tree and is used for taking wraps in a **load line**. As with the Port-a-Wrap™, the number of wraps needed varies with the size of the tree section to be lowered. The large diameter of the cylinder provides a favorable bend ratio, which minimizes strength loss in the rigging line. This type of device is more appropriate than a Port-a-Wrap™ for very heavy loads.

Some bollard-type lowering devices are designed with a ratcheting system that allows the arborist to remove slack from the line or even lift a load and then lower it. The Hobbs Lowering Device™ is an example of a ratcheting bollard.

FIGURE 9.18 **Friction devices have been designed for tree work, and they have some obvious control advantages over taking wraps around the tree. The wear on the rope is much less, and damage to the tree can be avoided. With a friction device, wraps can be taken in the middle of the rope.**

The Good Rigging Control System (GRCS)™ is a self-tailing nautical winch that can be mounted on a tree. The winch provides a powerful, efficient means of lifting. The modular design allows a fixed aluminum bollard to replace the winch in the frame strapped to the tree for use in controlling friction when there will be heavy shock-loading. This will save wear on the winch.

A number of other devices have been developed for similar rigging or belaying purposes. Most are designed with steel or aluminum piping, around which wraps can be taken with a rope. They are significantly less expensive than heavy-duty lowering devices, but most should not be used for heavy loads.

Any friction device dissipates energy from the falling wood by converting it to heat, rather than stretching the rigging line. Therefore, arborists must be aware of possible heat damage (glazing) to rigging lines running on metal surfaces. Some bollards are designed with cooling systems to help with heat dissipation.

As with all equipment, it is important to receive proper training before using these devices. Most manufacturers provide instructions and safety precautions for use. A new piece of equipment or technique should not be put in service without first gaining experience by using it in situations where damage is unlikely.

BASIC RIGGING TECHNIQUES

Knowledge and experience will improve a climber's arsenal of rigging techniques. As learning progresses, a climber will come to understand more of the variables to be considered. It is important for novice riggers to be introduced to the thought processes involved in planning a rigging operation. What are the limitations of the tree and site? What equipment and techniques will be employed? Skill in planning for different options comes with experience and can make rigging operations safer and more efficient.

The tools and techniques used in rigging vary with the situation. When removing limbs from a tree that is being pruned, care must be taken not to damage the remaining branches and trunk. When rigging for removal, the climber has more options in how to work the tree.

Sometimes the branches or wood to be removed can be landed safely on the ground without the use of ropes or rigging, that is, by using the **cut-and-chuck method**.

If pieces must be roped down, the generally preferred technique is to position the rigging point above the work. This technique helps minimize the load on the rigging line and provides more control of the piece. A load line (rigging line) is run through a rigging point above the limb or piece to be removed and then tied to the piece.

The simplest form of rigging involves the use of ropes, wraps on the trunk, and natural branch unions as rigging points. More sophisticated techniques require a better understanding of the advantages and limitations of the equipment and methods involved.

There is always more than one way to get the wood and brush to the ground, but the best method is the one that is both safe and productive. An investment in equipment and education about the science behind the equipment can pay off by making the work easier, reducing wear on tools, and allowing larger sections to be removed safely.

The first choice to be made is whether to run ropes through a natural branch union or through a block installed as a rigging point. Natural unions can be fast and effective, but the running rope can injure the tree (if it is not being removed) and increases wear on the rope. Because of this friction, only ropes that are resistant to abrasion should be used. Another disadvantage to natural branch union rigging is that the amount of friction is not very predictable.

Installing a Block as a Rigging Point

The use of arborist blocks for rigging points has gained widespread use—and with good reason. They provide more consistent friction than natural branch unions. Also, because there is minimal friction with an arborist block, the entire rigging line can function to distribute the load in the line. Placement is not limited to the location of natural branch unions.

The block should be as high as practical and away from the climber's tie-in point. Having more rope in the system can reduce shock load. Therefore, height can be an advantage for force reduction. The rigging point and the climber's tie-in point should always be in different parts of the tree whenever possible. Whenever possible, the block is positioned so limbs swing away from the climber and obstacles. Ideally, the rigging point is positioned so that the piece being removed will not become entangled in the rigging, the climber's line, or other parts of the tree. The block should be placed so that the rigging line will not contact the climbing line, because a running rigging line can damage or melt a climbing line. Care must be exercised when setting blocks away from the main stem. Bending from the reaction forces on limbs can cause limb failure.

The spliced-eye rope sling that holds the block should have a working-load limit *twice* that of the rigging line. Reaction forces at the block (and its attachment point) can be as much as twice the load in the rigging line (discounting friction).

FIGURE 9.19 **The spliced-eye rope sling that holds the block should have a working-load limit twice that of the rigging line. Reaction forces at the block (and its attachment point) can be as much as twice the load in the rigging line (discounting friction).**

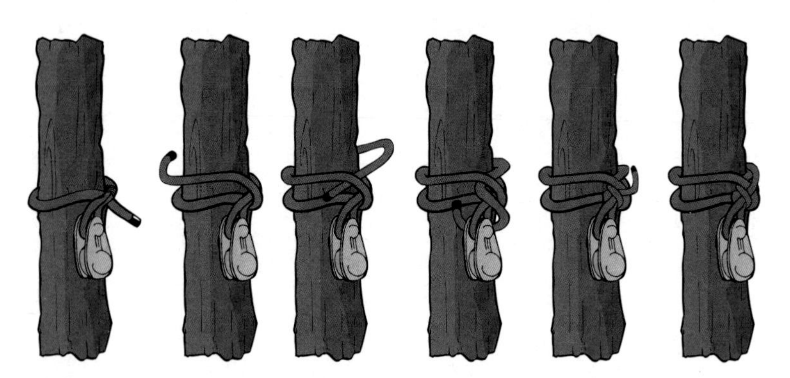

FIGURE 9.20 **An arborist block can be attached to a tree using a sling tied with a cow hitch.**

The block is usually attached to the tree with a **cow hitch**, which is essentially a girth hitch with a **half hitch** tied around the splice so it jams against the bight formed earlier. Then, excess rope is wrapped between the tree and the turns of the hitch. It is important to make sure that the rigging sling used to attach the block is snug and tight to minimize dynamic loading at the block and attachment point.

Tying Off the Wood

Most limbs or wood sections are tied off with one of two knots, a **running bowline** or a **clove hitch** with two half hitches. A running bowline is easily tied and removed, even after loading. It can be tied at a distance from the desired attachment point and pulled along the line to where it is cinched. If a clove hitch is used, it must be followed up with two half hitches to prevent the hitch from rolling out and losing the load. With a clove hitch, bends in the knot are more favorable (less strength loss) than with the running bowline, but it takes longer to tie and untie than the running bowline.

FIGURE 9.21 **Most limbs or wood sections are tied off with one of two knots, a running bowline or a clove hitch with two half hitches.**

If the rigging line is attached at the butt end of the piece to be removed, it is said to be **butt-tied**. The piece will normally drop tip down. The climber must be positioned to avoid contact with the rigging line or being hit by the butt of the branch.

FIGURE 9.22 If the rigging line is attached at the butt end of the piece to be removed, it is said to be butt-tied. The piece will normally drop tip down.

Tip-tying attaches the rigging line toward the tip of the branch being removed. If the limb is tip-tied and cut, the butt end will drop away from the cut, and the swing of the limb will depend on the placement of the rigging point. The climber must be positioned to avoid being struck by the swinging limb. A limb might also be tip-tied and lifted to avoid hitting an obstacle below.

At times, it is essential to minimize the swing or drop of a limb. Rather than tip-tying or butt-tying, a separate rope tool can be used to **balance** the limb, keeping either the butt or tip from dropping. Balancing can also help reduce swing and dynamic loading. An advantage is that it may allow the climber to remove a limb as one piece. Also, dynamic loading can be minimized, especially if the rigging point is directly above the work. Various types of equipment and procedures can be used with this technique.

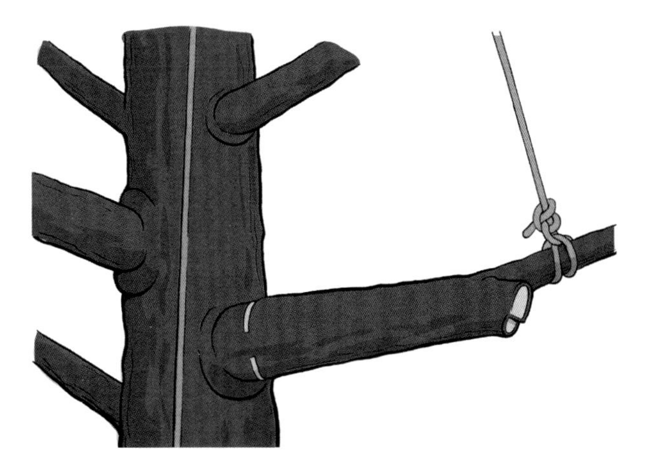

FIGURE 9.23 If the rigging line is attached at the tip of the piece to be removed, it is said to be tip-tied. The piece will normally drop butt down.

FIGURE 9.24 Rather than tip-tying or butt-tying, a separate rope tool can be used to balance the limb, helping reduce swing and dynamic loading.

A balancer can be nothing more than a length of rope tied to the limb at the tip and butt with running bowlines (or other means of attachment). A separate loop is tied into a Prusik at the center and provides a way to adjust in order to find the balance point. The rigging line can have either a loop tied into the end or an eye splice to clip a heavy-duty steel carabiner (or other heavy-duty connecting link) to the Prusik loop. Other techniques incorporate a section of rope (a spider leg

FIGURE 9.25 Another balancing technique incorporates one or more sections of rope (spider leg balancers) attached to the lowering line using friction hitches, with the ends of the spider legs and the lowering line attached to the butt and tips of the pieces. Adjusting the friction hitches provides a means of balancing the load.

balancer) attached to the lowering line via a friction hitch, with the ends of the spider leg and the lowering line attached to the butt and tip of the piece and the friction hitch providing a means of balancing the load. Whatever technique is used,

FIGURE 9.26 A tagline may be attached to help the ground worker control the piece being removed.

it is a good idea to consider whether the limb will swing and whether a tagline is needed.

A **tagline/pull line** is a rope tied to the piece to be removed and controlled by a ground worker, but which is neither run through a rigging point nor used for lowering. A tagline may be used with any of the other techniques.

It can be attached at any point to help control the swing or direction of the limb, or it may be pulled or tied off to prevent unwanted movement. A tagline may be attached to pull over the top of a tree (pull line) or pulled to cause a limb to swing in a particular direction (as with a limb hinged to the side).

As mentioned previously, it is always preferable to establish a rigging point above the work. There are situations, however, where a rigging line cannot be anchored above the work, such as in removals. After the last of the branches is removed, the climber no longer has an overhead rigging point to use. Without any overhead options, all rigging points will be below the piece of wood being cut. Rigging from below, sometimes called butt-hitching or negative rigging, is a common technique in which a piece is tied with the rigging line above the point where it will be cut and the line is run through a block or branch union below the cut. This can be one of the most

FIGURE 9.27 Rigging from below (negative rigging) is a technique in which a piece is tied with the rigging line above the point where it will be cut and the line is run through a block or branch union below the cut.

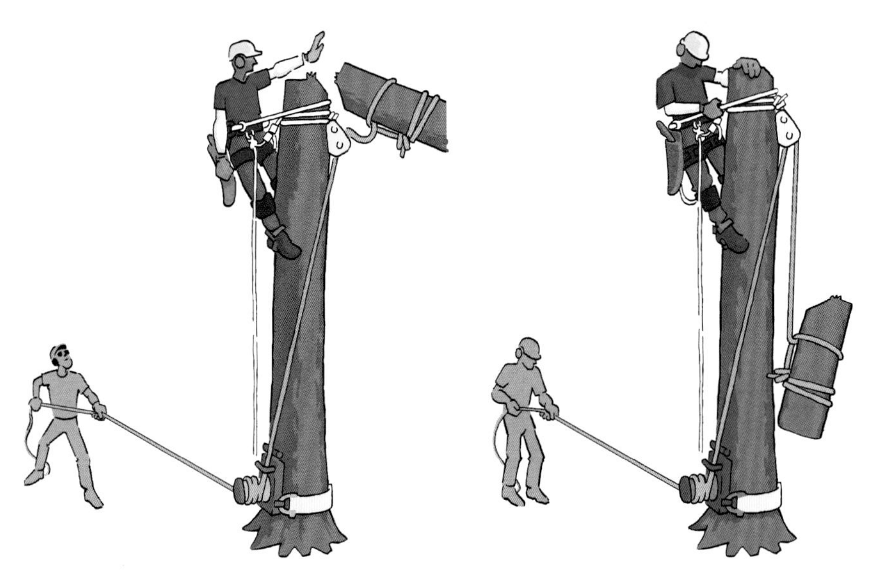

FIGURE 9.28 Rigging from below can be one of the most demanding techniques for a rope (as well as the hardware and the tree) because of the potential for shock-loading.

demanding techniques for a rope (as well as the hardware and the tree) because of shock-loading. Because there are no high tie-in points, it can also be dangerous for the climber. Specific training for this technique is essential.

This text is introductory in nature and presents only the most basic of rigging techniques. Arborists wanting to advance their skill and knowledge of rigging should seek qualified, hands-on training and are encouraged to study *The Art and Science of Practical Rigging*, an eight-part video series and study guide published by the International Society of Arboriculture. This series details many of the more advanced rigging techniques and discusses the science involved.

FIGURE 9.29 When using a chain saw, arborists often form the top cut directly above the undercut to avoid getting the bar stuck in the kerf of the cut as the limb breaks free.

CUTTING TECHNIQUES

Once the limb is rigged for removal, the climber must decide on the appropriate method of cutting the limb. The **drop cut**—the classic three-point cut—dates back to the early years of arboriculture and appears in almost every pruning text as the recommended technique for removing large limbs. It consists of an undercut and a top cut farther out on the limb, then a final cut to remove the stub after the limb has been removed. When using a chain saw, arborists often form the top cut directly above the undercut to avoid getting the bar stuck in the **kerf** of the cut as the limb breaks free.

A cut that is handy for controlling relatively small sections of wood that may not require roping is the **snap cut** (bypass cut). This cut is made by cutting slightly more than halfway through a section from one side, then cutting from the opposite side, about an inch or more offset from the first cut. The distance apart will need to be larger for larger limbs. The two cuts will bypass, but the fibers should hold. The saw can then be shut off and the remaining piece broken off manually. A snap cut can be made on the top and bottom sides of a branch stub from a large branch that has been removed.

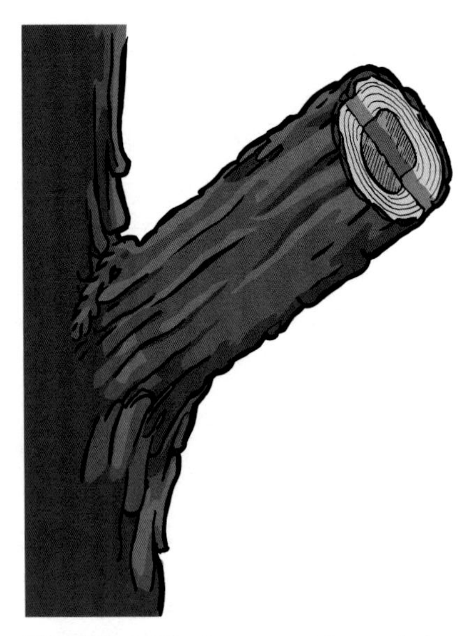

FIGURE 9.30 A snap cut is made by cutting slightly more than halfway through a section from the side, then cutting from the opposite side, about an inch or more offset from the first cut.

The **hinge cut** is a variation of standard tree-felling techniques (described in Chapter 10) and is referred to as a topping cut when taking a vertical top out of a tree. It employs the use of a **notch** and back cut to form a hinge that controls the direction the limb falls. It can be used to swing a limb around rather than simply dropping the branch to the ground. Unless the limb is supported with a rigging line, there is a limit to how much the climber will be able to swing the limb before the hinge breaks. If the hinge is formed too far around the side of the limb, the hinge may be ineffective and may break before the limb swings.

FIGURE 9.31 A hinge cut employs the use of a notch and back cut to form a hinge that controls the direction the limb falls.

The strategy for piecing out a tree depends on the circumstances. The climber must plan the order of removal to avoid being left with a limb that is too difficult or dangerous to remove. A general rule of thumb is to clear a pathway for the limbs, removing brush first. It is often better to leave a few limbs with brush for **damping** the rigging forces (dissipating the energy), especially when taking out the top. Removing the easiest limbs first can sometimes cause problems when trying to rig limbs later.

As with all aspects of removal, the key to safety is to use equipment that can handle the load and to ensure that the tree can handle the load. It is important to understand that the choices made in rigging setup can affect the loads experienced. Workers must avoid trying to take out a section that is too big. The whole crew should always consider what could happen if some component of the rigging failed. The climber and all ground workers must be clear of danger in the event of something breaking unexpectedly.

FIGURE 9.32 Small "kerf" cuts can be made to prevent the fibers from tearing too far back and damaging limbs that will remain.

ROLE OF THE GROUND WORKER

Ground workers are an essential part of a rigging operation; they set up friction devices, run lines, detach ropes, and send equipment and lines up to the climber. Safety is dependent on good communication between the climber and the ground workers. Ground workers can monitor the steps of the rigging process and play a key role in reducing the likelihood of mistakes.

The **drop zone (landing zone)** is the area beneath the tree where pieces are to be dropped or lowered. The drop zone must allow for swing, roll, or bounce of pieces being removed. Some companies create a visual boundary for the drop zone by marking it with cones or some other visual marker. This helps to identify it as a place of caution and acts as a visual reminder for crew members to communicate with the climber before entering the landing zone.

There must be a clear and efficient means of communication between climbers and ground workers so that each knows when it is safe for a ground worker to enter the drop zone. The voice **command-and-response system** ensures that warning signals are heard, acknowledged, and acted upon. The climber warns, "Stand clear," but does not proceed until hearing the acknowledgment, "All clear." It is best if one person on the ground is assigned the task of ensuring that all workers are clear before giving the response. Additionally, when ground workers want to enter the drop zone, they must communicate with the climber to indicate that they want to come underneath and must wait for the acknowledgment before entering.

The ground worker's primary role in rigging operations is "running the ropes." The ground worker takes wraps with the rigging line, either on the trunk of a tree or on a friction device. These wraps add friction into the system for controlled lowering.

FIGURE 9.33 The drop zone (landing zone) is the area beneath the tree where pieces are to be dropped or lowered. Ground workers must be aware of what is happening at all times, including where they are standing and how the ropes and cut pieces are moving.

FIGURE 9.34 The voice command-and-response system ensures that warning signals are heard, acknowledged, and acted upon. The climber warns, "Stand clear," but does not proceed until hearing the acknowledgment, "All clear."

HANDLING THE ROPES IN RIGGING

Never wrap a line around any part of your body or stand where you could be entangled in running lines.

Once a piece is cut and begins to fall, it will create a dynamic load on the rigging line. A skillful ground worker can minimize this effect by gradually letting out more rigging line into the system before bringing the piece to a gradual stop. This is called "letting it run," and it is a skill that should be practiced. It can be used only if the situation allows for the piece to be lowered in this manner. Ground workers should wear gloves made of leather or other heat-resistant material when running rigging lines.

It is common sense not to stand under the piece being lowered, but that is not enough. All workers must consider the direction the load will drop or swing and what would happen if any element of the rigging system failed or if a section of the tree were to break off. This means staying "outside" of the rigging so that if a rope snaps or a piece of equipment breaks, nobody will be struck. Ground workers must never stand on a rope or in a position where the rope feeds from behind them to reduce the likelihood of getting caught in the rope as it "runs." The climber's line must be kept from becoming tangled in rigging lines or limbs on the ground. Rope bags are a big help in keeping the lines clear and clean.

In addition to sending up equipment and running and returning the lines, ground workers can also assist the climber in judging distances and loads and in selecting methods. Climbers and ground workers function most safely and efficiently when they learn to work as a team.

KEY CONCEPTS

1. Managing friction is the key to controlling loads in all rigging operations.
2. Dynamic loads damage ropes and other equipment more quickly than equivalent static loads. Stopping a falling load puts a shock load (sudden dynamic load) on the rope, hardware, and the tree that is much greater than the weight of the object itself.
3. Understanding the design and limitations of each piece of equipment employed, as well as the tree itself, is an important part of setting up a safe and efficient rigging system.
4. Using an arborist block as a rigging point provides more consistent friction than using a natural branch union. More of the rigging line length can function to absorb loads, and wear on the rigging line is reduced. Placement is not limited to the location of natural branch unions.
5. Rigging from above the load is preferred, when possible, because rigging from below can create large, dynamic loads.
6. Proficiency in rigging comes with good training and experience. Understanding the potential loads and selecting appropriate equipment, rigging methods, tying techniques, and cutting techniques can help manage friction and the loads experienced.
7. Managing the placement of workers on the jobsite is just as important as the placement of equipment in the tree. Make sure the lines of communication are established before beginning rigging operations.

WORKBOOK

MATCHING 1

_____ tensile strength	A. rope that controls swing of piece
_____ clevis/shackle	B. heavy-duty pulley for rigging
_____ sling	C. breaking strength under static load
_____ arborist block	D. attach rope to the far (brush) end of limb
_____ shock load	E. length of rope or webbing to attach hardware
_____ butt-tied	F. used to connect ropes and equipment
_____ tip-tie	G. strong, sudden dynamic load
_____ tagline	H. tied off at large end of limb

TRUE/FALSE

1. T F Shock-loading results when ropes are used to stop heavy limbs in motion or free fall.
2. T F The greater distance a limb drops before its motion is stopped, the greater the load on the rope, hardware, and tree.
3. T F The use of knots increases the working-load limit of a rope.
4. T F Dividing the published tensile strength of a rope or piece of equipment by the design factor yields the working-load limit (WLL).
5. T F Tensile strength is determined under a static load.
6. T F Dynamic loads can damage ropes, equipment, and trees more quickly than equivalent static loads.
7. T F Heat and friction are not a problem with synthetic ropes.
8. T F Carabiners are always oval and aluminum, and have a spring-loaded, auto-locking gate.
9. T F Compared to running lines through natural branch unions, blocks can decrease wear on ropes, reduce dynamic loading, and limit damage to the tree.
10. T F Rescue pulleys are heavy-duty pulleys, with a large rotating sheave for the lowering line and a smaller fixed sheave to accept a rope sling.
11. T F The advantages of friction devices over taking wraps on the tree trunk include reduced wear on the rope and ease of taking up slack.

12. T F In tree work, a bollard is a cylinder that straps to the tree and is used for taking wraps in a load line.
13. T F Using pulleys can reduce the wear on rigging lines.
14. T F If the load line is rigged at the brushy end of a limb, it is butt-tied.
15. T F Taglines, or pull lines, are used for lowering heavy limbs.
16. T F An advantage to balancing a limb is that it can help reduce swing and dynamic loading.
17. T F A hinge cut is made by cutting slightly more than halfway through a section from the side, then cutting from the opposite side, about an inch or more offset from the first cut.
18. T F A cut that is handy for controlling relatively small sections of wood that may not require roping is the snap cut.
19. T F A skillful ground worker can minimize the effect of dynamic loading created by stopping a falling limb with the rigging line by "letting it run."
20. T F Ground workers should never wear gloves when operating the ropes in rigging operations.

MATCHING 2

_____ drop cut	A. force opposite the relative motion
_____ running bowline	B. used to take wraps on load line
_____ snap cut	C. area where pieces are dropped or lowered
_____ friction device	D. classic three-point cut
_____ drop zone	E. forces on stationary objects
_____ mechanical advantage	F. knot used to tie off limbs
_____ statics	G. can multiply pulling power
_____ friction	H. bypassing cuts made from opposite sides

SAMPLE TEST QUESTIONS

1. An advantage to using an installed block instead of a natural branch union as a rigging point is
   a. more flexibility in placement of the rigging point
   b. the friction is more controlled
   c. it minimizes damage to the tree
   d. all of the above

2. The reaction force at the rigging block can be

   a. approximately half the load in the rigging line
   b. approximately twice the load in the rigging line
   c. greater when lifting limbs
   d. increased if a low-friction block is used

3. Dynamic loads in a rigging system are a concern because

   a. the load can be many times the weight of the piece
   b. shock-loading is tougher than static-loading on ropes and hardware
   c. they can be more difficult to estimate or predict
   d. all of the above

CHAPTER

10

REMOVAL

LEARNING OBJECTIVES

The tree worker will be able to:

- Summarize the steps required for safe tree felling.
- Describe techniques used for estimating tree height.
- Contrast the types of notches and back cuts.
- Explain how the hinge formed by the notch and back cut controls a tree's fall.
- Discuss the precautions used for safe limbing and bucking of felled trees.

IMPORTANT TERMS

back cut
barber chair
block and tackle
bore cut
bucking
cant hook
conventional notch
escape route
hinge
Humboldt notch
limbing
mechanical advantage
notch
open-face notch
peavey
pull line
tagline

INTRODUCTION

Tree removal is a significant part of the tree care profession. Trees may have to be removed for a variety of reasons. Often, trees must be removed because they pose a hazard to people or structures. Some trees have to be removed for future construction. The most obvious reason for removal is the death of the tree in a location where the dead tree poses an unacceptable risk.

Rigging concepts and techniques were described in the "Rigging" chapter. This chapter focuses on felling and the important preparations and planning that must take place before any cuts are made. The techniques and cuts used to fell a tree are explained. Limbing and bucking, the process of cutting up the felled tree, are also explored. As always, the primary emphasis is safety.

FIGURE 10.1 Before beginning, always inspect the tree and site for potential hazards and obstacles, or anything that could affect the removal operation.

PREPARATION

Assessment of the Tree and Site

Before beginning any felling operation, it is important to inspect the tree and site and to check for potential hazards. As with all tree care operations, a job briefing and work plan are essential before beginning work. The surrounding area should be checked and cleared of movable obstacles, such as lawn furniture and play equipment. Tree height and width of the crown must be noted. There must be no doubt of adequate space to fell the tree. The tree feller must also be aware of any utility lines in the vicinity. The feller has to consider the possibility of branches breaking off upon impact and being hurled from the tree. If necessary, windows and other structures in the area must be protected. It is also important to protect underground utilities, such as septic tanks and sprinkler heads.

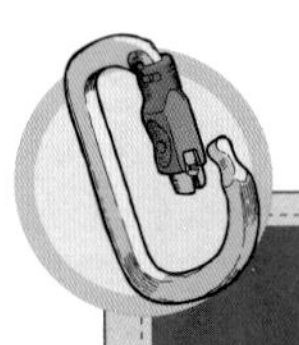

> **PRE-FELLING SITE AND TREE INSPECTION**
>
> Identify:
>
> - Electrical conductors and communication lines
> - Obstacles and structures
> - Potential safety hazards
> - Tree conditions such as cavities, decay, dead or broken limbs, hanging branches, cracks, etc.
> - Size and lean of the tree
> - Safe path for an escape route

It is essential to consider the condition of the tree, being aware of decay, broken or dead branches, cracks, cavities, vines, and other defects or conditions that may affect the felling operation. Extra precautions must be taken when felling decayed or hollow trees to control the direction of fall.

The shape and lean of the tree are important. These factors affect not only the felling direction but also where the saw operator should stand when making the cut. If there is side lean, for example, the feller may want to adjust the aim of the face notch and should finish the felling cut on the side opposite the lean. Forward or back lean can affect the choice of notch angle and back cut, whether to employ felling wedges, and the risks involved. It is also important to take the weight distribution of the crown into account. An experienced tree worker is familiar with the properties of various trees, such as wood strength and weight.

Another important factor to consider is the direction of the wind and its force. Is it steady and regular or gusty? A strong gust of wind can alter the direction in which a tree falls. It may be best to avoid felling operations on very windy days.

When a tree is felled, it has the potential to cause damage where it lands. To avoid damage to turf, pavement, or landscape plantings, tree workers often lay cut limbs and/or brush in the landing zone to cushion the falling tree or protect obstacles.

Estimation of Height

It is important for tree workers to be able to estimate the height of the tree (and thus its position when felled). Accurate height estimation will help avoid hitting obstacles. It is important to consider that the height of the felling cut will affect the distance that the top of the tree reaches when it is felled.

> **TIP!**
>
> **THE STICK METHOD**
>
> Hold the stick so that the distance from your eye to your hand equals the distance from your hand to the top of the stick. Hold your arm horizontally and the stick vertically. Walk forward or backward until the distance from your hand to the top of the stick is proportional (visually equal) to the distance from the felling cut to the top of the tree.

Most techniques for height estimation are based upon a geometric principle of similar right triangles. There are devices and cell phone apps available to assist workers with height estimation. A simple field technique employs nothing more than a straight stick. The technique is known as the stick method (see "TIP" box).

There are some limitations to the stick method of height estimation. The estimation technique assumes that the tree is vertical, the ground is level, and the top of the tree can be seen. Also, it may be necessary to adjust for the difference

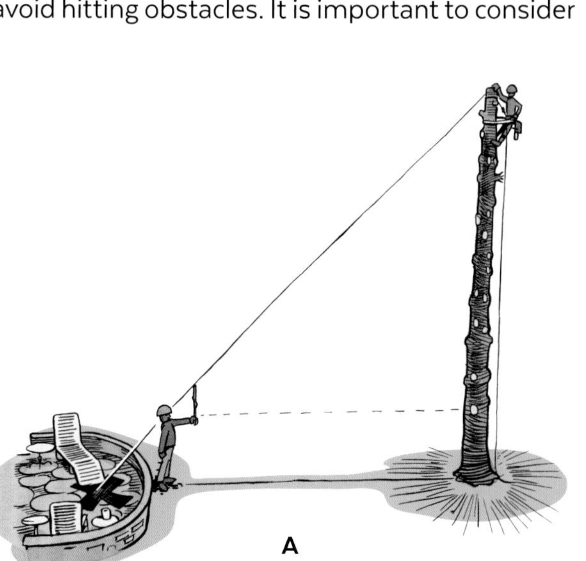

FIGURE 10.2 (A) Most techniques for height estimation are based upon a geometric principle of similar right triangles. (B) Find the position at which the distance from your hand to the top of the stick visually equals the height of the tree from the cut.

between the viewing height and the height of the felling cut.

Planning

Once the site has been prepared and the tree inspected, the felling operation should be planned. The workers must decide what method will be used to fell the tree and what equipment will be needed. Planning also includes determining the direction of fall, considering the need for a pull line, figuring out what types of cuts will be used and where they will be placed, deciding whether felling wedges will be employed, securing the site, and establishing where all workers need to be positioned for their duties. All workers must have a clear understanding of their responsibilities.

FIGURE 10.3 A pull line can be installed without climbing the tree and will offer additional control in tree felling.

Many times, in the conditions under which arborists work, trees must be rigged for removal. Other times, they can be felled using a **tagline** (**pull line**) for added control. A pull line can often be installed without climbing the tree. A pull line can be set using a throwline to get a line in the desired branch union. The pull line can then be attached to the throwline and pulled through a branch union. A running bowline can be tied at ground level and pulled up into the tree. Workers must ensure that the pull of the line is in a direct line that will not create a twisting or torquing pull. If the line detours around a limb, creating a dogleg in the line, the tree may pivot, breaking the hinge and misdirecting the fall. Another technique is to install the pull line in the tree and tie it off at the base. The advantages of this technique are that the line can be moved to another position in the tree, if necessary, and can be tied in a configuration to avoid twisting. A disadvantage is that it requires a longer rope.

FIGURE 10.4 A pulley added to the system can create mechanical advantage when rigged correctly.

FIGURE 10.5 A mechanical advantage system, such as a block and tackle, may be used to apply extra tension to a line.

FIGURE 10.6 Workers who are not directly involved in the removal operation should be two tree lengths away from the tree being felled. Those involved, including those on the tagline, must be at least one and a half tree lengths away, have an established means of communication with the feller, and have a planned escape route.

The amount of forward or back lean of the tree should be considered when estimating the amount of pull needed. **Mechanical advantage** systems such as a **block and tackle** may be used to apply extra tension to a line or to compensate for the lean of a tree. Felling wedges, another form of mechanical advantage, are sometimes employed to aid in felling the tree.

Workers who are not directly involved in the removal operation should be at least two tree lengths away from the tree being felled. Those involved, including those on the tagline, must be at least one and a half tree lengths away, have an established means of communication with the feller, and have a planned escape route. The preferred **escape route** for the chain saw operator in a felling operation is 45° on either side of a line drawn opposite the intended direction of fall. The escape route should be cleared of debris and obstacles prior to cutting. When the tree starts to fall, the chain saw operator should move away in this direction while maintaining eye contact with the fall of the tree.

FIGURE 10.7 The preferred escape route for the chain saw operator in a felling operation is 45° on either side of a line drawn opposite the intended direction of fall.

FELLING

The Notch, the Hinge, and the Back Cut

Trees should be felled using a **notch** and **back cut**. Together, the notch and the back cut establish the **hinge**. Felling notches and back cuts should be made high enough above ground level to enable the chain saw operator to begin the cut safely, control the saw, and have freedom of movement for escape. A number of notch configurations can be used for felling trees, including an **open-face notch**, a **conventional notch**, and a **Humboldt notch**. Historically, a 45° (conventional) notch was the most widely used notch, based on cutting techniques that predated the chain saw. However, a conventional notch does not allow the hinge to work long enough to maintain control of the tree all the way to the ground. An open-face notch of

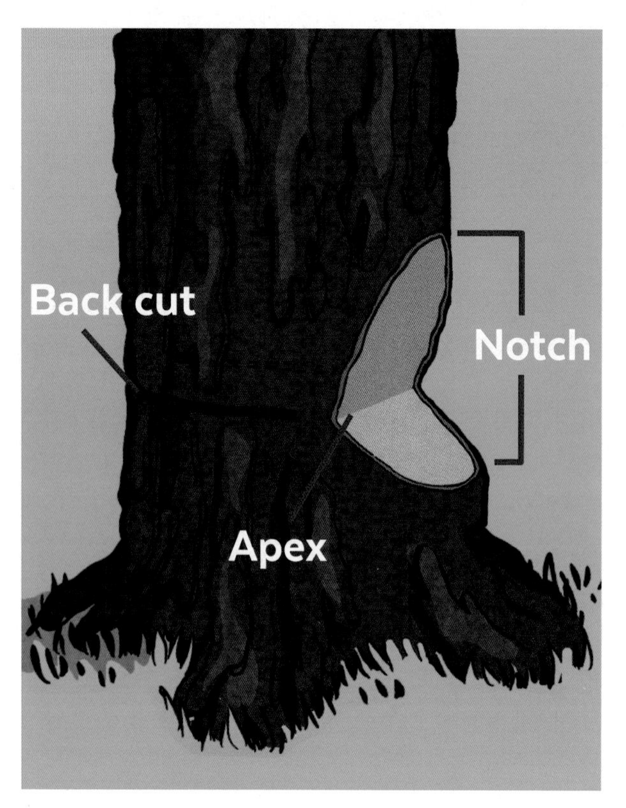

FIGURE 10.8 Trees should be felled using a notch and back cut. Together, the notch and the back cut establish the hinge.

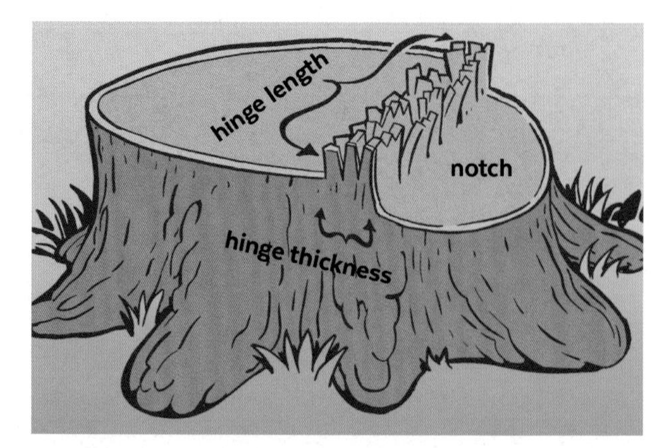

FIGURE 10.9 The hinge length should be about 80 percent of the tree's diameter. The rule of thumb for hinge thickness is about 10 percent of the tree's diameter.

70° or more allows the hinge to control the tree longer. The amount of face notch opening affects how long the hinge will control the direction of fall. In most trees, 70° is sufficient, but in a tree with heavy back lean, a notch of 90° may provide longer control.

A rule of thumb for the depth of the notch is 20 to 25 percent of the diameter of the tree. Remember: a small notch can be enlarged, but it is impossible to correct a notch that is too deep. The length of the hinge should be about 80 percent of the tree's diameter. If possible, the notch should not be placed in the vicinity of cracks, decay, or cankers, because it is important to have solid fiber to form the hinge. When cutting the notch, it is very easy to bypass the apex—the point where the top and bottom cuts that form the notch meet—when making the cuts. Bypassing cuts sever the crucial fibers of the hinge and may cause the hinge to fail earlier than intended, leading to a loss of control. If a bypass is created, it must be corrected before felling the tree.

The hinge is critical in controlling the direction of fall. If the hinge is the proper thickness, the wood fibers should control the falling tree until the face notch closes, causing the hinge fibers to break. The guideline for felling trees is to allow a hinge with a thickness of no more than 10 percent of the tree's diameter, but flexibility in this guideline is in order. For example, when cutting short sections up in a tree, a hinge thickness of 10 percent may be too much for the climber to break off with limited leverage. Also, for large diameter trees, establishing a hinge of less than 10 percent may be necessary for the hinge to function effectively. It is important to avoid cutting into the hinge when making the back cut.

The traditional, straight back cut is made by starting the cut from the back of the tree toward the notch. The hinge is formed as the back cut approaches the notch. It is easy to cut through the hinge while making the back cut, especially if the saw operator is looking toward the top of the tree. Most experts recommend making the back cut slightly higher than the apex of the notch—a

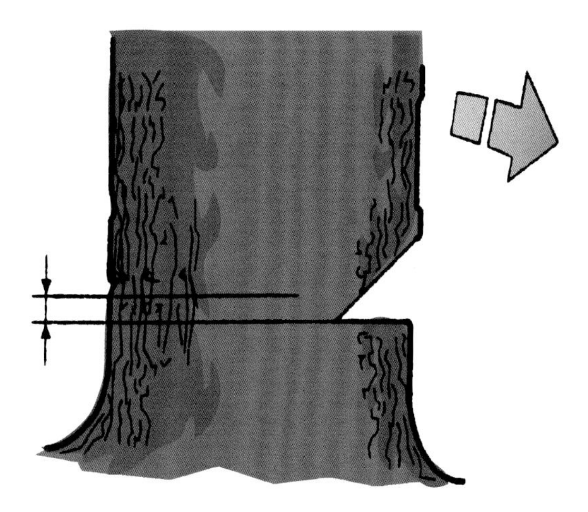

FIGURE 10.10 A "stepped" back cut can reduce the possibility of the tree kicking back toward the operator when the hinge breaks. It is made slightly higher than the apex of the notch. Using a stepped back cut is important when using a conventional (45°) notch, or a notch that is less than 70°.

FIGURE 10.11 An open-face notch of 70° or more allows the hinge to control the tree longer.

"stepped" back cut—to reduce the possibility of the tree kicking back toward the operator when the hinge breaks. This is important when using a conventional (45°) notch, or a notch that is less than 70°. With only 45° of movement until the notch closes and the hinge breaks, the trunk is then free to potentially slip off the back of the stump toward the saw operator when the tree is only about halfway to the ground. This is especially important when felling trees in a dense stand, where the tree's crown will contact other trees during its fall.

Most instructors now teach the open-face notch, which allows the hinge to control the fall of the tree longer than with the conventional (45°) notch. With the open-face notch, the back cut may not need to be stepped higher. It can usually be cut at the same level as the apex of the notch, which makes it easier to align the cut and not undermine the hinge. In some instances, however, it may be helpful to use a stepped back cut with an open-face notch. If the tree has significant forward lean, or could hang up in another tree when felled, the stepped back cut can reduce the likelihood of the cut trunk pushing back off the stump and striking the saw operator.

FIGURE 10.12 The worker aligns the notch facing the desired direction of fall. Sometimes the notch direction is adjusted for side lean.

Sometimes, if the tree is leaning in the direction of fall or has internal faults, or if there is too much tension on a pull line, the tree can split upward from the back cut. This is called a **barber chair**, and it can be very dangerous. It happens very quickly and the split trunk can hit the person felling the tree, which is often fatal.

One technique that can reduce the chance of creating a barber chair is to use a **bore cut**. The

FIGURE 10.13 Sometimes, if the tree is leaning in the direction of fall or has internal faults, or if there is too much tension on a pull line, the tree can split upward from the back cut. This is called a barber chair, and it can be very dangerous. The split trunk can hit the person felling the tree, which is often fatal.

bore cut is made by boring into the tree several inches behind the apex of the notch. The cut is started well behind the desired position of the hinge. Once the chain saw bar is in, the cut is made to establish the hinge to the desired thickness behind the apex of the notch. Once the hinge is established, the back cut is made from the hinge toward the back of the tree, leaving a strap of wood in the back as holding wood. An advantage of this technique is that the operator can stop if necessary without being committed. This can allow the operator to do a final safety check of the area prior to making the final cut.

If the tree is larger than the bar length of the saw, the "bad" side, or the side the tree is leaning toward, should be cut first, taking care to cut less than 50 percent through the diameter. Then the good side is cut, meeting the cut from the other side. If the tree has side lean or significant decay on one side, the feller should be sure to finish the back cut on the "good" side of the tree. Wedges can also be used to help support the hinge on the bad side of the tree.

Bore cutting requires effective training and practice to perfect but is an important skill to know. It provides a much higher degree of safety, control, and reliability than a traditional back cut, and it effectively eliminates the possibility of a barber chair.

Additional Safety Techniques

Specific training in cutting techniques for felling trees with lean or with flaws can reduce the possibility of a barber chair occurring. Also, a load strap or chain could be secured around the tree above the notch to reduce or prevent splitting. No other workers should be in the area directly behind the tree. The worker making the back cut should plan an escape route at a 45° angle to either side of a line drawn opposite the intended direction of fall.

It is a good idea to have felling wedges ready when making the back cut. Wedges can be driven into the back cut to prevent the tree from closing

FIGURE 10.14 When limbing a felled tree, workers should stand away from the possible roll of the tree. If necessary, the log should be blocked to prevent rolling.

on the back cut and pinching the bar of the chain saw. They may also be used to help initiate the fall.

FIGURE 10.15 When bucking, the worker should cut three-fourths of the way through each cut (left), then roll the log over to finish the cuts (right).

LIMBING AND BUCKING

After the tree has been felled, it must be sawed up, using a process called **limbing** and **bucking**. Limbing is the process of cutting off all of the side or lateral branches of the tree. Cutting up the main logs and trunk after limbing is called bucking. Proficiency with chain saw skills is important, both for safety and for efficiency. It is best to have formal chain saw training; some countries require completion of specific chain saw qualifications. A few basic safety principles should also be remembered.

All chain saw safety regulations and guidelines apply when limbing and bucking trees. The chain brake must be engaged when taking one hand off the saw to move a limb or when taking more than two steps with the saw running. It is easy to trip or lose balance when walking around logs and limbs.

The worker should always be aware of the tension of the logs and branches. Branches bent

FIGURE 10.17 When bucking a log, the worker should be positioned away from the chain saw path.

FIGURE 10.16 The worker should position the saw to keep the bar of the saw from touching the ground.

FIGURE 10.18 Debris should be cleared to minimize risk of creating a kickback situation.

FIGURE 10.19 If the limb is under downward pressure, the worker should start with a small undercut, then finish from the top.

under tension can be hazardous. When tension is released while making the cut, branches can spring back toward the worker. A worker must be able to anticipate where a limb will go after being cut so they can position themselves safely. If the worker cuts from the wrong side (the compression side) of a limb under tension, the saw may become pinched. Sometimes a small face notch and back cut can be employed to safely release tension or control the direction of a limb. If the limb is under downward pressure, pressure can be reduced by starting with a small undercut (or a small notch on the underside of the limb). The cut is then finished from the top to release the branch. If there is an upward tension, a small top cut or notch should be made on the top side and then the cut finished from the bottom side. An easy way to remember this is to always identify which side is under tension and which is under compression, then start with a small cut on the compression side and finish on the tension side.

If more than one worker is cutting in the area, extra care should be taken. Each worker must be aware of what the other workers are doing, and care must be taken when approaching a saw operator. Workers should stay on the uphill side of the tree or log and avoid working where the tree could roll toward them. If necessary, the log should be blocked to prevent rolling.

When bucking up the major logs or trunk, wedges can be used to prevent binding of the guide bar. Another tip is to place smaller logs under the trunk before it drops to relieve the tension and allow the worker to cut all the way through with the chain saw. If large logs must be rolled, a **cant hook** or **peavey** should be used as illustrated in Figure 10.21.

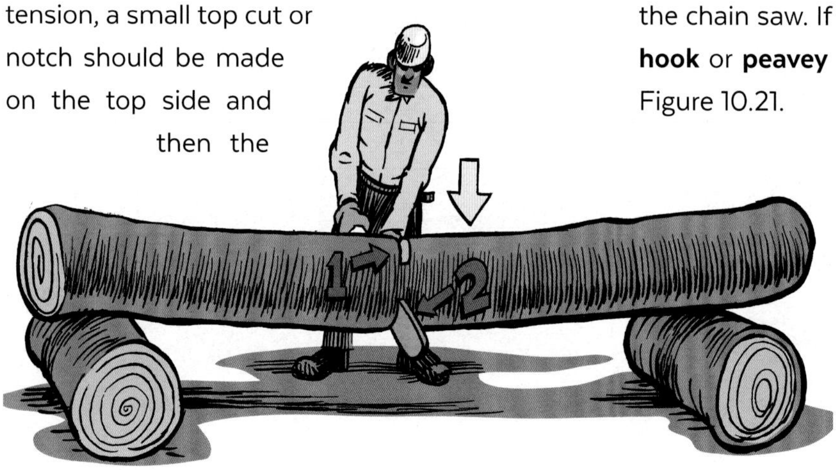

TIP! CUTTING UPROOTED TREES

If working on a tree that has been uprooted, there is a possibility of the root ball settling back when bucking. This can happen very quickly and with great force. It is important to consider the possibility of the root ball settling prior to limbing and bucking, and to always be aware of the tree's movement when cutting.

FIGURE 10.20 If there is upward pressure on the limb, the worker should start with a small top cut and finish from below.

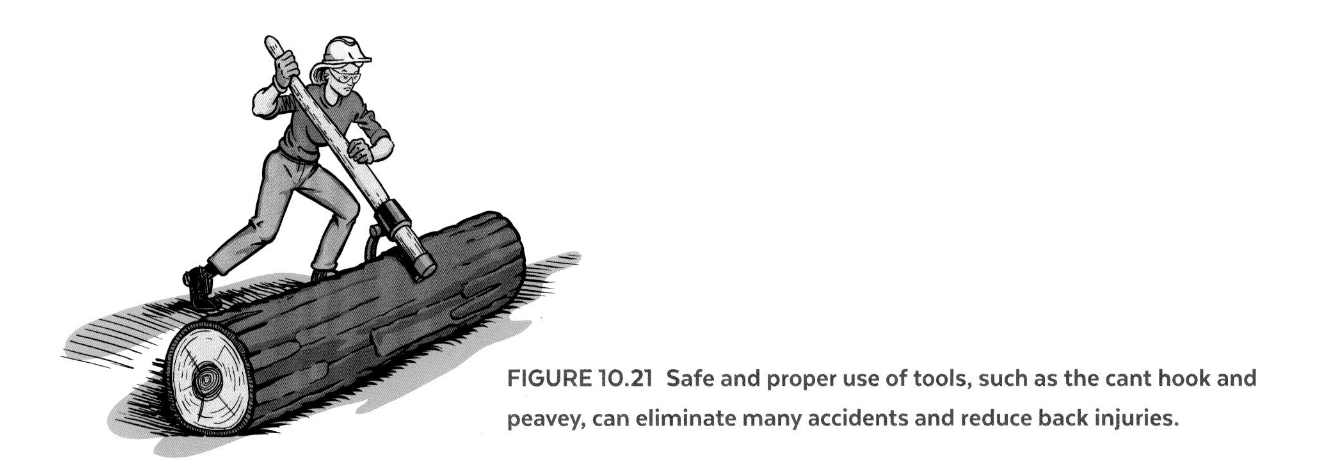

FIGURE 10.21 Safe and proper use of tools, such as the cant hook and peavey, can eliminate many accidents and reduce back injuries.

KEY CONCEPTS

1. Preparation for felling includes inspecting the tree and site for hazards and obstacles, preparing a felling plan, and conducting a job briefing.
2. For most arboricultural felling operations, a tagline (pull line) should be installed for added control.
3. Accurate height (and breadth) estimation of the tree to be felled will help avoid hitting obstacles.
4. Assessing the leans (or weights) of the tree will determine the types of cuts used and safe positioning for the cutter.
5. An open-face notch of 70° or more allows the hinge to control the tree longer.
6. The hinge is critical in controlling the direction of fall. If the hinge is the proper thickness, the wood fibers should break when the face notch closes.
7. The worker making the back cut should plan an escape route at a 45° angle to either side of a line drawn opposite the intended direction of fall, and use that route once the tree starts to fall.
8. Limbing is the process of cutting off all of the side or lateral branches of the tree. Cutting up the main logs and trunk is called bucking. It is best to have formal chain saw training, and some countries require completion of specific chain saw qualifications.

WORKBOOK

MATCHING

_____ cant hook	A. typically greater than 70°
_____ notch cut	B. device used to roll large logs
_____ bucking	C. should never cut into the hinge
_____ limbing	D. helps steer the tree in a felling operation
_____ open-face notch	E. removing side limbs of felled trees
_____ barber chair	F. wedge-shaped cut to direct tree fall
_____ back cut	G. cutting log into smaller lengths
_____ hinge	H. tree pivots or splits up behind hinge when felling

TRUE/FALSE

1. T F Before beginning any felling operation, the tree and site should be inspected for potential hazards.
2. T F Hollow trees can present difficulties in controlling the direction of fall.
3. T F The lean and shape of the tree are important, but species characteristics are irrelevant in felling operations.
4. T F It is best to plan a tree's removal before any cuts are made.
5. T F The preferred escape route for the chain saw operator in a felling operation is 45° on either side of a line drawn opposite the intended direction of fall.
6. T F A pull line and/or wedges can be used to help control a tree's fall.
7. T F When felling a tree, the notch should be cut at least 50 percent of the way through the tree.
8. T F A "dogleg" in the pull line can cause the tree to rotate on the cut, misdirecting the fall.
9. T F A rule of thumb for the depth of the notch is one-third or less of the diameter of the tree.
10. T F The hinge of wood formed behind the notch controls the tree's direction of fall.
11. T F The back cut should always be made slightly lower than the apex of the notch.
12. T F An advantage of the open-face notch is that it controls the fall of the tree longer.
13. T F After a tree has been felled, bucking should take place before limbing.

14. T F Branches or logs that are under tension can present a hazard when cut.

15. T F The height of a tree can be estimated using a stick and the principle of similar right triangles.

SAMPLE TEST QUESTIONS

1. Cutting large logs into smaller sections is known as

    a. felling
    b. limbing
    c. bucking
    d. notching

2. If a tree pivots or splits upward during felling, it is sometimes called

    a. bucking
    b. barber chairing
    c. hinging
    d. wedging

3. When felling a tree using the conventional 45° notch, the back cut should be made

    a. even with the apex of the notch
    b. just below the apex of the notch
    c. just above the apex of the notch
    d. directly through the apex of the notch

CHAPTER

11

CABLING

LEARNING OBJECTIVES

The tree worker will be able to:

- Summarize the objectives of cable installation in trees.
- Contrast dynamic and static cable systems.
- Describe the hardware used in cabling trees.
- Contrast dead-end and through-hardware applications.
- Explain appropriate placement of cables in trees to achieve the objective.
- Contrast common-grade cable and extra-high-strength cable and the hardware required to form their terminations.
- Summarize the steps for installing a static cable.
- Discuss various cable configurations and their applications.

IMPORTANT TERMS

amon-eye nut
cable aid
cable-stop termination
cabling
Chicago™ grip
codominant branches
come-along
common-grade, 7-strand, galvanized cable
dead-end grips
dynamic cable
extra-high-strength (EHS) cable
eye bolt
eye splice
Haven grip
heavy-duty washer
included bark
lag hook
peen
ship auger
static cable
swage-stop termination
thimble
threaded rod

FIGURE 11.1 Trees with codominant stems may have included bark in the branch union and may be candidates for cabling.

INTRODUCTION

Cables are installed in trees to limit branch movement and provide extra support. When used wisely, they may extend the life of a tree or reduce the risk of failure.

Whenever hardware is installed in the wood of a tree, the tree is wounded. Once wounded, there is the risk of decay advancing into wood that supports or holds the hardware. Therefore, the situation must be assessed carefully when deciding whether to install steel cables or dynamic (rope) cables, to prune out the potentially hazardous limbs, or to remove the tree.

In determining whether cabling is warranted, the condition, species, and value of the tree should be considered. If the root system is not structurally sound or if the tree contains excessive decay, removal may be preferable. Cables cannot be relied upon to make a hazardous tree safe; they can only help to reduce the likelihood of failure.

Sometimes the most revealing inspection of tree defects is made aloft by the tree climber. Thus, it is important that the tree climber be able to recognize tree defects and be able to predict risk potential. If a cable has been called for but the tree's structure is unsound, it is up to the climber to notify the job supervisor. Installing a cable in an unstable or declining branch or tree may create a false sense of security and could be a source of legal action should the limb fail and result in personal injury or property damage. Any cable installation should be accompanied by a commitment by the owner to ongoing inspections.

This chapter introduces cabling as a tree support system. Reasons for installing cables are discussed, and various hardware and installation tools are presented. Rigid and dynamic cable types are contrasted, and common steel cable and extra-high-strength cable are introduced. Various installation and attachment options are described.

REASONS FOR INSTALLING CABLES

Cables should not be installed in trees without a clear objective. The following are some objectives for installing cables (**cabling**):

1. Limit movement of branches or stems
2. Support split or decayed branch unions
3. Support **codominant branches**, especially those that contain **included bark**
4. Support heavy limbs or limbs that extend over structures or high-traffic areas

5. Support wide-spreading branches or multi-stemmed trees that may be threatened by ice, snow, or other loads

HARDWARE AND TOOLS

It is important to select the appropriate hardware for cabling a tree. Cables, eye bolts, and other cabling hardware come in various sizes, types, and materials. Each has advantages and limitations. Consideration must be given to the size of the limbs, the weight to be supported, loads from wind and other factors, and the presence of decay when choosing materials. If the hardware is too small or inadequate, the cable support system may fail.

Steel Cables

Steel cable is sometimes referred to as **static cable** or rigid cable because it does not stretch or flex much. It is very strong and, if an appropriate size and type is used, it is rarely the component of a cable system that fails. Steel cables have been installed in trees for decades without significant degradation or problems. A disadvantage is that installation requires wounding of the tree.

STEEL CABLES

Advantages

- Very strong
- High longevity
- Not visually intrusive

Limitations

- No stretch
- Requires drilling through branch
- EHS can be difficult to work with

Two types of steel cable are commonly used in cabling trees: **common-grade, 7-strand, galvanized cable** and **extra-high-strength (EHS) cable**. The common-grade cable is relatively malleable (bendable) and easy to work with. The EHS cable is much stronger but less flexible than common-grade cable. Both are available in a wide range of sizes. Cables ranging in diameter from 3/16 to 3/8 in (and comparable metric sizes) are commonly used in trees.

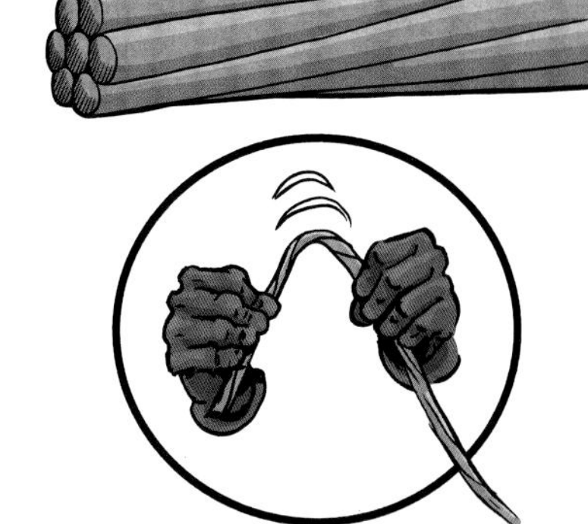

FIGURE 11.2 Common-grade, 7-strand cable.

Dynamic Cables

Another option is to use dynamic, fiber cables. **Dynamic cables** use some form of rope or flexible strap material that is typically wrapped around a stem. Several systems use a hollow-braid, polypropylene rope, which enables the use of simple splices for attachment. Several proprietary brands are available and are widely used in Europe. These systems share many properties, but their materials and installations differ.

Dynamic cables may reduce the potential for shock-loading the system, which can occur if two stems move in opposite directions with great force. It is also thought that by allowing more movement, dynamic support systems may increase the likelihood that the tree will develop wood to strengthen weak branches or unions. Some systems include an additional shock-absorbing rubber component; others incorporate an overload indicator, which can signal that the system was overstressed and thus prompt the arborist to perform a closer inspection or possibly replace the system.

Dynamic cables do have some limitations. The

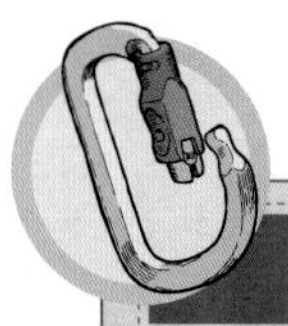

DYNAMIC CABLES

Advantages
- Absorbs some shock through stretching
- Fast installation
- No drilling (with sling-type attachment)

Limitations
- UV degradation
- Animal chewing
- Potential for girdling

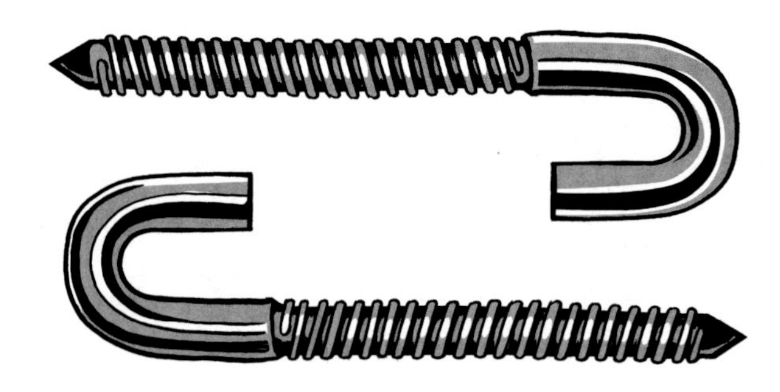

FIGURE 11.3 Lag hooks, or J-lags, work well on small limbs and trees with strong wood, but should not be installed in limbs greater than 10 in (25 cm) in diameter.

fiber materials used for dynamic cables lose strength over time to UV degradation. Another potential problem is that some wildlife (birds and squirrels, for example) have been known to chew on dynamic cables, which could lead to failure.

Lag Hooks

A **lag hook**, or J-lag, is a threaded device in the shape of a "J." It is made out of steel and is usually hot-dipped galvanized or bent metal that has been zinc plated to slow rusting. The long end of the J-shaped lag is threaded with wood screw threads. Standard lag sizes used in tree cabling are 5/16 in (8 mm), 3/8 in (10 mm), 1/2 in (13 mm), and 5/8 in (16 mm) in diameter. Lag hooks come with right- and left-handed threads, so that when each end is twisted into the branch to complete installation, the lay of the cable strands will not come unwound.

Lag hooks are installed by screwing into a predrilled hole that is smaller in diameter than the lag. The hole should be drilled 1/16 to 1/8 in (1.5 to 3 mm) smaller than the lag. The lags should be screwed into the tree (after the cable is attached) so that the open end of the J is just contacting the bark, without injuring the bark. It is not uncommon for a cable to "jump off" a lag when a gap has been left between the open end of the lag and the bark. If the lag must be installed at an angle that will prevent screwing it in completely, it may be preferable to install an eye bolt or other anchoring hardware.

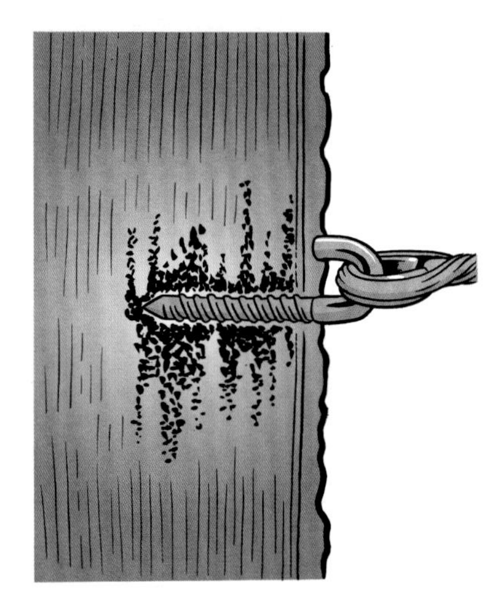

FIGURE 11.4 Lag hooks should NOT be installed in decayed wood.

Lag hooks work quite well on small limbs and trees with strong wood, but should not be installed in limbs that are greater than 10 in (25 cm) in diameter. Lag hooks should never be installed in limbs with decay. The decay will limit the holding capacity of the lags and may spread into healthy wood. Lags are generally considered less reliable than hardware that bolts through the limb.

Eye Bolts and Amon-Eye Nuts

When lag hooks are not appropriate, **eye bolts** or **threaded rods** with **amon-eye nuts** may be used. Some companies make this a standard

FIGURE 11.5 A: Threaded rod with amon-eye nut. B: Eye bolt.

FIGURE 11.6 Installation of an eye bolt.

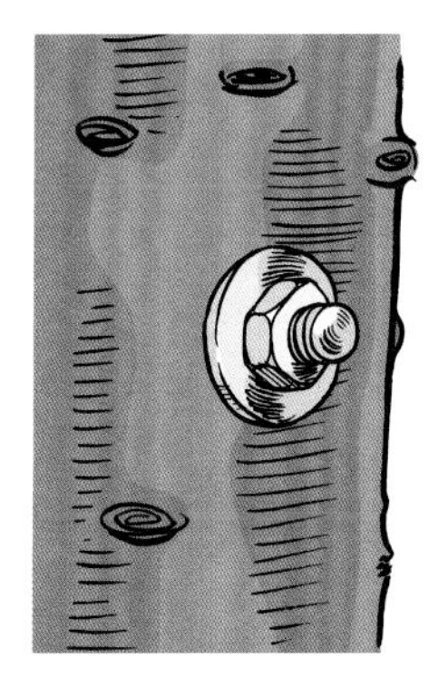

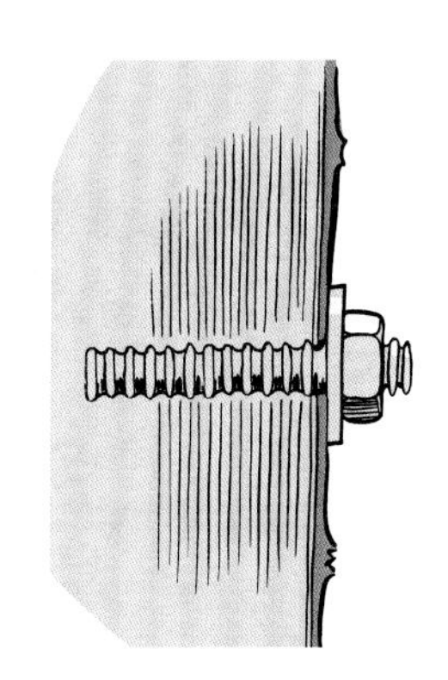

FIGURE 11.7 The washer should be seated against the bark. On trees with very thick bark, the outer, furrowed bark should be chiseled away to allow the washer to sit flat, taking care not to wound live tissue.

installation practice. Both are drop forged and machine threaded, and their installation is similar. A hole, usually 1/16 to 1/8 in (1.5 to 3 mm) larger than the hardware, is drilled through the limb to be cabled. The eye bolt or threaded rod is installed with a round, **heavy-duty washer** and nut on the outside end. The washer should be seated against the bark. On trees with very thick bark, the outer, furrowed bark should be chiseled away to allow the washer to sit flat, taking care not to wound live tissue. Excess rod should be cut off, and the exposed threads on the end of the eye bolt and both ends of the threaded rod used with the amon-eye should be **peened** to prevent the nut from unscrewing.

Drop-forged eye bolts are considered slightly stronger than amon-eye nuts used with threaded rods. However, an advantage of the amon-eye system is that the length of the rod can be adjusted easily for any job.

Thimbles, Splices, and Dead-End Grips

When attaching the cable to its anchoring hardware, **thimbles** must be used. The purpose of the thimble is to increase the diameter of the bend

FIGURE 11.8 Cut off excess just beyond the nut.

FIGURE 11.9 Peen the end of the bolt to prevent the nut from backing off.

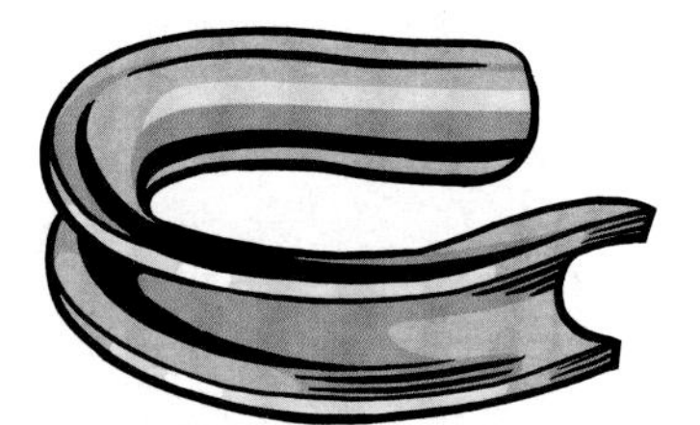

FIGURE 11.10 A thimble is used to increase the diameter of the bend and to protect the cable from excessive wear.

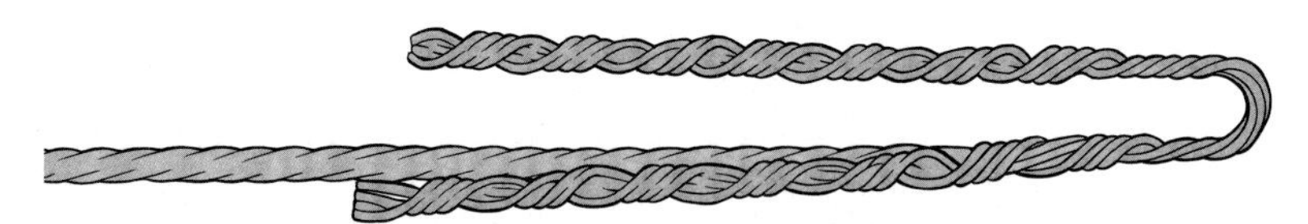

FIGURE 11.11 Wrapping a dead-end grip onto the cable. The thimble must be installed before wrapping the other side.

FIGURE 11.12 Dead-end grip and EHS cable. Note the use of a thimble.

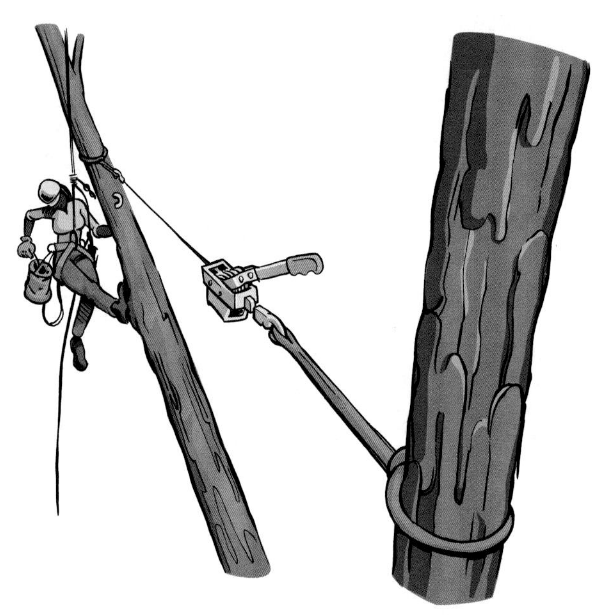

FIGURE 11.13 A come-along may be used to pull the limbs closer together in order to install the cable so that it will be taut.

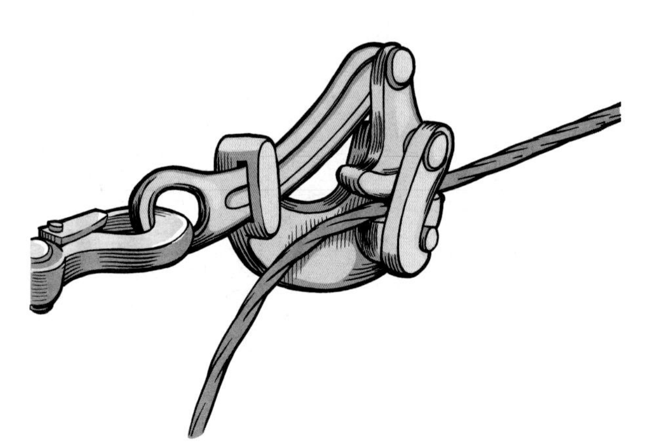

FIGURE 11.14 Haven grips clamp onto the cable and are used to pull tension.

and to protect the cable from excessive wear. If cables or grips are installed directly on the hardware, the steel-to-steel contact and abrasion may eventually cause wear and cable breakage. For common-grade cable, thimbles are closed after installing on the eye bolt. For EHS cable, thimbles are left open to conform to the bend in the **dead-end grips**, which must be used.

Dead-end grips are installed over the thimble and then wrapped upon the cable. They are used to attach EHS cable to the anchor hardware. The cable is not malleable enough to form an eye splice.

Cable grips have been found to be quite satisfactory for small- and medium-sized trees. However, cable grips are not designed to withstand the dynamic loads that can be created by branches twisting and swaying, particularly in gusting winds. Excessive wind sway in large trees may cause metal fatigue in the dead-end grips, which could lead to failure. When installing this hardware in large trees, it is important to take into account the wind conditions and potential for twisting.

Another way to terminate steel cables is to use manufactured **cable-stop** or **swage-stop termination** devices. These are fasteners that hold the cable after the cable is passed through the

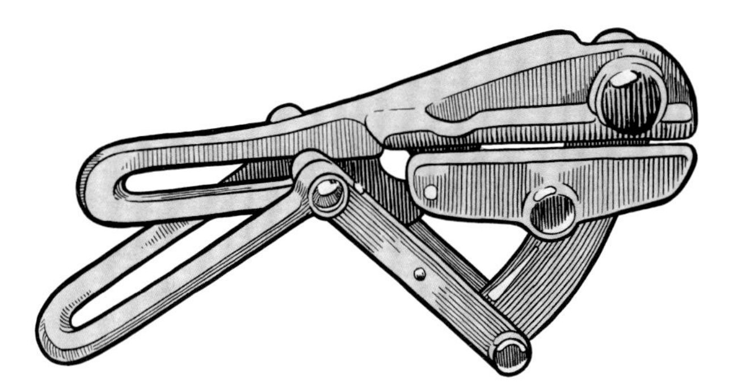

FIGURE 11.15 Chicago™ grips are designed for use with EHS cable. They tend not to kink the cable.

FIGURE 11.16 Drilling for hardware installation.

branch. These devices work well when there is minimal lateral cable movement that could enlarge the opening.

Cabling Tools and Equipment

The installation of cables in trees requires a number of tools. Sometimes, especially when installing lag hooks, a **come-along** is used to bring two branches closer together. The use of a come-along is illustrated in Figure 11.13. A

FIGURE 11.17 A ship auger is used to predrill the holes for cable hardware installation.

second commonly used tool is a **Haven grip**. This cammed device is used to grip the cable and help the climber pull the cable for tensioning or attaching to anchor hardware. The **Chicago™ grip** is designed for use with EHS cable.

In order to install the hardware in the tree, holes must be drilled. This can be accomplished using either a brace and bit, a gas-powered drill, or an electric drill. Though fast and efficient, corded electric drills can be difficult to work with in the tree, and an electrical source is not always available. Battery-powered, rechargeable drills offer a solution to these problems. With all drill types, the bit should be a **ship auger**. This will work more efficiently in green wood and will pull the shavings from the hole.

Another handy piece of equipment is the **cable aid**. A cable aid can be used to spread open thimbles, to tighten lags, and to help wrap dead-end grips onto the cable. A cable aid is illustrated in Figure 11.18.

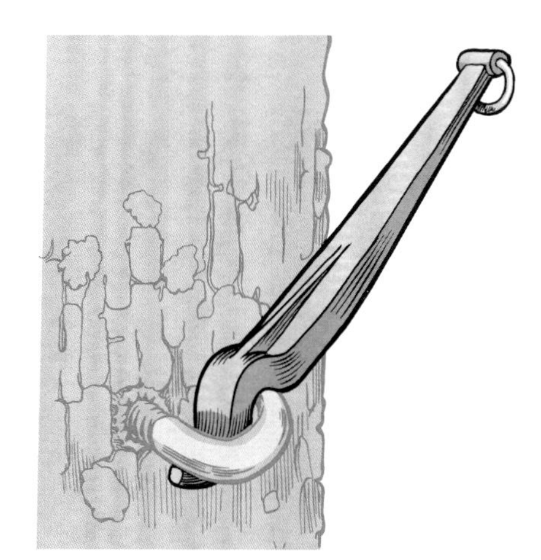

FIGURE 11.18 A cable aid may be used for tightening hardware.

Other tools that are useful in cabling operations include cable cutters, hack saws, hammers, chisels and mallets, slings, and wire cutters. It is helpful for a climber to carry these tools in a bag, bucket, or belt that will prevent the tools from being dropped accidentally. Some companies require that all hand tools be tethered to prevent dropping.

ATTACHING THE CABLE TO THE HARDWARE

Steel Cable Attachment

As previously mentioned, if EHS cable is used, it must be attached to the hardware using dead-end grips. However, if common-grade cable is used, there are alternatives. Common-grade, 7-strand cable is usually attached to the hardware using an **eye splice**. An eye splice is actually a series of wraps and not a true splice. A thimble is always used to form the eye at the end of the cable. It is important to use the right size of thimble for the cable. If the bend in the thimble is too tight, the cable will be weakened. The eye splice is made by wrapping the end of the cable around the thimble, then separating the cable strands. Each strand is wrapped individually around the cable two to three complete turns per strand in the same direction. When complete, the finished splice will have a neat appearance and will provide optimal holding capacity.

FIGURE 11.19 Common-grade, 7-strand cable is often attached to the hardware using an eye splice. The eye splice is made by wrapping the end of the cable around the thimble, then separating the cable strands. Each strand is wrapped individually around the cable two to three complete turns per strand in the same direction.

Dynamic Cable Attachment

Dynamic systems use ropes and belts, sheaths, or straps instead of cables and anchors. Most dynamic cables are ropes that are wrapped around a stem. These cables do not require the climber to drill into the tree. The potential for girdling or damaging is reduced by using a strap or band that distributes the load over a wider area than the unsheathed cable. Some systems call for the formation of loops of cable, which are intended to accommodate tree growth and further minimize the potential for girdling.

One hybrid system uses the traditional through-hardware installation with rope between the anchors. The goal of this system is to provide the shock-absorbing properties of dynamic cable without the potential for girdling.

Cable-Stop and Swage-Stop Terminations

Cable-stop and swage-stop terminations are installed at the end of the cable without attaching to other hardware. A hole approximately 1/16 in (1.5 mm) larger than the cable is drilled directly through the limb. The cable is threaded through the hole. The termination device is then installed

FIGURE 11.20 Dynamic cabling uses ropes and belts, sheaths, or straps instead of cables and anchors. Some hybrid types are installed with hardware anchors.

at the end of the cable to prevent the cable from pulling through the predrilled hole.

An advantage to using a cable-stop or swage-stop device is that additional hardware is not needed to form the termination. A disadvantage, however, is that sometimes branch movement can widen the hole at the point where the cable enters.

CABLE INSTALLATION

Before installing cables in a tree, the tree should be pruned as needed. Hazardous limbs should be removed. If necessary, the tree should be pruned for risk reduction and to reduce excessive weight.

A general rule of thumb is to install the cable at least two-thirds the distance from the weak union to the ends of the limbs. Exact placement will depend upon the location of lateral branches and defects. The branches at the point of cable attachment must be large enough and solid enough to provide adequate support of the hardware.

The angle of the cable and its distance from the branch union determine its strength and effectiveness. Support can be maximized by installing the cable directly across the branch union being supported and at or near two-thirds the distance up. “Directly across” can be determined by setting the cable perpendicular to (at a 90° angle with) an imaginary line through the center of the branch union.

Hardware should be installed with the pull of the cable in a direct line with the installed bolt or lag. If the cable is installed correctly, at right angles with the line that bisects the branch union, the

FIGURE 11.21 Cables should be installed two-thirds the distance up from the branch union to the branch tips.

FIGURE 11.22 The cable should be installed perpendicular to (at a 90° angle with) an imaginary line that bisects the branch union.

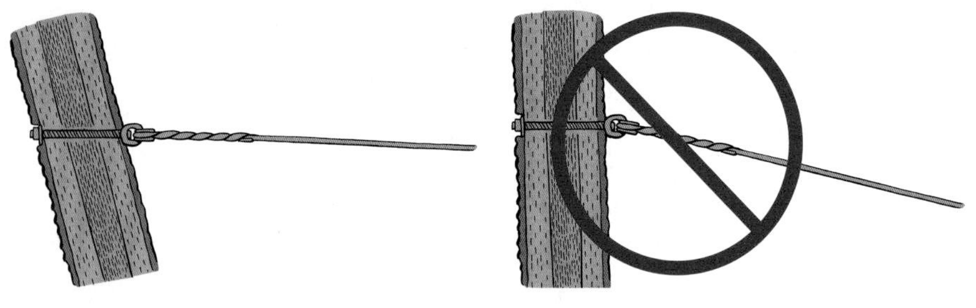

FIGURE 11.23 Hardware should be installed with the pull of the cable in a direct line with the installed bolt or lag.

defect or causing the hardware to pull out. If the cable is installed while the tree is in leaf, it should be tight enough that it will not be slack after the leaves have fallen. If the cable is installed while the tree is not in leaf, it should not be too taut, as the branches will be heavier in the summer and it may otherwise be pulled too tightly.

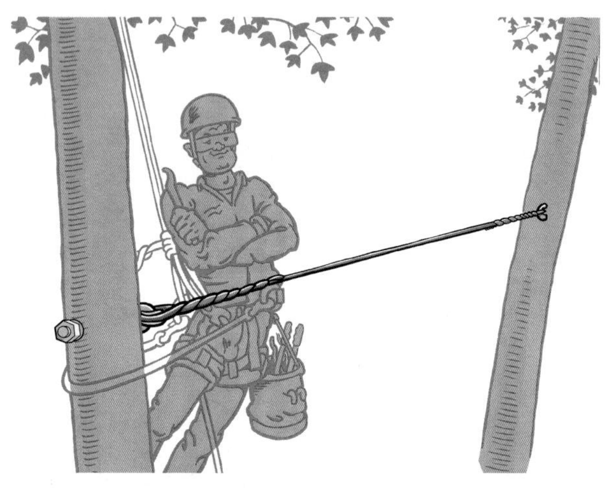

FIGURE 11.24 A properly installed cable should look neat and professional.

hardware will usually not be installed perpendicular to either branch. To maximize the strength of the system, it is important not to have the cables pull at an angle to the hardware.

Once installed, the cable should be just taut. A cable that is too tight may put excessive stress on the wood fibers, resulting in more damage at the

The most common cable installation is the simple or direct cable (one cable between two limbs). Sometimes a tree will require more than one cable. Several cabling systems are illustrated in Figure 11.26. If multiple cables are required, extra stability can be added to the system by cabling the branches together in threes (in a triangle). If more crown movement is desired, a box or rotary system can be installed.

When more than one cable is being installed on the same limb, vertical spacing between the hardware should be greater than or equal to the diameter of the limb if possible. An anchor should not be installed directly above another anchor. Only one cable should be attached to each bolt or lag.

TIP! CABLE INSTALLATION

When installing a direct cable, the branches can be brought closer together with ropes or slings and a come-along. This will make the installation easier, and the cable should be taut when the limbs are released.

FIGURE 11.25 The most common cable configuration is a single direct cable.

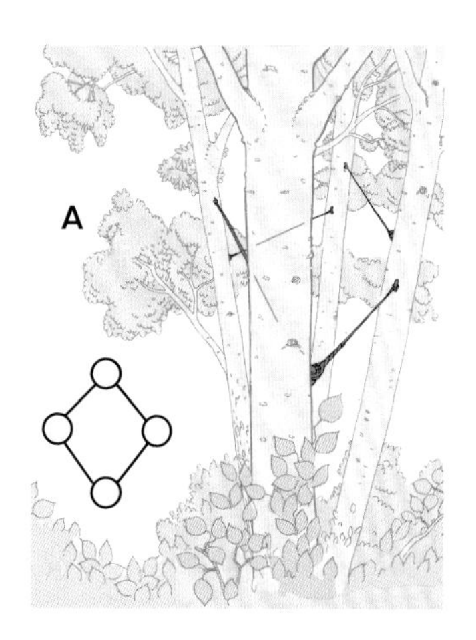

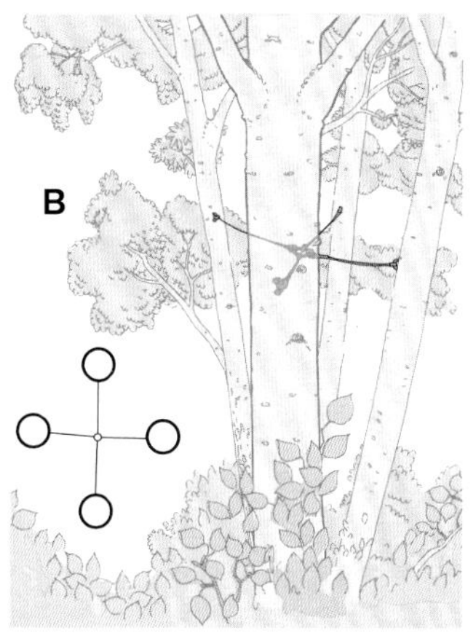

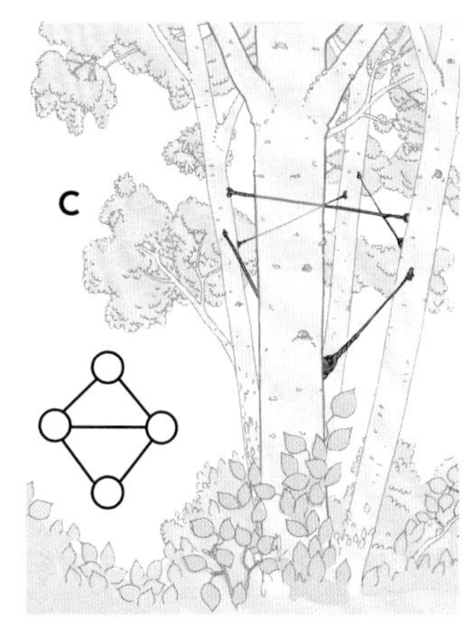

FIGURE 11.26 Cabling systems. A) box system, B) hub-and-spoke system, C) triangulated system.

FIGURE 11.27 When more than one cable is installed on the same limb, vertical spacing between the hardware should be greater than or equal to the diameter of the limb, if possible. An anchor should not be installed directly above another anchor.

FIGURE 11.28 Only one cable should be attached to each bolt or lag.

The installation of cables in a tree represents an ongoing responsibility. Cables should be inspected annually, including checking to see that the hardware remains securely anchored. As the tree grows older and taller, new cables may need to be installed higher in the tree. Trees that have been cabled may need to be pruned periodically to remove excess weight and reduce wind resistance.

KEY CONCEPTS

1. Cables are installed in trees to limit branch movement and provide extra support.
2. There are two main types of cabling: static and dynamic. Each requires a different set of tools, supplies, and installation requirements.
3. Static (steel) cables are strong and have minimal degradation, but have limited flex and could create shock-loading of stems.
4. Dynamic (fiber) cables allow movement and limit shock-loading, but can girdle stems and are subject to UV degradation and wildlife chewing.
5. Through-bolts can be installed in any size limb and are preferred for larger limbs or those with decay. They are installed in a hole 1/16 to 1/8 in (1.5 to 3 mm) larger than the bolt. J-lags or lag hooks (dead-end terminations) are best installed in smaller limbs or those without decay, in a hole 1/16 to 1/8 in (1.5 to 3 mm) smaller than the lag.
6. Cables should be installed directly across the union they support, approximately two-thirds the distance to the branch tips from the union being supported, with the anchor hardware in direct line with the cable.
7. Cabling should come with a commitment from the tree owner for ongoing inspection.

WORKBOOK

MATCHING

_____ lag hooks	A. brings limbs closer together
_____ eye splice	B. used with threaded rod
_____ eye bolt	C. increases bend size and reduces wear on cable
_____ amon-eye nut	D. attaches soft cable to hardware
_____ ship auger	E. do not use in decayed wood
_____ thimble	F. helps pull cable taut
_____ Haven grip	G. for predrilling holes
_____ come-along	H. hardware that is through-bolted

TRUE/FALSE

1. T F In most cases, a tree should be pruned, if needed, before cables are installed.
2. T F Dynamic (fiber) cables allow movement and limit shock-loading, but can girdle stems and are subject to UV degradation and wildlife chewing.
3. T F Cables should be installed one-third the distance from the branch union to the branch tips.
4. T F Properly installed cables should be parallel to the ground.
5. T F Cables should always be installed perpendicular to the larger limb.
6. T F When properly installed, the cable should be just taut.
7. T F Cables installed while a tree is in leaf may slacken following leaf drop.
8. T F Lags should only be used in limbs less than 10 in (25 cm) in diameter and when no decay is present.
9. T F When installing more than one cable on a limb, the cables must be installed directly over each other.
10. T F Two cables should never be installed on a single eye bolt or lag.
11. T F If EHS cable is used, dead-end grips must be used to attach the cable to the hardware.
12. T F Thimbles are not required with dead-end grips.
13. T F When installing lags, the hole should be drilled approximately 1/16 to 1/8 in (1.5 to 3 mm) smaller than the lag diameter.
14. T F An eye splice cannot be formed when using common-grade, 7-strand cable.

15. T F Swage-stops, or cable-stops, are fasteners that hold a cable after the cable is passed through the branch.
16. T F The cable should be installed in direct line with the hardware.
17. T F Most dynamic cable systems are attached to a tree exactly the same way steel cables are attached.
18. T F A shock-absorbing component can be installed with some dynamic cabling systems.
19. T F If a cable is installed correctly, at right angles with the line that bisects the branch union, the hardware will usually be installed perpendicular to both branches.
20. T F If multiple cables are required and crown movement is desired, a box or rotary system can be installed.

SAMPLE TEST QUESTIONS

1. A device commonly used to bring two limbs closer together in cabling operations is a

    a. Haven grip
    b. come-along
    c. cable aid
    d. cable clamp

2. When installing extra-high-strength (EHS) cable, the cable can be attached to the hardware using

    a. dead-end grips
    b. an eye splice
    c. cable clamps
    d. all of the above

3. The recommended height/distance for installing cables is

    a. as close to the branch union as possible
    b. one-third the distance from the branch union to the tips
    c. half the distance from the branch union to the tips
    d. two-thirds the distance from the branch union to the tips

ANSWERS TO WORKBOOK QUESTIONS

CHAPTER 1 - TREE HEALTH AND SCIENCES

MATCHING 1

F	xylem	A.	trees that lose all their leaves annually
D	absorbing roots	B.	food-conducting tissues
G	included bark	C.	water vapor loss through leaves
B	phloem	D.	usually in the upper 8 in (20 cm) of soil
E	photosynthesis	E.	sugar production by plants
H	cambium	F.	carries water up through the tree
C	transpiration	G.	bark within a branch union
A	deciduous	H.	zone of diameter growth in trees

TRUE/FALSE

1. **TRUE** Small fibrous roots serve to take up water and minerals.
2. **FALSE** The root system of a tree looks like a mirror image of the top (crown).
3. **TRUE** Roots tend to grow where moisture and oxygen are available.
4. **FALSE** Tree roots rarely grow beyond the drip line of the tree.
5. **TRUE** Starches are stored throughout the trunk and branches of a tree.
6. **FALSE** The cambium is located in the center of the trunk and branches.
7. **FALSE** The phloem carries sugar only to the roots.
8. **FALSE** The xylem is located directly beneath the bark.
9. **TRUE** In most cases, each growth ring represents one year of growth.
10. **TRUE** The thickness of the growth rings is often an indication of growing conditions in previous years.
11. **FALSE** The heartwood conducts water and minerals up through the tree.
12. **TRUE** In most tree species, only the outermost rings of sapwood conduct water.
13. **TRUE** Rays are storage sites for starch and play a role in defense against decay.
14. **TRUE** The bulge at the base of a branch at the point of attachment to the trunk is called the branch collar.
15. **TRUE** Leaves may be considered the "food factories" of a tree.
16. **TRUE** A vigorous tree will compartmentalize decay to limit its spread.
17. **FALSE** Most of the time, if a tree is stressed, the cause is an insect problem.

18.	**TRUE**	Compaction reduces the pore space in the soil, which reduces water and oxygen availability.
19.	**TRUE**	Generally, with deciduous trees, insects or diseases that affect only the foliage of the tree are not fatal.
20.	**TRUE**	Insects or diseases that affect the vascular system of a tree are usually serious.
21.	**TRUE**	Photosynthesis means "made with light."
22.	**TRUE**	Loss of water evaporating from the leaves helps pull water up from the roots.
23.	**FALSE**	Compound leaves have one bud for each leaflet.
24.	**TRUE**	Trees that lose their leaves for the winter are called deciduous.
25.	**FALSE**	The bud at the end of a twig is known as the axillary bud.

MATCHING 2

F	conk	A.	areas between soil particles
D	simple leaf	B.	teeth along the leaf margin
G	compound leaf	C.	bark pushed up in the branch union
C	branch bark ridge	D.	one blade per leaf
A	pore spaces	E.	bud at the tip of a twig
E	terminal bud	F.	sign of decay within the tree
B	serration	G.	leaf with multiple leaflets

SAMPLE TEST QUESTIONS

1. Most absorbing roots are located

   a. very deep in the soil
   b. along the surface of the tap root
   c. in the upper 8 in (20 cm) of soil
   d. within the drip line of the crown

2. If two buds arise across from one another on a stem, the arrangement is called

   a. alternate
   b. axillary
   c. whorled
   d. opposite

3. Which evergreen trees have needles in bundles?

   a. pines (*Pinus*)
   b. hemlocks (*Tsuga*)
   c. firs (*Abies*)
   d. spruces (*Picea*)

CHAPTER 2 - SAFETY

MATCHING

F	shall	A.	leg protection for chain saw use
G	approved	B.	advisory recommendation
C	CPR	C.	cardiopulmonary resuscitation
D	direct contact	D.	body touches energized conductor
B	should	E.	US safety standard for tree work
H	indirect contact	F.	mandatory requirement
E	ANSI Z133	G.	meets applicable safety standards
A	chaps	H.	touching an object in contact with an energized conductor

TRUE/FALSE

1. **FALSE** Head protection need only be worn while there are climbers in the trees.
2. **FALSE** Eye protection is a good idea but is not required for tree work.
3. **TRUE** Hearing protection may be in the form of earplugs or earmuff-type devices.
4. **TRUE** Workers must not wear gauntlet-type gloves while chipping brush.
5. **TRUE** The voice command-and-response system ensures that warning signals are heard, acknowledged, and acted upon.
6. **TRUE** The job briefing summarizes, among other things, what has to be done and who will be doing each task; the potential hazards and how to prevent or minimize them; what special PPE may be required; and emergency procedures.
7. **TRUE** Employers must instruct their employees in the proper use of all equipment.
8. **FALSE** Carrying a first-aid kit on each truck is recommended but optional.
9. **FALSE** The first-aid kit should be left on the truck at all times, except when in use.
10. **TRUE** Gas-powered equipment should not be started or operated within 10 ft (3 m) of the refueling site.
11. **TRUE** All power and communication wires shall be considered charged with potentially fatal voltages.
12. **TRUE** An electrical conductor is defined as any overhead or underground electrical device, including wires and cables, power lines, and other such facilities.
13. **FALSE** Rubber footwear and gloves provide absolute protection from electrical hazards.

14. **FALSE** Drop starting is the recommended method for starting a chain saw.

15. **FALSE** On the ground, both hands are required for chain saw operation, but one hand can be used in the tree.

16. **TRUE** Chain saw engines must be stopped for refueling.

17. **TRUE** Kickback can occur when the upper tip of the chain saw guide bar contacts an object.

18. **FALSE** A well-trained climber, in good condition, should be able to dodge the kickback of a chain saw.

19. **TRUE** The most common injury causing missed work among tree workers is back injury.

20. **FALSE** When chipping brush, you should stand directly behind the chipper infeed chute to feed branches in.

SAMPLE TEST QUESTIONS

1. Which of the following should be considered energized with a potentially fatal voltage?

   a. overhead electric lines
   b. underground electric lines
   c. telephone and cable TV wires
   d. all of the above

2. Head protection is required for tree workers

   a. whenever performing tree care operations
   b. when specified by the supervisor
   c. whenever there are climbers working aloft
   d. only if chain saws or chippers are in use

3. To avoid chain saw kickback, you should

   a. avoid cutting with the top of the bar
   b. never operate a chain saw on its side (cutting horizontally)
   c. not allow the upper tip of the guide bar to contact an object
   d. not allow the lower tip of the guide bar to contact an object

CHAPTER 3 - ROPES AND KNOTS

MATCHING

E	braided rope	A.	curve or arc in a rope
F	working end	B.	also known as a climbing hitch
H	butterfly knot	C.	used to secure hardware to a tree
C	cow hitch	D.	core and cover share the load
G	figure-8 knot	E.	rope construction commonly used for tree climbing
D	double braid	F.	the end of a rope in use
B	friction hitch	G.	used as a stopper knot
A	bight	H.	often used to form a midline loop

TRUE/FALSE

1. **TRUE** Polyester and polyester blends are the materials most commonly used for arborists' ropes.
2. **FALSE** A 3-strand rope is known for its high strength, high price, and resistance to twisting and hockling.
3. **FALSE** Double-braid lines are recommended for rigging through natural branch unions.
4. **TRUE** A line has a working end and a standing end, or the ends in use (usually forming a knot) and not in use, respectively.
5. **TRUE** "Knot" is the general term given for all knots, hitches, and bends.
6. **TRUE** A hitch is a type of knot used to secure a rope to an object, another rope, or the standing part of the same rope.
7. **TRUE** "Dressing" a knot aligns the parts; "setting" it tightens the knot in place.
8. **TRUE** Most of the "advanced" friction hitches are tied with a separate hitch cord.
9. **TRUE** One limitation of Blake's hitch is a tendency to glaze on a long or rapid descent.
10. **TRUE** An advantage to using the running bowline to tie off limbs is that it is easy to untie after loading.
11. **FALSE** The standard figure-8 knot is a good example of a "slipped" knot.
12. **TRUE** A midline clove hitch is commonly used to send equipment up to a climber.
13. **TRUE** When using an endline clove hitch to tie off limbs, it should be backed up by at least two half hitches.
14. **FALSE** There are very few knots that can be "slipped."

15. **TRUE** The knot known as the slip knot is a slipped overhand knot.

16. **FALSE** The primary purpose of a sheet bend is to form a Prusik loop.

17. **TRUE** A knot is said to be directional if it performs differently when loaded (pulled) from opposite directions or ends.

18. **TRUE** When tying a timber hitch in a sling to attach hardware to a tree, you should always make at least five wraps and spread them at least two-thirds of the way around the stem.

19. **TRUE** A sheet bend is used to join two ropes of unequal diameters and is often used to send a line up to a climber.

20. **TRUE** Natural fibers are generally not as strong as the new, synthetic fibers and can rot over time.

SAMPLE TEST QUESTIONS

1. A type of knot used to secure a rope to an object, another rope, or the standing part of the same rope is a

    a. bend
    b. bight
    c. hitch
    d. slip

2. A common, easy-to-untie knot for forming a loop is a

    a. bowline
    b. clove hitch
    c. tautline hitch
    d. sheet bend

3. Which of the following can be used to join two ropes of unequal diameter?

    a. clove hitch
    b. sheet bend
    c. running bowline
    d. butterfly

CHAPTER 4 - CLIMBING EQUIPMENT

MATCHING

D	hitch cord	A.	personal protective equipment
H	friction-saving device	B.	weighted cord used to set a line
C	bridge	C.	attachment point on harness
E	quick link	D.	cordage (often smaller diameter) used to tie a friction hitch
A	PPE	E.	connecting link; can be tightened with a wrench
F	ascender	F.	rope-gripping climbing aid
B	throwline	G.	light-duty pulleys, often used to tend slack
G	micropulley	H.	installed to reduce friction at the tie-in point

TRUE/FALSE

1. **TRUE** It is possible to buy gear that does not meet standards or regulations for tree climbing gear.
2. **TRUE** Advantages to using a friction-saving device when tying in include reduced wear on the climbing line and less chance of damaging the tree.
3. **TRUE** If a carabiner is used, it must be loaded only along its major axis.
4. **TRUE** Carabiners and snaps used for climbing must have a minimum tensile strength of 5,000 lb (23 kN).
5. **FALSE** Old, worn, or cut climbing lines must be used for rigging applications only.
6. **TRUE** Work-positioning lanyards must meet the same strength requirements for ropes and hardware.
7. **TRUE** Climbing ropes should be inspected daily before use.
8. **TRUE** Climbing helmets are more comfortable and better-fitted, offer additional side protection, and stay in place much better than standard hard hats.
9. **FALSE** Climbing spurs are acceptable for use in climbing trees whenever the spurs' marks will not be obvious.
10. **FALSE** Earmuff-type hearing protection is suitable for tree work, but earplugs do not meet safety standards.
11. **TRUE** A throwline can be used to set a climbing line in a tree.
12. **FALSE** Because it is used in climbing, a throwline is considered life-support equipment.

13. **FALSE** Ropes with spliced eyes cannot be used for tree climbing.
14. **TRUE** Gear inspections should be conducted daily, periodically, and after any incident.
15. **TRUE** Some friction-saving devices can be installed and retrieved from the ground.
16. **TRUE** Mechanical friction devices function in place of, or in addition to, a friction hitch.
17. **FALSE** Hitch cords are typically larger in diameter than the climbing line to which they are tied.
18. **TRUE** It is a good idea to alternate the ends of the climbing line, if practical, to the opposite end of the line so that the line wears evenly.
19. **TRUE** All climbing gear employed must meet applicable standards, be used according to manufacturers' recommendations, and be maintained in good working order.
20. **TRUE** As a general rule, textiles and plastics have a specified shelf life, beginning from the date of manufacture.

SAMPLE TEST QUESTIONS

1. All of the following are a requirement of carabiners used for climbing *except*:

   a. be self-closing and self-double locking
   b. have a minimum tensile strength of 5,000 lb (23 kN)
   c. be constructed of stainless steel
   d. only be loaded along the major axis

2. In addition to being a safety device, the climbing line helps a climber to

   a. access branch tips
   b. maintain balance in the tree
   c. keep both hands free for working
   d. all of the above

3. Climbing gear must be inspected

   a. daily before use, visually for wear and defects
   b. periodically, including a functionality test
   c. after any incident in which the gear was involved
   d. all of the above

CHAPTER 5 - PREPARING TO CLIMB

MATCHING

G	conk	A.	tool used to "sound" for decay
D	access line	B.	thin, slick cordage for installing a climbing line
B	throwline	C.	tree without branches
A	mallet	D.	second climbing line pre-installed for emergency
H	gaffing out	E.	bringing an injured climber to the ground
F	trunk flare	F.	root crown
C	spar	G.	fruiting body of a decay fungus
E	aerial rescue	H.	climbing spikes dislodging from a tree

TRUE/FALSE

1. **TRUE** If there are electrical conductors nearby, workers must know and abide by minimum approach distances (MAD).
2. **FALSE** The pre-climb inspection is limited to checking for electrical hazards and tree defects.
3. **TRUE** Signs of decay in the root crown (trunk flare) could indicate a defect that can lead to whole-tree failure.
4. **TRUE** Snow, vines, debris, soil, and landscaping could hide conks or fruiting bodies of decay organisms, which indicate decay in the tree.
5. **FALSE** Dieback in the top of the tree could indicate root damage but is never a serious concern.
6. **TRUE** Along the trunk, included bark, cankers, and other structural defects could result in trunk failure.
7. **TRUE** A throwing knot can be used in an open or closed form; the closed version will not come undone when the rope is thrown.
8. **FALSE** If friction from tree bark makes it challenging to get a throw weight down to the ground, the only option is to pull the line out and begin again.
9. **TRUE** A poorly managed throwline can easily become a rat's nest of tangled string when some loose twigs and leaves get involved.
10. **TRUE** Sloughing of fronds is a leading cause for fatalities among climbers in fan palms, as they can pose an asphyxiation risk, which is why climbing and pruning from under the skirt must be avoided.

11.	**FALSE**	Ladders are never an acceptable means of entering a tree.
12.	**TRUE**	Using climbing spikes to climb trees for pruning is generally unacceptable and strongly discouraged because it can do irreparable damage to a tree.
13.	**TRUE**	When using climbing spikes, the correct placement of the feet should be at a comfortable, natural-feeling distance apart on the tree, approximately shoulder-distance apart.
14.	**TRUE**	Lanyards that have a wire core should not be assumed to provide protection from cutting with a chain saw.
15.	**TRUE**	The tie-in method for working on a spar must allow the climber to be secured while working, but should also allow for quick and easy descent, if necessary.
16.	**FALSE**	When calling for emergency assistance, it is best to give the location information as quickly as possible, then hang up and return to the victim.
17.	**FALSE**	The rescue kit should be kept on the truck at all times so that every worker knows where to look for it in an emergency.
18.	**FALSE**	Emergency personnel will generally defer to crew members to perform an aerial rescue.
19.	**TRUE**	A victim should not be moved unless necessary, such as to perform CPR or control serious bleeding.
20.	**TRUE**	In an aerial rescue, both the victim and the rescuer must remain secured at all times.

SAMPLE TEST QUESTIONS

1. When performing a pre-climb inspection, in addition to looking for hazards, the climber should

   a. perform a thorough root crown excavation to look for decay
   b. always use both a mallet and a probe on each tree climbed
   c. plan the climb, look for a tie-in point, and consider loads
   d. determine each branch to prune or remove in the tree

2. The main limitation to using a throwline to install a climbing line in a tree is

   a. that the line cannot be installed higher than 30 ft (10 m)
   b. the inability to inspect the tie-in point from the ground
   c. that it is not possible to install a line over a branch and around the main stem
   d. that the line must always pass over only one branch

3. When considering whether to attempt an aerial rescue, it is essential to consider

   a. electrical and other potential hazards to the rescuer
   b. the safety of the rescuer and other workers
   c. whether the victim can self-rescue
   d. all of the above

CHAPTER 6 - MOVING ROPE SYSTEMS

MATCHING

E	split-tail	A.	change in the path of the climbing line
H	open hitch	B.	inefficient ascent technique used with MRS
B	body-thrust	C.	tied in a tail to prevent it from slipping through
F	closed hitch	D.	device to reduce friction at the tie-in point
C	stopper knot	E.	separate cord used to tie the friction hitch
A	redirect	F.	tied with both ends of the hitch cord connected
D	friction-saving device	G.	rope ascent technique that utilizes ascenders
G	rope walking	H.	friction hitch with a "loose" unconnected tail

TRUE/FALSE

1. **TRUE** Climbing systems can be divided into two main types: moving rope systems (MRS) and stationary rope systems (SRS).
2. **FALSE** Moving rope systems are so named because the climbing line moves through the friction hitch.
3. **TRUE** Because the climbing line is doubled in MRS, the climber's weight is split between the two parts of the line, creating a mechanical advantage for the climber.
4. **TRUE** With MRS ascent, though only half of the climber's body weight must be pulled when ascending, the climber advances only 1 ft (30 cm) for every 2 ft (60 cm) of line pulled.
5. **TRUE** The position of the tie-in point affects the climber's ability to access various parts of the tree.
6. **FALSE** Because the tie-in point is not part of life support, a strong branch union is not needed.
7. **TRUE** Generally, when selecting a tie-in point, it is desirable to pick a high, central location in the tree.
8. **TRUE** The more vertical the climbing line, the more secure the climber.
9. **TRUE** Friction-saving devices can reduce wear on the climbing line and damage to the tree, and, in some cases, can facilitate climbing.
10. **FALSE** A sheath-type friction-saving device cannot be installed or removed from the ground.

11. **TRUE** Ring-style friction-saving devices can be installed from the ground, but they take some time to learn how to install, adjust, and retrieve, as well as inspect.

12. **TRUE** When tying in with a tautline hitch or a Blake's hitch, a stopper knot such as a figure-8 must be tied in the tail of the friction hitch to prevent the end from going through the friction hitch.

13. **FALSE** Even if a climber uses a climbing line with a spliced eye and attaches to bridge hardware using an approved carabiner, a termination knot is still required.

14. **TRUE** When climbing MRS, the climber will need a climbing line at least twice as long as their final tie-in point is high.

15. **TRUE** A climber must always be tied in or otherwise secured while entering or working in a tree.

16. **FALSE** The body-thrust technique for ascending can be used most effectively when the climbing line is set well away from the trunk of the tree.

17. **FALSE** The rope walking technique for ascent is best applied if the climbing line is set directly adjacent to the tree trunk.

18. **TRUE** When ascending large trees, it may be necessary to reset the climbing line several times.

19. **TRUE** If an MRS climber has to cross around multiple branches or through branch unions, the added friction can make a simple movement much more difficult.

20. **TRUE** A climber uses the climbing line to ascend the tree, access branch tips, maintain balance, and move freely within the tree.

21. **TRUE** The location of the tie-in point affects the climber's ability to keep the line taut and at a good angle for working.

22. **FALSE** The preferred method of limb walking is to walk forward along the limb to prevent tension in the climbing line.

23. **TRUE** Ideally, the angle formed by the trunk below the tie-in point and the climbing line should not exceed 45°.

24. **TRUE** The simplest redirect is achieved by descending down through a branch union above the work.

25. **TRUE** The equipment used for the redirect must meet the same safety standards as other climbing equipment, and the attachment point must be able to support the climber.

26. **TRUE** Using a redirect not only helps improve rope angles, it also can help to achieve safe and efficient work positioning.

27. **FALSE** Double-tying involves installing the climbing line through two branch unions at the tie-in point.

28. **TRUE** Equipment, other than the hand saw, is usually sent up to the climber on the climbing line after the climber is set in the tree.

29. **TRUE** Chain saws should be shut off, with the chain brake engaged, when the climber moves to another position.

30. **TRUE** Throughout the climb, the climber should be pulling the tail of their climbing line through branch unions and untangling it as they go.

SAMPLE TEST QUESTIONS

1. Which of the following is a limitation of MRS climbing?

   a. The climber advances only 1 ft (30 cm) for every 2 ft (60 cm) of line pulled.
   b. Much of the work is done by the upper body, which can be exhausting for the climber.
   c. Both ends of the climbing line must be isolated over a single branch.
   d. All of the above.

2. Most of the time, the best way to install the climbing line at the tie-in point is to pass it

   a. over a lateral branch at least 3 ft (1 m) out from the trunk of the tree
   b. wrapped around a lateral branch, then passed around the trunk of the tree
   c. through a union, around the larger limb or trunk, and over the smaller or lateral branch
   d. wrapped around the trunk a full wrap and over a lateral branch

3. Which of the following is NOT an MRS ascent technique?

   a. body-thrusting
   b. lanyard crawl
   c. secured footlocking
   d. rope walking

CHAPTER 7 - STATIONARY ROPE SYSTEMS

MATCHING

G	basal anchor	A.	changes the path of the climbing line
D	canopy anchor	B.	does not require returning to dismantle
H	ergonomic	C.	functioning together in a system without damage
E	isolated	D.	climbing line tied off at a branch union
F	PSP	E.	passing over only one branch
A	redirect	F.	primary suspension point
B	retrievable	G.	climbing line tied off at the base of a tree
C	compatible	H.	efficient, comfortable, and minimizing bodily damage

TRUE/FALSE

1. **TRUE** While trying new equipment, techniques, and systems, it is essential to read the user manuals and to understand the equipment's intended use, application, and working-load limits.
2. **FALSE** When climbing using stationary rope systems, the rope runs over a branch union or through a friction-saving device, constantly moving as the climber navigates the tree.
3. **TRUE** SRS climbing lines can run through one or more branch unions and are held taut at an anchor point, either at the base of the tree or within the canopy.
4. **TRUE** Climbers may choose to ascend the tree using SRS and transfer to MRS once in the canopy.
5. **TRUE** With stationary rope systems, because the climber's entire body weight is on the single leg of the climbing line, the friction from a friction hitch is insufficient.
6. **TRUE** Using SRS, the climber will often "walk" up the rope, taking small steps, allowing the knee ascender to grip first, followed by the foot ascender.
7. **TRUE** Because it can be fatiguing and transferring to another system for working the tree can be tricky, footlocking has largely been replaced with other SRS methods.
8. **FALSE** An advantage of using a canopy anchor is that it can be configured in ways that make the climbing system lowerable.
9. **FALSE** The line for a basal anchor must be isolated over a single branch union.
10. **TRUE** To install a basal anchor, either the rope can be cinched around the trunk or a separate basal anchoring sling or loop can be installed.

11. **TRUE** The line for a canopy anchor is cinched most often using one of two knots: a running bowline with a Yosemite finish, or an alpine butterfly.

12. **TRUE** When using a basal anchor, a 200 lb (90 kg) climber will be balanced out by about 200 lb of force holding the load at the base of the tree, which will translate to nearly 400 lb (180 kg) in the canopy.

13. **FALSE** The type and size of ropes used with toothed ascenders are not important.

14. **TRUE** With basal anchors, there is so much added rope in the system, the additional stretch can make the system bouncy and challenging.

15. **TRUE** A mechanical friction device serves to provide friction on the climbing line, allowing a climber to ascend and, in some cases, to work the tree and descend.

16. **TRUE** Equipment is compatible when the various components work properly together, function as a system, and do not cause damage to any component.

17. **TRUE** Toothed ascenders are designed for ascent only and cannot be used for work positioning or lateral movement.

18. **TRUE** With SRS, the rope at the PSP is stationary; friction is consistent and is controlled with the friction hitch/device as the climber moves along the stationary rope.

19. **FALSE** Because the friction remains unchanged, redirects are rarely used with SRS climbing.

20. **TRUE** With SRS, when returning from a long limb walk, the climber is now pulling a large portion of their body weight while advancing along the line using a pushing motion.

SAMPLE TEST QUESTIONS

1. An advantage associated with SRS ascent is that

   a. the line pull equals the upward advancement
   b. it is more ergonomic and less fatiguing
   c. the body is in a more upright, comfortable position
   d. all of the above

2. The load at the primary suspension point, with no redirects, would be highest using a/an

   a. basal anchor
   b. canopy anchor
   c. MRS tie-in point
   d. friction-saving device

3. In SRS, a technique that can be employed to make returning from a limb walk much easier is

   a. installing a carabiner in the climbing line and passing the tail of the line through it to create mechanical advantage
   b. installing a redirect above the work area and passing the tail of the climbing line through it and back to the harness
   c. adding a hitch-tending pulley above a mechanical friction device as a mechanical advantage mechanism
   d. reversing the position of the hitch-tending pulley to add friction back into the climbing system

CHAPTER 8 - PRUNING

MATCHING

G	topping	A.	removes a branch back to its point of origin
E	scabbard	B.	hand pruning shears
C	raising	C.	removal of lower branches
H	included bark	D.	excessive removal of inner branches
F	branch collar	E.	sheath for pruning saw
B	secateurs	F.	"swollen" zone at base of branch
D	lion tailing	G.	poor crown reduction technique
A	branch removal cut	H.	sometimes found in codominant branch unions

TRUE/FALSE

1. **TRUE** Improper pruning can cause permanent damage to a tree.
2. **FALSE** Anvil-type hand pruners are preferred over the bypass blade type.
3. **FALSE** Hedge shears are the best tool for pruning most small trees.
4. **FALSE** Most pruning saws are designed to cut on the forward or push stroke.
5. **TRUE** "Bleeding" that results when certain trees are pruned in the spring has little negative effect on the tree.
6. **TRUE** The final pruning cut in branch removal should be made just outside the branch collar.
7. **TRUE** Large or heavy branches should be removed using the three-cut technique.
8. **TRUE** It is preferable to develop a sturdy scaffold branch structure while the tree is young.
9. **FALSE** The branch bark ridge is located under the branch.
10. **FALSE** A tree's growth habit and rate are irrelevant in pruning.
11. **TRUE** Removing a large limb from a very mature tree can cause significant stress.
12. **TRUE** Young trees are generally more tolerant of severe pruning than older, mature trees.
13. **TRUE** Included bark in a branch union can weaken branch attachment.
14. **TRUE** If a young tree has more than one leader, usually one leader should be selected and the others reduced or removed.
15. **FALSE** Topping is the recommended technique for crown reduction.
16. **TRUE** Lion-tailed branches tend to whip and break in the wind because they are slender and end-weighted.

17. **TRUE** Restoration pruning may improve the structure and appearance of a tree that has been topped or storm damaged previously.

18. **FALSE** Pollarding, topiary, espalier, and pleaching are specialty systems of pruning, which are not appropriate for trees.

19. **FALSE** Large, mature trees are generally very tolerant of severe pruning.

20. **FALSE** Tree wound dressings are widely recommended to accelerate healing and prevent insect and disease penetration in wounds.

SAMPLE TEST QUESTIONS

1. The goal in pruning for structure is to

   a. establish a good framework with sturdy branches
   b. encourage development of strong branch unions
   c. reduce future risk of branch failure
   d. all of the above

2. The final cut in removing a branch should be made just outside the

   a. branch collar
   b. cambium layer
   c. trunk taper
   d. internode

3. One result of topping or lion tailing is often the production of

   a. excessive taper
   b. scaffold branches
   c. bark inclusions
   d. watersprouts

CHAPTER 9 - RIGGING

MATCHING 1

C	tensile strength	A.	rope that controls swing of piece
F	clevis/shackle	B.	heavy-duty pulley for rigging
E	sling	C.	breaking strength under static load
B	arborist block	D.	attach rope to the far (brush) end of limb
G	shock load	E.	length of rope or webbing to attach hardware
H	butt-tied	F.	used to connect ropes and equipment
D	tip-tie	G.	strong, sudden dynamic load
A	tagline	H.	tied off at large end of limb

TRUE/FALSE

1. **TRUE** Shock-loading results when ropes are used to stop heavy limbs in motion or free fall.
2. **TRUE** The greater distance a limb drops before its motion is stopped, the greater the load on the rope, hardware, and tree.
3. **FALSE** The use of knots increases the working-load limit of a rope.
4. **TRUE** Dividing the published tensile strength of a rope or piece of equipment by the design factor yields the working-load limit (WLL).
5. **TRUE** Tensile strength is determined under a static load.
6. **TRUE** Dynamic loads can damage ropes, equipment, and trees more quickly than equivalent static loads.
7. **FALSE** Heat and friction are not a problem with synthetic ropes.
8. **FALSE** Carabiners are always oval and aluminum, and have a spring-loaded, auto-locking gate.
9. **TRUE** Compared to running lines through natural branch unions, blocks can decrease wear on ropes, reduce dynamic loading, and limit damage to the tree.
10. **FALSE** Rescue pulleys are heavy-duty pulleys, with a large rotating sheave for the lowering line and a smaller fixed sheave to accept a rope sling.
11. **TRUE** The advantages of friction devices over taking wraps on the tree trunk include reduced wear on the rope and ease of taking up slack.
12. **TRUE** In tree work, a bollard is a cylinder that straps to the tree and is used for taking wraps in a load line.

13. **TRUE** Using pulleys can reduce the wear on rigging lines.
14. **FALSE** If the load line is rigged at the brushy end of a limb, it is butt-tied.
15. **FALSE** Taglines, or pull lines, are used for lowering heavy limbs.
16. **TRUE** An advantage to balancing a limb is that it can help reduce swing and dynamic loading.
17. **FALSE** A hinge cut is made by cutting slightly more than halfway through a section from the side, then cutting from the opposite side, about an inch or more offset from the first cut.
18. **TRUE** A cut that is handy for controlling relatively small sections of wood that may not require roping is the snap cut.
19. **TRUE** A skillful ground worker can minimize the effect of dynamic loading created by stopping a falling limb with the rigging line by "letting it run."
20. **FALSE** Ground workers should never wear gloves when operating the ropes in rigging operations.

MATCHING 2

D	drop cut	A.	force opposite the relative motion
F	running bowline	B.	used to take wraps on load line
H	snap cut	C.	area where pieces are dropped or lowered
B	friction device	D.	classic three-point cut
C	drop zone	E.	forces on stationary objects
G	mechanical advantage	F.	knot used to tie off limbs
E	statics	G.	can multiply pulling power
A	friction	H.	bypassing cuts made from opposite sides

SAMPLE TEST QUESTIONS

1. An advantage to using an installed block instead of a natural branch union as a rigging point is

   a. more flexibility in placement of the rigging point
   b. the friction is more controlled
   c. it minimizes damage to the tree
   d. all of the above

2. The reaction force at the rigging block can be

   a. approximately half the load in the rigging line
   b. approximately twice the load in the rigging line
   c. greater when lifting limbs
   d. increased if a low-friction block is used

3. Dynamic loads in a rigging system are a concern because

   a. the load can be many times the weight of the piece
   b. shock-loading is tougher than static-loading on ropes and hardware
   c. they can be more difficult to estimate or predict
   d. all of the above

CHAPTER 10 - REMOVAL

MATCHING

B	cant hook	A.	typically greater than 70°
F	notch cut	B.	device used to roll large logs
G	bucking	C.	should never cut into the hinge
E	limbing	D.	helps steer the tree in a felling operation
A	open-face notch	E.	removing side limbs of felled trees
H	barber chair	F.	wedge-shaped cut to direct tree fall
C	back cut	G.	cutting log into smaller lengths
D	hinge	H.	tree pivots or splits up behind hinge when felling

TRUE/FALSE

1. **TRUE** Before beginning any felling operation, the tree and site should be inspected for potential hazards.
2. **TRUE** Hollow trees can present difficulties in controlling the direction of fall.
3. **FALSE** The lean and shape of the tree are important, but species characteristics are irrelevant in felling operations.
4. **TRUE** It is best to plan a tree's removal before any cuts are made.
5. **TRUE** The preferred escape route for the chain saw operator in a felling operation is 45° on either side of a line drawn opposite the intended direction of fall.
6. **TRUE** A pull line and/or wedges can be used to help control a tree's fall.
7. **FALSE** When felling a tree, the notch should be cut at least 50 percent of the way through the tree.
8. **TRUE** A "dogleg" in the pull line can cause the tree to rotate on the cut, misdirecting the fall.
9. **TRUE** A rule of thumb for the depth of the notch is one-third or less of the diameter of the tree.
10. **TRUE** The hinge of wood formed behind the notch controls the tree's direction of fall.
11. **FALSE** The back cut should always be made slightly lower than the apex of the notch.
12. **TRUE** An advantage of the open-face notch is that it controls the fall of the tree longer.
13. **FALSE** After a tree has been felled, bucking should take place before limbing.
14. **TRUE** Branches or logs that are under tension can present a hazard when cut.
15. **TRUE** The height of a tree can be estimated using a stick and the principle of similar right triangles.

SAMPLE TEST QUESTIONS

1. Cutting large logs into smaller sections is known as

   a. felling
   b. limbing
   c. bucking
   d. notching

2. If a tree pivots or splits upward during felling, it is sometimes called

   a. bucking
   b. barber chairing
   c. hinging
   d. wedging

3. When felling a tree using the conventional 45° notch, the back cut should be made

   a. even with the apex of the notch
   b. just below the apex of the notch
   c. just above the apex of the notch
   d. directly through the apex of the notch

CHAPTER 11 - CABLING

MATCHING

E	lag hooks	A.	brings limbs closer together
D	eye splice	B.	used with threaded rod
H	eye bolt	C.	increases bend size and reduces wear on cable
B	amon-eye nut	D.	attaches soft cable to hardware
G	ship auger	E.	do not use in decayed wood
C	thimble	F.	helps pull cable taut
F	Haven grip	G.	for predrilling holes
A	come-along	H.	hardware that is through-bolted

TRUE/FALSE

1. **TRUE** In most cases, a tree should be pruned, if needed, before cables are installed.
2. **TRUE** Dynamic (fiber) cables allow movement and limit shock-loading, but can girdle stems and are subject to UV degradation and wildlife chewing.
3. **FALSE** Cables should be installed one-third the distance from the branch union to the branch tips.
4. **FALSE** Properly installed cables should be parallel to the ground.
5. **FALSE** Cables should always be installed perpendicular to the larger limb.
6. **TRUE** When properly installed, the cable should be just taut.
7. **TRUE** Cables installed while a tree is in leaf may slacken following leaf drop.
8. **TRUE** Lags should only be used in limbs less than 10 in (25 cm) in diameter and when no decay is present.
9. **FALSE** When installing more than one cable on a limb, the cables must be installed directly over each other.
10. **TRUE** Two cables should never be installed on a single eye bolt or lag.
11. **TRUE** If EHS cable is used, dead-end grips must be used to attach the cable to the hardware.
12. **FALSE** Thimbles are not required with dead-end grips.
13. **TRUE** When installing lags, the hole should be drilled approximately 1/16 to 1/8 in (1.5 to 3 mm) smaller than the lag diameter.
14. **FALSE** An eye splice cannot be formed when using common-grade, 7-strand cable.

15. **TRUE** Swage-stops, or cable-stops, are fasteners that hold a cable after the cable is passed through the branch.

16. **TRUE** The cable should be installed in direct line with the hardware.

17. **FALSE** Most dynamic cable systems are attached to a tree exactly the same way steel cables are attached.

18. **TRUE** A shock-absorbing component can be installed with some dynamic cabling systems.

19. **FALSE** If a cable is installed correctly, at right angles with the line that bisects the branch union, the hardware will usually be installed perpendicular to both branches.

20. **TRUE** If multiple cables are required and crown movement is desired, a box or rotary system can be installed.

SAMPLE TEST QUESTIONS

1. A device commonly used to bring two limbs closer together in cabling operations is a

   a. Haven grip
   b. come-along
   c. cable aid
   d. cable clamp

2. When installing extra-high-strength (EHS) cable, the cable can be attached to the hardware using

   a. dead-end grips
   b. an eye splice
   c. cable clamps
   d. all of the above

3. The recommended height/distance for installing cables is

   a. as close to the branch union as possible
   b. one-third the distance from the branch union to the tips
   c. half the distance from the branch union to the tips
   d. two-thirds the distance from the branch union to the tips

GLOSSARY OF ARBORICULTURAL TERMS

3-strand rope—rope construction in which three strands are twisted together in a spiral pattern

12-strand rope—for arborist ropes, a braided-rope construction consisting of 12 strands, with most being coreless; there are two types of 12-strand construction: a tight braid that is not easily spliceable, used for climbing and rigging lines, and a loose, easily spliceable "hollow" (e.g., coreless) braid, commonly used for slings

16-strand rope—for arborist ropes, a rope construction that has a 16-strand, braided, load-bearing cover and a filler core that is not significant in load carrying

24-strand rope—for arborist ropes, a braided rope that has a 24-strand cover and a core

abiotic—nonliving

absorbing roots—fine, fibrous roots that take up water and minerals; most absorbing roots are within the top 12 in (30 cm) of soil

access line—second climbing line hung in a tree to reach a victim in an emergency

aerial rescue—bringing an injured worker down from a tree or aerial lift device

alternate leaf arrangement—one leaf or bud at each node, situated at alternating positions along the stem; in this arrangement, the leaves are not directly across from each other

amon-eye nut—specialized nut used in cabling trees that has a large eye for attaching a cable to a threaded rod; used as part of the cable anchor in the tree

anatomy—1) study of the structure and composition of plants and other living organisms. 2) structure and composition of plants and other living organisms

anchor—1) in SRS climbing, the point at which the climbing line is secured. 2) in rigging, the point at which the rigging system is secured or where friction is controlled. 3) in cabling, hardware to which support cable is affixed

anchor hitch—knot commonly used to attach a line to a piece of hardware

ANSI Z133 standards—in the United States, industry-developed, national consensus safety standards of practice for tree care

approved—in the context of standards and specifications, that which is acceptable to federal, state, provincial, or local enforcement authorities or is an accepted industry practice

arboriculture—practice and study of the care of trees and other woody plants in the landscape

arborist—a professional who possesses the technical competence, through experience and related training, to provide for or supervise the management of trees and other woody plants in residential, commercial, and public landscapes

arborist block—heavy-duty pulley with an integrated connection point (bushing) for attaching a rope sling, a rotating sheave for the rope, and extended cheek plates; used in tree rigging operations

ascender—a mechanical device that enables a climber to ascend a rope; attached to the rope, it will grip in one direction (down) and slide in the other (up)

axillary bud—bud in the axil of a leaf; lateral bud

back cut—cut made on a tree trunk or branch, opposite from the notch and toward the notch cut or face cut, to complete felling or branch removal

balance—in rigging, a technique for lowering a limb without allowing either end to drop

barber chair—dangerous condition created when a tree or branch splits upward vertically from the back cut, slab up

barrier zone—chemically defended tissue formed by the still-living cambium, after a tree is wounded or invaded by pathogens, to inhibit the spread of decay into new annual growth rings

basal anchor—in SRS climbing, the means of securing the climbing line at the base of a tree

bend—type of knot used to join two rope ends together

bend ratio—ratio of the diameter of a branch, sheave, or other object to the diameter of the rope that is wrapped around it

bight—curve or arc in a rope between the working end and the standing part

biotic—pertaining to living organisms

Blake's hitch—open friction hitch used by climbers, sometimes in place of the tautline hitch or Prusik knot

block—heavy-duty pulley used in rigging; designed for dynamic loading

block and tackle—a mechanism of pulleys and rope used to gain mechanical advantage in lifting and pulling

body-thrust—method of ascending a tree using a moving rope system

bollard—post on which wraps can be taken with a rope to tie it off or to provide friction for control

bore cut—back-cut technique in which the hinge is established by plunge cutting through the stem, then cutting back away from the hinge; plunge cut

bowline—loop knot used to form an endline loop in a rope, often to attach items to the rope

branch bark ridge—raised strip of bark at the top of a branch union, where the growth and expansion of the trunk or parent stem and adjoining branch push the bark into a ridge

branch collar—the swollen area where a branch joins the trunk or another branch, created by the overlapping vascular tissues from both the branch and the trunk

branch protection zone—chemically and physically modified tissue within the trunk or parent branch at the base of a subordinate branch that retards the spread of discoloration and decay from the subordinate stem into the trunk or parent branch

branch removal cut—cut that removes a branch at its point of origin

branch union—point where a branch originates from the trunk or another branch

bridge—part of a climbing saddle (harness) intended for attachment to the climbing line, allowing the connecting device to slide for increased mobility

bucking—cutting of a tree trunk or log into shorter, manageable sections

burr—undesirable raised sliver of metal on a piece of equipment which can damage rope or other gear

butterfly knot—knot that can be used to form a loop in the standing part of a line; midline loop knot

butt-hitching—method of lowering pieces when the rigging point is below the work, traditionally without the use of a block

buttress roots—roots at the trunk base that help support the tree and equalize mechanical stress

butt-tied (butt-tying)—tying off a limb at the butt end for rigging

cable aid—device used to tighten lags and aid in cable installation

cable-stop termination—in tree support systems, metal fitting that can be affixed to the ends of steel cable strands to terminate a cable installation

cabling—installation of steel or synthetic cable in a tree to provide supplemental support to weak branches or branch unions

caliper—thickness or diameter of the trunk of a tree taken at a standard height, used in specifying nursery stock

cambium—thin layer(s) of meristematic cells that give rise (outward) to the phloem and (inward) to the xylem, increasing stem and root diameter

Canadian Standards Association (CSA)—Canadian not-for-profit association made up of representatives from government agencies, industry, and other stakeholders, providing standards documentation and training materials; serves a similar role as the American National Standards Institute (ANSI) in the United States

canker—a discrete, localized, usually necrotic area on stems, roots, and branches; often sunken and discolored

canopy anchor—in SRS climbing, the means of securing the climbing line in the canopy of the tree

cant hook—a long-handled lever fixed with a blunt metal end to handle logs; includes a swinging metal hook opposing the blunt end to create leverage

carabiner (karabiner)—aluminum or steel connecting device used in climbing and static rigging that is opened and closed by a spring-loaded gate

cardiopulmonary resuscitation (CPR)—an emergency procedure in which chest compressions are used to maintain circulation when the heart has stopped beating

cavity—open or closed hollow within a tree stem, branch, or root, usually associated with decay

chain saw protective pants—trousers manufactured with a protective layer designed to slow or stop a chain saw chain

chaps—form of leg protection or personal protective equipment (PPE) worn over trousers when operating a chain saw

Chicago™ grip—a device designed to clasp and hold EHS cable

chipper—equipment used to grind tree branches into wood chips

clevis—U-shaped fitting with a pin running through it; shackle

climbing harness—work-positioning harness (saddle) designed for climbing trees

climbing helmet—a plastic shell equipped with an adjustable suspension system and a chinstrap, designed to disperse the energy of an object falling on the head; some helmets may be designed to take side, front, and back impacts

climbing hitch—hitch used to secure a tree climber to the climbing line, permitting controlled ascent, descent, and work positioning

climbing line—rope that meets specifications for use in tree climbing

climbing saddle—work-positioning harness designed for climbing trees

climbing spikes / climbing spurs—sharp devices strapped to a climber's lower legs to assist in climbing poles or trees being removed; also called spikes, gaffs, irons, hooks, or climbers

closed hitch—a hitch with both ends of the line captured

clove + half hitches—a combination of knots sometimes used to secure a rope to a tree section in rigging

clove hitch—knot used to secure an object to a rope or a rope to an object

codominant branches / codominant stems—forked branches nearly the same size in diameter, arising from a common junction and lacking a normal branch union

come-along—portable device, consisting of cable winches or rope winches, used to draw two objects closer together; simple arrangement of rope knots and loops to create mechanical advantage

command-and-response system—system of vocal communication in tree care operations used to convey critical information and ensure understanding by another worker, often between a worker aloft and a ground worker

common-grade, 7-strand, galvanized cable—steel cable construction in which seven strands are twisted together in a spiral pattern; often used to add structural support to trees; terminated by wrapping onto itself

compartmentalization—natural defense process in trees by which chemical and physical boundaries are created that act to limit the spread of disease and decay organisms

Compartmentalization of Decay in Trees (CODIT)—model for the natural defense process in trees by which chemical and physical boundaries are created that act to limit the spread of disease and decay organisms

compatible—components that are approved by the manufacturer(s) for use together, and thereby work properly together, function as a system, and do not cause damage to any other component

compound leaf—leaf with two or more leaflets; compare to *simple leaf*

configuration—the selection and arrangement of components of a climbing system

conifer—cone-bearing tree or other plant that has its seeds in a structure called a cone

conk—fruiting body or nonfruiting body (sterile conk) of a fungus, often associated with decay

connecting link—component of a rigging or climbing system that connects other components

conventional notch—a 45° notch with a horizontal bottom cut; used in removing trees or branches; also called common notch; compare to *Humboldt notch* and *open-face notch*

cordage—general term for ropes and lines

cow hitch—knot commonly used to attach hardware to a tree; should be backed up with a half hitch

crack—separation in wood fibers; narrow breaks or fissures in stems or branches; if severe, may result in tree or branch failure

crazing—producing a network of fine cracks on a surface

crown—upper part of a tree, consisting of the branches and foliage; its length is measured from the lowest branch to the top of the tree

cut-and-chuck method—method of removing a tree in small sections without rigging

cycles to failure—number of times a rope or other piece of equipment can be used with a given load before mechanical failure

daily inspection (gear)—visual inspection of climbing gear, ropes, and other equipment before use each day

damping—decrease in the amplitude (magnitude) of oscillation (movement back and forth) such as the movement of a spar tree when the top is removed

dead-end grips—manufactured wire wrap cable-termination devices that must be used to terminate extra-high-strength cable; may be used to terminate common cable

dead-end hardware—lag-threaded cable anchor or bracing rod that is screwed directly into an undersized, predrilled hole in the tree but which does not pass through to the other side; compare to *through-hardware*

dead-eye sling—rope sling with a single eye spliced in one end; also called an eye sling, a fixed-eye sling, or a spliced-eye sling

deadwooding—removing dead and dying branches from a tree

decay—1) n. a substance undergoing decomposition. 2) v. process of degradation by microorganisms

deciduous—tree or other plant that sheds all of its foliage annually

design factor—factor by which the rated or minimum breaking strength of a rope or piece of equipment is divided in determining its working-load limit

dieback—condition in which the branches in a tree die from the tips toward the main stem

direct contact—any part of the body touching an energized electrical conductor; compare to *indirect contact*

directional knot—knot that performs differently when loaded (pulled) from opposite directions or ends

Distel hitch—a closed friction hitch similar to the tautline hitch, except both ends of the hitch are captured in a connecting link

double braid—rope construction consisting of a braided rope within a braided rope, both of which carry part of the load

double fisherman's knot (bend)—knot commonly used to join two ropes or two ends of the same rope, as when forming a Prusik loop

double-locking (gate)—pertaining to a carabiner, requiring two distinct motions to prepare the gate to open

double-tying—tying in with both ends of the climbing line, or with two climbing lines, in two separate tie-in points

D-rings—D-shaped metal rings on a climber's saddle for attaching ropes and snaps

drip line—imaginary boundary on the soil surface defined by the branch spread of a single plant or group of plants

drop cut—branch-removal technique consisting of an undercut and then a top cut, usually made farther out on the branch

drop zone—predetermined area beneath workers aloft where cut branches or wood sections will be dropped or lowered from a tree, and where the potential exists for struck-by injuries; landing zone

dynamic cable—any of several cabling systems that utilize elastic materials (usually rope of various constructions) for tree support systems

dynamic load—forces created by a moving load; load that changes with time and motion; compare to *static load*

electrical conductor—any body or medium allowing the passage of electricity; while working on trees, this generally would be any overhead or underground electrical wires; includes communication cables and power lines that have electricity or have the potential to carry electricity

emergency response—predetermined set of procedures by which emergency situations are assessed and handled

endline knots—knots tied at the end of a line (such as a bowline or clove hitch)

ergonomic—efficient, comfortable, and minimizing long-term musculoskeletal damage

escape route—in felling operations, the direction for chain saw operator to move while tree is falling; generally 45° on either side of a line drawn opposite the intended direction of fall

espalier—1) n. pruning system that develops a plant in a plane, such as along a wall or a fence. 2) n. a plant trained in that manner. 3) v. to train plants in that manner

evergreen—tree or other plant that does not shed all of its foliage annually

extra-high-strength (EHS) cable—type of 7-strand, steel cable, often used to cable trees; stronger but less flexible than common-grade cable; terminated with dead-end tree grips

eye bolt—cable anchor with a closed eye, usually machine-threaded; only drop-forged eye bolts are accepted and approved for tree support systems in the United States

eye splice—1) closed-eye termination, hand-formed in common-grade cable, to attach the cable to eye bolts or lags. 2) rope termination forming an eye and made by splicing the rope back upon itself

eye-and-eye sling—sling (usually a length of spliced rope) with an eye at each end; also called eye-to-eye sling

eye-spliced rope—a length of rope that has been spliced back upon itself to form an eye in the end

fall—in rigging, the part of the line from the rigging point to the anchor point; compare to *lead*

false crotch—device installed in a tree to set ropes during climbing or rigging because there is not a suitable natural branch union available, or to protect an available union, and/or to reduce wear on ropes

fascicle sheath—the tubular encasement of conifer needles (especially pines) at the point of attachment to the stem

figure-8 knot—knot often used as a safety knot or stopper knot tied in the end of a line

first aid—emergency care or treatment of the injuries or illnesses of a person to stabilize his or her condition before medical help is available

footlock (footlocking)—to climb up a suspended rope by pulling with the hands and arms and pushing upward with the feet; see *secured footlock*

force—any action or influence causing an object to accelerate/decelerate; calculated as mass multiplied by acceleration; is a vector quantity

friction—specific type of force that resists the relative motion between two objects in contact; the direction is always opposite the motion

friction device—in rigging, a device used to take wraps in a load line to provide friction for controlled lowering or climbing

friction hitch—any of numerous knots used in tree climbing or rigging that may alternately slide along and then grip a rope

friction-saving device—type of artificial tie-in point used to reduce damage to the tree and climbing line

frond—large, divided leaf structure found in palms and ferns

fruiting body—reproductive structure of a fungus; the presence of certain species may indicate decay in a tree; see *conk*

gaff—pointed, spur portion of a climbing spike

gaffing out—unexpected slip or fall that occurs when a climber's spikes become dislodged from a tree

girdling root—root that encircles all or part of the trunk of a tree, or other roots, that constricts the vascular tissue and inhibits secondary growth and the movement of water and photosynthates

girth hitch—simple knot used to attach a line, spliced eye, or endless loop to an object

growth rings—rings of xylem that are visible in a cross section of the stem, branches, and roots of some trees; in temperate zones, the rings typically represent one year of growth and are sometimes referred to as annual rings

half hitch—simple knot used to temporarily attach a line to an object; also used as a backup in combination with other knots

hand pruners (hand pruning shears)—tool used for pruning small twigs of less than 1/2 in (13 mm) in diameter

hard hat—protective hat made of a rigid material, usually without a chinstrap, that must be worn when performing ground operations; a form of personal protective equipment (PPE); contrast with *climbing helmet*

Haven grip—device used to clasp and hold common-grade cable

heading cut (heading back)—a pruning cut that removes a branch or stem between nodes (leaving a stub), to a bud, or to a live branch that is less than one-third the diameter of the stem being removed

heartwood—the central wood in a branch or stem characterized by being composed of dead cells; more resistant to decay, generally darker, and harder than the outer sapwood; trees may or may not have heartwood; contrast with *sapwood*

heavy-duty washer—heavy-duty steel hardware installed on through-hardware between the tree surface and the nut; heavy-duty washers are made of thicker metal than standard-duty washers and have a larger outside diameter

hedge shears—manual tool used to trim (shear) hedges

hinge—strip of wood fibers created between the face cut or notch and the back cut that helps control direction in tree or limb removal

hinge cut—sequence of cuts used to control the direction of a limb being removed

hitch—type of knot made when a rope is secured around an object or its own standing part

hitch cord—short length of cordage used to tie a friction hitch in climbing or rigging

hitch-tending pulley—a micropulley installed in a climbing system to advance the friction hitch as the climber ascends

hollow braid—rope construction consisting of a braided rope with no core

Humboldt notch—felling notch that is horizontal on the top and angled on the bottom; also called Humboldt scarf or reverse scarf; compare to *conventional*, or *common, notch* and *open-face notch*

included bark—bark that becomes embedded in a crotch (union) between branch and trunk or between codominant stems; causes a weak structure

indirect contact—touching any conductive object that is in contact with an energized electrical conductor; compare to *direct contact*

internode—region of the stem between two successive nodes

isolate—setting a line in a tree such that it passes over only one branch and both ends of the line follow the same path to the ground

job briefing—the communication of at least the following subjects for arboricultural operations: hazards associated with the job, work procedures involved, special precautions, electrical hazards, job assignments, and personal protective equipment

kerf—space created by a saw cut (the width of the chain or blade)

kernmantle—rope with a cover and a parallel core in which the cover is primarily intended to protect the load-bearing core

kickback—sudden, sometimes violent and uncontrolled backward or upward movement of a chain saw

kickback quadrant—upper quadrant of the tip of a chain saw bar

knot—any of various fastenings formed by looping and tying a rope (or cord) upon itself or to another rope or to another object; general term referring to all knots, bends, and hitches

lag hook (J-lag)—lag-threaded cable anchor with an open eye (J-shaped)

landing zone—predetermined area where cut branches or wood sections will be dropped or lowered from a tree

lanyard—short rope equipped with carabiners, snaps, and/or eye splices; work-positioning lanyards are used for temporarily securing a climber in one place; tool lanyards are used to secure tools or chain saws

lanyard crawl—an ascending technique used in MRS climbing that uses a work-positioning lanyard to assist with upward progress

lateral branch—a branch arising from a larger stem or branch

lateral bud—vegetative bud on the side of a stem; contrast with *terminal bud*

lead—part of a rigging line from the rigging point to the load; compare to *fall*

leader—primary terminal shoot or trunk of a tree; large, usually upright stem; a stem that dominates a portion of the crown by suppressing lateral branches

leaf scar—scar left on the twig after a leaf is shed

leaflet—separate part of a compound leaf blade

leg protection—chaps or other chain saw-resistant clothing worn over the legs when operating a chain saw

leglock method—method of starting a chain saw in which the saw's top handle is held with the left hand and the back of the saw is held tightly between the operator's legs, leaving the right hand free to pull the starting cord; the chain brake must always be engaged when starting a saw

lenticel—small opening in the bark that permits the exchange of gases

life-support equipment—components of climbing gear that are involved with keeping the climber aloft

limb walking—technique of moving laterally along limbs while keeping the climbing line taut

limbing—cutting off the side branches of a felled tree

lion tailing (lion's tailing)—poor pruning practice in which an excessive number of branches is thinned from the inside (lower part) of limbs into a clump of terminal foliage

load line—rope used to lower a tree branch or segment that has been cut

lobe—leaf segment that projects outward, creating voids (sinuses) between the segments

locking (gate)—pertaining to carabiners and snaps, requiring at least one distinct motion to prepare the gate to open (to unlock) but not to actually open

locking snap—connecting device that is self-closing and requires one motion to unlock and a separate motion to open the gate; used by tree climbers primarily for connecting the climbing line to the climbing saddle

lopping shears (loppers)—pruning tool with two long handles used to cut woody stems, typically up to 1 in (2.5 cm) in diameter

lowerable—capable of being lowered from a tree; specific reference commonly refers to a system with the possibility to lower an injured climber

mallet—broad-headed hammer made of wood, plastic, or resin used in the context of tree risk assessment for sounding a tree to detect internal decay

mechanical advantage—system by which effort can be multiplied

mechanical friction device—device used to provide friction for controlled climbing, either in place of, or together with, a friction hitch

Michoacán—type of closed friction hitch (climbing hitch) similar to those in the French Prusik group

micropulley—small, light-duty pulley used in climbing and rigging operations; often used as a knot tender

midline knot—knot tied in the standing part of a line

mineral—naturally occurring, inorganic solid that has a definite chemical composition and possesses characteristic physical properties; certain minerals are considered essential elements for tree growth and development

minimum approach distance (MAD)—the closest distance an employee may approach or bring any conductive object near an energized or utility system grounded object; or the closest distance the employee may be to an energized or utility system grounded object

moving rope system (MRS)—climbing system in which the rope adjustment device advances along a moving climbing line; the doubled rope technique (DdRT) is an example of a moving rope system; contrast with *stationary rope system*

mycorrhizae—symbiotic association between certain fungi and the roots of a plant

natural pruning—an informal system of pruning used to retain and promote the characteristic form of the species in its current location

node—point on a stem from which leaves, branches, and aerial roots are attached

notch—wedge cut into a log or tree for felling

Occupational Safety and Health Administration (OSHA)—in the United States, the federal agency responsible for establishing and enforcing safety work rules in accordance with the Occupational Safety and Health Act

open hitch—hitch with one or both ends not captured or secured

open-face notch—wedge-shaped cut (about 70° or greater) used in felling trees or removing tree sections; compare to *conventional*, or *common, notch* and *Humboldt notch*

opposite leaf arrangement—leaves or branches situated two at each node, across from each other on the stem; compare to *alternate leaf arrangement*

palm skirt—layers of dead fronds that may remain attached and hanging along some or all of the length of the trunk of certain palms

peavey—stout, wooden lever fitted with a strong, sharp spike and a hook; used for rolling logs

peen—act of bending, rounding, or flattening the end of through-hardware for the purpose of preventing the nut from backing off

periodic inspection—inspection that is conducted regularly (often monthly or quarterly), depending on applicable regulations or the extent of use

personal protective equipment (PPE)—personal safety gear such as hard hat, safety glasses, hearing protection, and chain saw-protective trousers or chaps

phloem—plant vascular tissue that transports photosynthates and growth regulators; situated on the inside of the bark, just outside the cambium; is bidirectional (transports up and down); compare to *xylem*

photosynthesis—process in green plants (and in algae and some bacteria) by which light energy is used to form glucose (chemical energy) from water and carbon dioxide

physiology—in arboriculture, the study of the life function of a tree

pleaching—pruning system that trains one or more plants to achieve a desired shape or form through a combination of pruning and interweaving or tying small branches to one another or to a preformed frame

pole pruner—long-handled, scissors-like tool used to make small pruning cuts to branches that cannot be reached with hand tools

pole saw—long-handled tool with a pruning saw on the end

pollarding—semiformal pruning system that maintains crown size by initial heading of branches on young trees or young portions of older trees, followed by removal of sprouts to their point of origin at appropriate intervals, without disturbing the resulting pollard heads

pore space—air- and water-filled spaces between soil particles

post-incident inspection—inspection of gear or equipment following an unplanned event

primary suspension point (PSP)—the position in the tree where the climbing line is anchored or crosses over that experiences the highest loads during the climb; this term is used mostly with SRS

probe—stiff, small-diameter rod, stick, or wire that is inserted into a cavity or crack to estimate its size or depth

pruning saw—hand saw designed for pruning trees, generally with a bowed blade and teeth oriented for cutting on the pull stroke

Prusik hitch—type of multi-wrapped friction hitch used in climbing and rigging; a common use is to attach the Prusik loop to the climbing line when footlocking

Prusik loop—loop of rope used to form a Prusik hitch for climbing or rigging

pull line—line attached near the top of a tree or tree section to be felled, or to any tree section being removed, to help pull or guide it in the desired direction or to control its swing

pulley—device consisting of a rotating, grooved wheel between two side plates; used to change the direction of pull in a line

quick link—metal connector hardware with a screw-type fastener, used to attach ropes or other climbing hardware

radius—distance from the center to the perimeter of a circle

raising—selective removal of lower limbs from a tree to provide clearance; lifting

ray—parenchyma tissues that extend radially across the xylem and phloem of a tree and function in transport, storage, and defense

reaction zone—natural boundary formed chemically within a tree to separate damaged wood from existing healthy wood; important in the process of compartmentalization; compare to *barrier zone*

reactive force—force generated in response and opposite to another force, often demonstrated when operating a chain saw

redirect—1) v. change the path of a climbing or rigging line to modify the forces on, or the direction of, the line. 2) n. system installed to change the path of a climbing or rigging line

reduction—pruning to decrease height and/or spread of a branch or crown

reduction cut—pruning cut that removes the larger of two or more branches or stems, or one or more codominant stems, to a live lateral branch, typically at least one-third the diameter of the stem or branch being removed

rescue kit—climbing gear and emergency equipment that should be set out on every jobsite and available to conduct an aerial rescue and apply first aid

rescue pulley—light-duty pulley used in light rigging operations

restoration—1) pruning to improve the structure, form, and appearance of trees that have been severely headed, vandalized, or damaged. 2) management and planting to restore altered or damaged ecosystems

retrievable—capable of being removed or dismantled without returning to the point of attachment

rigging—method of using ropes and hardware to control or direct the descent of cut material or to handle heavy loads

rigging point—placement in the tree (in a natural branch union, installed arborist block, or any other point through which the load line passes) to control rigging operations

risk reduction pruning—pruning that is designed to reduce the risk of tree failure and mitigate potential safety hazards

root crown—area where the main roots join the plant stem, usually at or near ground level; root collar

root mat—dense network of roots; in palms, near the base of the stem

rope angle—in tree climbing, the angle at the tie-in point or redirect that the climbing line makes away from vertical, straight down

rope snap—connecting device used by tree climbers, primarily for connecting the work-positioning lanyard to the harness

rope walking—technique for ascending a rope using a combination of ascenders, including at least one knee or foot ascender to grip the line, allowing the climber to "walk" up the rope, maintaining a vertical body position

running bowline—bowline knot with the standing part of the line running through the loop; often used to tie off and control branches or tree sections that are to be removed

sapwood—outer wood (xylem) that actively transports water and minerals; compare to *heartwood*

sapwood decay—decay located in the sapwood; bark and/or cambium may be damaged or dead; signs of this classification of rot are usually numerous, but small, fruiting bodies along the bark's surface are common

scabbard—protective sheath for a pruning saw or other tool

scaffold branches—permanent branches that form the scaffold or structure of a tree

Schwabisch—type of closed friction hitch (climbing hitch) considered to be an asymmetric version of the Prusik

screw link—connecting device with a threaded closure mechanism; used to secure equipment or tree sections in rigging operations

secateurs—pruning tool intended for cutting single, small-diameter stems; also called pruning shears or hand pruners

secured footlock—method of ascending a rope by wrapping the rope around the feet, in which the climber utilizes an additional means of securing against a fall

self-double locking—when describing carabiners, requiring three distinct motions to open the gate and to auto-close and auto-lock when the gate is released

serration—sawtoothed margin of a leaf, with the teeth pointed forward

shackle—U-shaped fitting with a pin running through it; clevis

shall—word that designates a mandatory requirement within the ANSI standards or contract documents; compare to *should*

sheet bend—knot used to attach two lines; the lines can be of unequal diameter; *not* to be used for life support

ship auger—type of drill bit with an open spiral form; used to drill holes in trees for cable or bracing installation

shock-loading—dynamic, sudden force placed on a rope or rigging apparatus when a moving load or piece is stopped

shot pouch—weighted sack used to set climbing or rigging lines in trees; usually a shot-filled, teardrop-shaped canvas bag; also known as a throw weight or throwbag

should—word that designates an advisory recommendation in the ANSI standards or contract documents; compare to *shall*

simple leaf—single-bladed leaf; not composed of leaflets; compare to *compound leaf*

skinning—process of removing old leaf bases from palms

sling—device used in rigging to secure equipment or pieces being rigged

slip knot—slipped overhand knot

sloughing—the detachment of large sections of palm frond rings

snap cut—cutting technique in which offset, bypassing cuts are made so that a section can be broken off easily; also known as mismatch cut

spar—standing trunk or main stem of a tree without a crown and lateral limbs

spliced eye—a loop spliced into the end of cordage

split-tail—separate, short length of rope used to tie the friction hitch in a climbing system

spurs—see *climbing spikes/climbing spurs*

standing end—the end of a rope not in use; compare to *standing part* and *working end*

standing part—inactive part of a rope, as opposed to the working end; compare to *standing end* and *working end*

starch—chain of sugar molecules linked together that serves as a form of energy storage in plants

static cable—semi-rigid cabling material, typically made of steel

static load—constant load exerted by a mass due to its weight; compare to *dynamic load*

stationary rope system (SRS)—climbing system in which the rope adjustment device moves along a stationary climbing line; contrast with *moving rope system*

stomates—small apertures, between two guard cells on the undersides of leaves and other green plant parts, through which gases are exchanged and water loss is regulated

stopper knot—knot, usually a figure-8 knot, tied in the end of a line or in the tail of a knot to prevent the end or tail from passing through the knot

stress—factor that negatively affects the health of a tree

structural root zone (SRZ)—area around a tree that contains the minimum amount of roots required for tree stability

strumming—technique of plucking the cord of a throwline to help bring the throw weight to the ground

swage-stop termination—metal fitting used to terminate a cable

swivel—part of a connecting device, or device itself, that rotates to prevent lines from twisting, often installed on the bridge of a harness

tagline—rope used to control the swing of a limb being removed; rope used to control the direction or fall of a tree or limb being removed

taper—change in diameter over the length of trunks, branches, and roots

tautline hitch—type of friction hitch used by climbers for fall protection during ascent, descent, and work positioning

tensile strength—force at which a new piece of equipment or rope in testing fails under a static load

terminal bud—bud at the tip of a twig or shoot; apical bud; compare to *lateral bud*

tether—a short line or other device to connect components, often to control or restrict movement, or to pull a component along a line

thimble—1) device used in cabling to form and protect the termination loop in the cable. 2) a device used in rope attachment to increase the bend radius and reduce wear on the rope

thinning—selective pruning to reduce density of live branches; removing unwanted branches and limbs to provide light or air penetration through the tree or to lighten the weight of the remaining branches

threaded rod—machine-threaded steel rod used for through-brace installations; bracing rod

through-hardware—cable anchors or bracing rods that pass completely through an oversized, predrilled hole in a trunk or branch and are secured with nuts and washers; compare to *dead-end hardware*

throw weight—weighted sack used to set climbing or rigging lines in trees; usually a shot-filled, teardrop-shaped canvas bag; also known as a shot pouch or throwbag

throwing knot—series of loops and wraps tied in a rope to form a weight for throwing

throwline—thin, lightweight cord attached to a throw weight or used to set climbing or rigging lines in trees

tie-in point—position in a tree (in a natural branch union or installed device) through which the climbing line is set to serve as the top rope placement for work positioning; this term is used mostly with MRS

timber hitch—knot consisting of a series of wraps on a line and used to secure equipment to a tree

tip-tied (tip-tying)—tying a line on the tip (brush) end of a branch to be removed, allowing the branch to be lowered butt-end first

topiary—a formal pruning system that uses a combination of pruning, supporting, and training branches to orient a plant into a desired shape; hedging is a subset of topiary

topping—reduction of tree size by cutting live branches and leaders to stubs, without regard to long-term tree health or structural integrity

transpiration—water vapor loss through the stomata of leaves

triple-action carabiner—carabiner that requires three distinct motions to open the gate

trunk flare—transition zone from trunk to roots where the trunk expands into the structural roots; root flare

***Valdôtain tresse* (Vt)**—variation of the *Valdôtain* friction hitch with added braids; used in climbing and rigging

vascular bundle—grouping of xylem and phloem tissues in distinct units that serve to transport water and other materials

vascular system—phloem and xylem, the parts of a tree that conduct water or nutrients

vascular wilt—disease caused by xylem-colonizing pathogens that interfere with water transport and induce loss of turgor and rigidity of leaves or young stems

watersprout—upright, epicormic shoot arising from the trunk or branches of a plant above the root graft or soil line; although incorrect, also called a sucker, which is a shoot arising from the roots

webbing—sturdy fabric woven in narrow widths for use where a strong connector or redirect is required

whoopie sling—sling with one fixed eye and one adjustable eye, made from hollow-braid rope

whorled—leaves, twigs, or branches arranged in a circle around a point on the stem

work plan—the crew's strategy for how to complete the job, including work assignments

working end—end part of a rope in use for rigging or climbing; compare to *standing end* and *standing part*

working-load limit (WLL)—tensile strength divided by design factor; maximum load that should not be exceeded in a piece of equipment, rope, or rope assembly when performing its normal working function

work-positioning lanyard—a component of a climbing system, used for both body stabilizing and redundancy while cutting, consisting of a flexible line of rope or strap that may incorporate a knot or mechanical device to allow for adjustability

wound dressing—compound applied to tree wounds or pruning cuts

woundwood—lignified, differentiated tissues produced on woody plants as a response to wounding

xylem—main water- and mineral-conducting tissue in trees and other plants; provides structural support, becoming wood after lignifying; is unidirectional (conducts up only); compare to *phloem*

REFERENCES

American National Standards Institute. 2013. *American National Standard for Tree Care Operations—Tree, Shrub, and Other Woody Plant Management—Standard Practices (Supplemental Support Systems)* (A300, Part 3). Manchester (NH, USA): Tree Care Industry Association. 24 p.

American National Standards Institute. 2017. *American National Standard for Arboricultural Operations—Safety Requirements* (Z133). Champaign (IL, USA): International Society of Arboriculture. 74 p.

American National Standards Institute. 2017. American National Standard: *Tree, Shrub, and Other Woody Plant Management—Standard Practices (Pruning)* (A300, Part 1). Manchester (NH, USA): Tree Care Industry Association. 33 p.

Arborist Ropes [online course]. Atlanta (GA, USA): International Society of Arboriculture. Available from: https://wwv.isa-arbor.com/store/product/762

Arborists' Knots for Climbing and Rigging [DVD and workbook]. 2006. Champaign (IL, USA): International Society of Arboriculture.

Basic Training for Tree Climbers [DVD and workbook]. 1999. Champaign (IL, USA) and Londonderry (NH, USA): International Society of Arboriculture and Tree Care Industry Association.

Chainsaw Safety, Maintenance, and Cutting Techniques [DVD and workbook]. 1998. ArborMaster Training Video Series. Champaign (IL, USA): International Society of Arboriculture.

Dirr MA. 2011. *Dirr's Encyclopedia of Trees and Shrubs*. Portland (OR, USA): Timber Press. 951 p.

Donzelli PS, Lilly SJ, Arbor Master Training Inc. *The Art and Science of Practical Rigging* [DVD and book]. 2001. Champaign (IL, USA): International Society of Arboriculture. 172 p.

Introduction to Arboriculture: Climbing [online course]. Atlanta (GA, USA): International Society of Arboriculture. Available from: https://wwv.isa-arbor.com/store/product/757

Introduction to Arboriculture: Identification Principles [online course]. Atlanta (GA, USA): International Society of Arboriculture.Available from: https://wwv.isa-arbor.com/store/product/771

Introduction to Arboriculture: Principles of Pruning [online course]. Atlanta (GA, USA): International Society of Arboriculture. Available from: https://wwv.isa-arbor.com/store/product/752

Introduction to Arboriculture: Pruning Practices and Standards [online course]. Atlanta (GA, USA): International Society of Arboriculture. Available from: https://wwv.isa-arbor.com/store/product/753

Introduction to Arboriculture: Rigging [online course]. Atlanta (GA, USA): International Society of Arboriculture. Available from: https://wwv.isa-arbor.com/store/product/758

Introduction to Arboriculture: Safety [online course]. Atlanta (GA, USA): International Society of Arboriculture. Available from: https://wwv.isa-arbor.com/store/product/759

Introduction to Arboriculture: Tree Anatomy [online course]. Atlanta (GA, USA): International Society of Arboriculture. Available from: https://wwv.isa-arbor.com/store/product/738

Introduction to Arboriculture: Tree Physiology [online course]. Atlanta (GA, USA): International Society of Arboriculture. Available from: https://wwv.isa-arbor.com/store/product/739

Introduction to Arboriculture: Tree Support Systems [online course]. Atlanta (GA, USA): International Society of Arboriculture. Available from: https://wwv.isa-arbor.com/store/product/748

Jepson J. 2000. *The Tree Climber's Companion*. 2nd ed. Longville (MN, USA): Beaver Tree Publishing. 104 p.

Jepson J; illustrations by Kotwica B. 2009. *To Fell a Tree: A Complete Guide to Tree Felling and Woodcutting Methods*. Longville (MN, USA): Beaver Tree Publishing. 166 p.

Jepson J. 2013. *Knots at Work: A Field Guide for the Modern Arborist*. Longville (MN, USA): Beaver Tree Publishing. 184 p.

Lilly SJ. 2010. *Arborists' Certification Study Guide*. 3rd ed. Champaign (IL, USA): International Society of Arboriculture. 352 p.

Lilly SJ, Gilman EF, Smiley ET. 2019. *Pruning*. 3rd ed. Atlanta (GA, USA): International Society of Arboriculture. 63 p. (Best Management Practices).

Pruning Cuts [online course]. Atlanta (GA, USA): International Society of Arboriculture. Available from: https://wwv.isa-arbor.com/store/product/765

Smiley ET, Lilly S. 2014. *Tree Support Systems: Cabling, Bracing, Guying, and Propping*. 3rd ed. Champaign (IL, USA): International Society of Arboriculture. 50 p. (Best Management Practices).

INDEX